SAVAGE JUNGLE

*The True Story of an Australian
Soldier's Courageous Struggle to Survive
in World War II Malaya*

GW00569076

SAVAGE JUNGLE

An Epic Struggle for Survival

Iain Finlay

HIGH ADVENTURE PUBLISHING
HIGHADVENTUREPRODUCTIONS.COM

AUSTRALIA

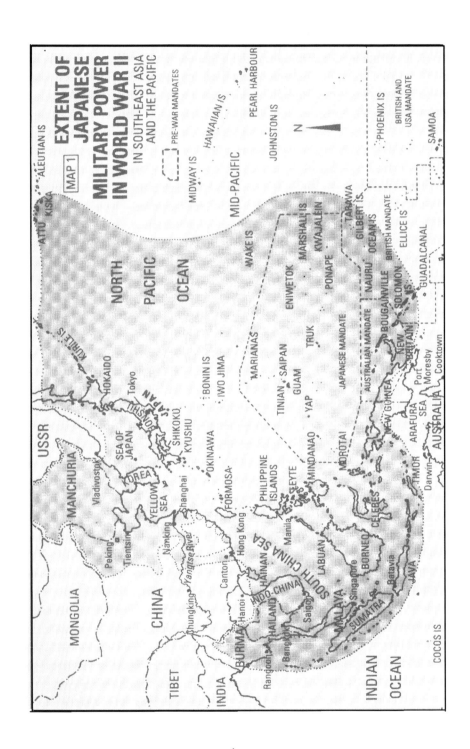

iv

MAP 2

JAPANESE INVASION OF MALAYA

DECEMBER 1941 TO FEBRUARY 1942

THAILAND

SINGORA (8.12.41)

PATANI (8.12.41)

ALOR STAR (13.12.41)

PENANG STAR

KOTA BHARU (8.12.41)

KEDAH

KETILI

PENANG

SELAMA

GRIK (17.12.41)

KUALA TRENGGANU (18.12.41)

PERAK

KELANTAN

TRENGGANU

KANGSAR

SOUTH CHINA SEA

KAMPAR

MALAYA

SLIM

PAHANG

KUANTAN (31.12.41)

STRAITS OF MALACCA

SELANGOR

KUALA SELANGOR (9.1.42)

KUALA LUMPUR (11.1.42)

Pahang River

PULAU TIOMAN

NEGRI SEMBILAN

GEMAS (13.1.42)

ENDAU (26.1.42)

PORT DICKSON (13.1.42)

MELAKA

Muar River

SEGAMAT

MERSING

JOHORE

MALACCA

YONG PENG (21.1.42)

KLUANG

N

MUAR

Area covered by MAP 7

BATU PAHAT

JOHORE BHARU (31.1.42)

SUMATRA

SINGAPORE (15.2.42)

v

First published in Australia in 1991 by
Simon & Schuster © Iain Finlay 1991

This 2015 Anzac Centenary edition published in Australia
By
High Adventure Publishing
highadventureproductions.com
Tumbulgum, 2490 Australia
© Iain Finlay 2015
ISBN 13:978-0-9807848-8-6
ISBN 10: 0980784883

National Library of Australia
Cataloguing in Publication data
Finlay, Iain, 1935—
Savage jungle an epic struggle for survival.

1. Shephard, Arthur, 1918-1984 — Fiction. 2. World War,
1939—1945—
Campaigns — Malaya ~ Fiction. 1. Title.
A8233

Map artwork by Iain Finlay, Greg Campbell Design
and
Design Illustrated

For Arthur. . .and Nancy

CONTENTS

oooooo

ILLUSTRATIONS

MAPS

AUTHOR'S NOTE

This book had a difficult birth. Its conception was back in 1979 when I first met Arthur Shephard and his wife Nancy in Adelaide and told them I would like to write Arthur's story. What happened during the twelve years between then and the book's first publication in 1991, to delay the manuscript would be too long and tedious to relate here. Suffice it to say that, like many authors before me, I became so distracted by the complexities of life, earning a living and bringing up teenage children, that there were long interruptions to the writing. My greatest regret and sorrow is that, during this long delay, Arthur Shephard died and did not see his story told.

The book, as it is now, is technically a work of non-fiction because it is about real people, in real places, and events which really occurred. Most of these people and the extraordinary history of their lives and deaths during the period 1942 to 1945 have sprung from the pages of Arthur Shephard's diary. But, as can be seen from the photograph of the diary, his record is an abbreviated, almost shorthand version of events.

My interviews with Arthur filled in many of the gaps, but for a story to come alive, the people in it have to come alive also: they have to speak. As there is no record of the actual words exchanged by the personalities involved, apart from the general idea of conversations that took place and the facts contained in them...as conveyed to me by Arthur... the dialogue in nearly all situations is my own. In that sense this book is also a work of fiction, or perhaps novelised non-fiction.

I must also acknowledge the great help given me by Arthur's wife, Nancy, who waited patiently as the book progressed, sometimes tortuously, and gave whatever information or advice that was needed.

AUTHOR'S NOTE

Appreciation is also due to those of Arthur's comrades in the- 2/29th Battalion who gave information that helped tell the story of the battles of Muar, Bakri and Parit Sulong, particularly Jim Kennedy, Jack Roxburgh, Max Robinson, Chris Nielson, Jack Haig, Bob Christie and T.E. (Borrie) Wiles.

The author also wishes to mention the exceptional archival and research facilities at the Australian War Memorial, an important national asset, and to acknowledge the assistance and guidance given by the Memorial's staff.

When this work was commenced, in the early 1980's, the writer sought the assistance of the Literature Board of the Australia Council which generously made special purpose and general writing grants to support the work. In the intervening years the writer's circumstances have changed for the better, but he gratefully acknowledges that without the Board's assistance, which was sorely needed at the time, the book may not have been started.

Throughout the book I have used imperial measurements (miles, yards, feet, inches etc.) instead of the metric rule. This is because, at the time of the story, these were the terms in use and it would seem clumsy and wrong for the characters who people this book to be speaking a different language.

The names of some of the places mentioned in the book have changed since Malaysia achieved its independence from British rule in 1957, but I have kept the names Arthur would have known.

FOREWARD

The Australian 8th Division was raised to fight Germany during the Second World War and was trained for the desert-like conditions of the Middle East. However, as the possibility of war with Japan threatened, the 22nd Brigade was sent instead to Malaya on 2 February 1941 – all other elements of the Division were spread throughout three separate operational theatres.

As war broke out Japanese forces based in Indochina quickly overran Thailand and successfully invaded Malaya. The demoralising loss of two British capital ships, HMS Repulse and HMS Prince of Wales, off Malaya, on 10 December 1941, neutralised Allied naval and air superiority, allowing the Japanese to conduct amphibious assaults on the Malayan coast with little resistance.

On 14 January, parts of the division went into action south of Kuala Lumpur at Gemas and Muar The 2/29th and the 2/19th Battalions were detached as reinforcements for the Indian 45th Brigade, which was in danger of being overrun near the Muar River. By 22 January, a mixed force from the two battalions, with some Indian troops, had been isolated and overrun – remnants hurriedly dispersing and seeking refuge in the unfamiliar and uninviting jungle. Hence begins the remarkable story of one man's epic quest for survival based solely on his courageous instincts, his practical approach to soldiering and his willingness to chance his luck with the native communist guerilla forces whose hatred for the Japanese fortunately outweighed their scorn for the British who ruled their adopted country.

In 1979, Iain Finlay, a well travelled and respected journalist came across the story of Arthur Shephard, a member of 2/29th Battalion, an Australian NCO who had survived in the jungles of Malaya for almost four years living under seemingly unpredictable and extremely testing conditions. Iain decided to follow up this story with the sole purpose of writing this book. Iain was astounded by the contents of Arthur's hand written diary and the clarity of his recall – truth really did have the capacity to be stranger and more exciting than fiction.

'Savage Jungle' reads like an action novel with a great introduction leading into the circumstances that Arthur Shephard and some of his mates found themselves in – the reader is then drawn along a path of running battles, countless illnesses, heartless executions, shortages of food, boredom, lack of English-speaking company, poor communications and ever-lasting friendships. This book however, is not an action novel, it is a true story that needed to be told. It is a book about the extraordinary will to survive and the strength of character that it took to make it to happen. True courage should never go unrewarded, Iain Finlay has provided that reward – thank you Iain for bringing this book to our shelves and highlighting this wonderful Australian's courage and determination.

It is fitting that this story be republished in the Centenary Year of ANZAC when Australia is celebrating the birth of its national character. Arthur Shephard ticks every box under the headings of courage, resolution, trust, discipline, resourcefulness, mateship and respect for others – he epitomised the Australian 'digger' of past legendary status and set the standard for subsequent generations - he should never be forgotten. Lest we forget.

Brian Vickery OAM
Lieutenant Colonel (Retired)
Royal Australian Infantry

[**juhng**-g*uh*]: A thick tangled mass of tropical vegetation. Also, a place of ruthless struggle for survival.

If you are alone in a great jungle, it is difficult not to ex-perience, amongst first impressions, a sense of awe and wonder. . .a feeling of insignificance. In some rainforests it could be lik-ened to being in a large cathedral where the soaring columns supporting the ceiling some thirty or forty feet above you are ac-tually ' enormous tree trunks, and the roof is a continuous can-opy formed by the interlocking of branches and leaves. But if you stand alone for more than a few minutes in such jungle sur-roundings, other sensations and emotions quickly surface. Ini-tially they may be feelings of pleasure and interest in the consid-erable beauty of the rainforest with its incredibly varied and sur-prising vegetation: great vines and creepers, thick rattan climb-ing the tallest trees to hang down in fern-like clumps from the branches, strange coloured moss, fungi and lichen covering the trunks of the trees to which endless varieties of tree-orchids also cling. At ground level, enormous ferns and rhododendron bushes form an impenetrable tangle of shrubs.

And then you notice the silence.

You realise how quiet it has been. You look around with a slight sense of unease, and begin to think that perhaps the jungle is really no place for humans.

The silence is suddenly broken by a loud tearing and crashing sound, and you jump with fright. But it is only a rotten tree falling through the tangled undergrowth. There is the sharp crack of a twig snapping nearby and, from that moment, the jun-gle is no longer beautiful. It has become fearsome and full of danger. It is damp and steamy and there is the odour of decay. Rain clouds cover what sun there is and the twilight of the dense forest turns to darkness. You discover several blood-sucking leeches clinging to your legs underneath your clothing. You quickly follow the path back out of the jungle to a grassy clearing which is broken only by serried rows of rubber trees stretching off into the distance and you are thankful you do not have to spend the night, let alone any longer period, in the Malayan jungle.

For much of its four hundred mile length, the central spine of the Malayan peninsula is covered by one of the densest tropical jungles in the world. To the west and east of this rugged mountain terrain, the peaks of which reach over seven thousand feet, the patterns of human development have been laid down on flat and fertile land over many centuries. The early inhabitants, indigenous Malay people, preferring the more settled occupations of agriculture and trade, shunned the jungle completely, leaving it to small groups of primitive and sometimes savage tribes-people who managed to find a way, like the Pygmies of Africa and the Indians of the Amazon basin, to successfully live on a permanent basis in the deepest jungle. But these primitives, the Sakais are perhaps the best known of those tribes that call the Malayan jungle their home have had generations of acclimatisation, hundreds of years to adapt to the ways of the deep forest, to understand its lores and the necessities of survival in such a savage world. And it is savage, not only in the sense of the predatory animals--tigers and panthers, poisonous Cobras and other snakes, ten-inch-long scorpions, centipedes and spiders-- that one might meet, but in the deadly and remorseless killers of human beings: malnutrition and diseases like malaria, dysentery, beri-beri, dengue, black-water fever, tropical ulcers and a host of other malignant plagues which attack any and all who would attempt to make the jungle a home.

This is the remarkable story of one such man, an Australian soldier, who managed to stay alive for three and a half years-- 1277 days--in the Malayan jungle, surviving incredible ordeals: bullet and shrapnel wounds, starvation, snakebite, a succession of terrible diseases, as well as delirium, fear, loneliness and the most savage of all oppressors--man.

1

JANUARY ON THE WESTERN SIDE of the Malayan peninsula is wet. . .very wet. For three months from December, the south-west monsoons sweep in from the Indian Ocean, drenching the great mountainous island of Sumatra and, across the Straits of Malacca, the coastal slopes of western Malaya. As the entire length of the four hundred mile peninsula lies less than seven degrees north of the equator, the temperature, except in the mountains, is always hot. On a typical January day, the sun will rise into an absolutely clear sky at about 6.30 am. The windless air, only marginally cooled during the night, is almost palpable. There is a thick moistness about it which is felt in colder climes only during fogs. In Malaya, however, the fog is both invisible and warm. For only a brief period in the mornings does the temperature remain within what are generally regarded as comfortable limits and even during this short hiatus, the air always holds the promise of great heat later in the day.

As the morning progresses and the mercury and humidity rise steadily, fluffy white clouds appear on the horizon as well as in the middle of the sky. Rapidly they grow in size, amalgamating with each other until the sky is filled with great cumulonimbus clouds, towering thunderheads carrying thousands of tons of rain, all seemingly just waiting for some signal. This usually comes around mid-afternoon when, with enormous thunderclaps and lightning bolts, the clouds open their flood-gates and let loose a tremendous downpour over thousands of square miles of land. The rain pours down for an hour or so and then, almost as suddenly as it began, it stops. As if satisfied with their job and

1

immensely relieved of their loads, the clouds disperse, melting away to leave the sky virtually clear again, with the ground and air washed clean as dusk approaches and the sun sets in a magnificent blaze across the Straits of Malacca.

Saturday, 17 January 1942, provided no exception to this pattern of nature. But in the north-eastern corner of Johore, the seven thousand-square mile State occupying the southern tip of the Malayan peninsula, there were few who were prepared to contemplate the dramatic skies as anything but a slight and perhaps inconvenient diversion from the more fateful human drama being acted out in the jungle and rubber plantations below.

For Arthur Shephard, the day and night preceding it had been a period of constant movement and feverish activity. Activity which helped only partially to alleviate the tension that he and his companions felt inside them. It wasn't really a fear of death or the pain it might involve-that was too definite. Perhaps it was a fear of the unknown. Perhaps it wasn't even fear at all. For Arthur, the feeling was vaguely familiar, somewhat like the sort of sensation he used to experience when his mother took him and his brothers and sisters to the circus. He recalled that, once a year, when the circus came to Melbourne, he would get so excited at the prospect that his stomach would just knot up into a ball and he'd throw up. Every time.

This, of course, was hardly the same thing. This was life or death...his own life or death. Not exactly the sort of thing to get excited about. And yet the feeling was there and, whether it was fear or excitement, or a combination of both, he knew it was something his companions felt too. The moment they had all been waiting for, and dreading, had arrived. Today, or tomorrow at the very latest, they would meet the Japanese Army. There was, Arthur admitted to himself, some comfort in the thought that he would not be doing it alone. The others, the rest of his platoon, and all eight hundred of his battalion (...well, closer to six hundred really, as D company had to remain in the Batu Anam area to support the 2/30th) would be there with him to face the advancing Japanese hordes.

Arthur Shephard, only six weeks past his twenty-fourth birthday, felt the pressure of leadership more than ever before. Technically, this was his first time as sergeant in the 2/29th. Up until recently he'd been a corporal of Signals. The unit already had a Signals Sergeant, Phil Simmons, but during the previous month, while his company had been based at Kahang airport, Sergeant Simmons had been sent to Officer Training School and Arthur was appointed to the rank of Acting Sergeant. Now, on this fateful day, his appointment as sergeant had been confirmed. In that fact at least, he felt some pleasure. There were quite a few privileges in being a sergeant, not the least of which was the sergeants' mess, always just that little bit better than the men's mess. And being a sergeant in a signals platoon was quite different from being in a rifle platoon. True, they were in an infantry battalion, but the atmosphere wasn't the same. There wasn't the same emphasis placed on drill and weapons. It was a more relaxed and, to a certain extent, a less disciplined set-up.

The actual command of the forty men in 1 Platoon, Headquarters Company, lay with Lieutenant Arthur C. Sheldon-'Twitty Mouse' the men called him, or sometimes just 'the mouse'. But, as often happens in infantry battalions, the commissioned officer could not quite command the same level of respect that his senior NCO, the platoon sergeant, held. There were several other platoons where the same situation applied. In Sergeant Shephard's platoon it wasn't that 'Twitty Mouse' Sheldon was disliked, it was just that he'd never really had any experience at handling men and, as 'Bomber' Wainright put it, "He was just a bloody office boy at the gas company before they sent him to OCS. He's hardly out of his flamin' nappies." Lieutenant Sheldon was just twenty-one. He was small and slightly-built with mousy-coloured hair and a blond, wispy attempt at a moustache straggling across his upper lip. He felt it was important to be liked by the men, but somehow it never really worked for 'the mouse'. He tried too hard. And, in many ways, he was naive.

"Look," he said to a bunch of his men one day on the troop ship when they were on the way to Singapore, "I know someone in the platoon has been saying I'm an office boy, that I don't know how to run the platoon. Now, I want to know who it is."

No reply.

He looked around at the faces of the men. "Now, I promise you there won't be anything further done if whoever it is owns up." But of course everybody knew that there'd be some form of retribution.

"I'm sure no-one would say a thing like that about you, Sir," Bomber said seriously. "That's not the sort of thing anyone in this platoon would say."

The lieutenant walked away mumbling something under his breath.

Although only slightly older than his platoon commander, and possessing no more practical experience of warfare, Arthur Shephard ('Shep' to most of his platoon), enjoyed widespread popularity within the unit. Shep was roughly the same height as his lieutenant, about five feet eight inches, but had a more solid and nuggety build. He had blond, curly hair, already beginning to thin out in the front. He liked his beer and knew what was happening on the Melbourne football scene, which gave him a decided advantage over 'Twitty Mouse' Sheldon. Not that Arthur felt in competition with his platoon commander, it was just the way things were. Most of the men in 1 Platoon ranged in age from eighteen to forty and they had, during the ten months of training in Australia and the four months in Malaya prior to the Japanese invasion, developed a reasonable rapport and a degree of trust in their NCOs, a trust Arthur now (too often) began to think might have been misplaced.

How would he stand up to battle? Would he be able to remain calm, or would he panic if a Japanese came rushing at him with a bayonet? Like all men facing real war for the first time, Arthur wondered how he would manage. And how would he lead his men? Up till now, this had only involved a few orders, orders that were usually passed on from someone higher up, anyway. And if the men didn't do as they were told, there'd be trouble. Now it was suddenly different. For the first time he felt that these forty men were largely his responsibility.

The signal ordering the battalion to move immediately from their present defensive position near the town of Buloh Kasap to a place called Muar had come late in the evening of the previous day, Friday the 16th. The whole unit had spent a good part of the night preparing for the move. Although Muar was only forty miles away as the crow flies, it was over one hundred miles by road. The idea of travelling such a long distance in broad daylight did not greatly appeal to Arthur Shephard or any of the other men in the 2/29th Battalion. They all knew that the Japanese had won almost total command of the skies in the five weeks since they had first landed on the Malayan peninsula. Flights of Zeros and the deadly fighter-bombers, which the Allies had dubbed 'Val' and 'Kate', patrolled the length of Malaya almost at will now, and they could wreak havoc in an army convoy the size of the one which was to take Arthur's battalion to Muar.

"Why the hell are we leaving, anyway?" Frank Fox asked his sergeant as he and several others in the platoon worked at stacking some of the Headquarters Company's signals equipment into the back of a Chevrolet truck. "I thought we were supposed to be relieving the bloody Thirtieth. That's what they told us this morning."

Frank Fox was a young farmer. He'd lived all of his life in the Colac district of Victoria where he was growing onions at the time he decided to enlist.

Arthur Shephard paused a moment. He wasn't exactly sure why they were moving either, although he'd been assured by Lieutenant Sheldon that it wasn't a retreat. "Well," he began, the Mouse told me. . ."

"Don't worry yer little mind about it, Frankie," Bomber Wainright interrupted. "You just do what yer told and it'll all come out in the wash sooner or later. They'll tell yer they know what they're doin', but there's no bloody chance of that. Now, at Gallipoli. . ."

When Bomber spoke, everybody listened. His real name was Gordon Wainright. He was only a signaller, roughly equivalent to a private first class, but he was older than everyone else in the platoon, somewhere in his mid-forties, although no-one knew exactly where. He was only small, about five feet seven inches and slightly built, but he was tough and wiry. He had a thin face with a long, pointed nose which was straddled on either side by two piercing blue eyes. His hair, originally sandy, was greying now although it showed little, shorn in military short-back-and-sides fashion. The cut did, however, accentuate his ears, making him look for all the world like a determined little ferret as he moved around the camp area.

Bomber was the only person in 1Platoon who had ever seen warfare, real warfare, and the stories of his exploits in Gallipoli and France had both intrigued and horrified the younger men. Bomber had won the Military Medal (and his nickname) in France when he broke up an enemy attack that had been launched against his platoon by throwing Mills Bombs, or hand grenades, at them. True, it had been static trench warfare and already it was very clear, from what had been happening in Europe since war had begun almost two years earlier, and now, here in Malaya, that things were very different from the kind of fighting that Bomber had seen in World War I. And yet Bomber was the voice of authority. He had 'experience'. The fact that he had joined up again when he could obviously have avoided conscription because of his age seemed to impress some of the younger men. It was almost as if he had rejoined for the fun of it. It made the whole thing seem more like a game that you had to be in or you'd be sorry you missed out. The way he always fooled around and cracked jokes somehow made it seem less deadly. '

"The way things are going," a third member of the work detail grunted as he heaved a heavy coil of field telephone wire into the back of the truck, "we're never going to get a bloody chance to have a crack at them. Just when it's our turn to give the little yellow bastards another nasty shock, they pull us out. Anyway, who's going to relieve Galleghan's mob now?"

The speaker was Jim Kennedy, a twenty-one-year-old accountancy student from Albury. He, Frankie Fox and two others-Jack Roxburgh and Tom Wiles...were Arthur Shephard's closest friends. They'd been together ever since the 2/29th had been formed in Australia, back in November 1941.

"What's happening, Shep?" he went on. "I mean, I can't see how we can just piss off to this place Muar when the bloody Nips are just down the road at Gemas. What's going to happen to the Thirtieth?"

Everybody knew that the Thirtieth, the 2/30th Infantry Battalion, must be tired. They had been the first Australian army unit to come into contact with the Japanese only three days previously, but they had inflicted stunning losses on the Japanese 9th Infantry Brigade's Mukaide Regiment. Under the command of Lieutenant Colonel F. G. Galleghan, the 2/30th had planned and carried out a brilliant ambush on the advancing Japanese column, killing hundreds of Japanese bicycle soldiers in the first encounter and then fighting, in the words of one of the Japanese military diarists, Colonel Masonobu Tsuji, 'with a bravery we had not previously seen'.

But now the Japanese were rushing their 5th Division, some fifteen thousand men supported by powerful armoured formations, as reinforcements to attempt to break through the Australian defences at the small town of Gemas, and so continue their drive down the main trunk road to Singapore. The plan had been for the 2/29th, of which Bomber, Frankie Fox, Jim Kennedy and the rest of Shep's platoon were a small but integral part, to take over from the 2/30th, to spell them for a few days and hold the advancing Japanese at bay. Most of the battalion felt completely confident that they could do it. They looked on the incredible succession of defeats suffered by the British and Indian army units to the north over the past few weeks as being shameful. There were many comments heard intimating that once the Japanese met Australian soldiers, they'd 'wonder what bloody well struck them!' And in the first day or so after Galleghan's Thirtieth had stopped the Mukaide detachment in their tracks, it looked as if they'd been right. Even the Commander of the 8th Australian Division, General Gordon Bennett, shared this view. For a few hours after the dramatic stand at Gemas, he felt that the Australian troops had the will and the ability not only to stop the Japanese progress south, but to turn them back.

But now, for some reason, the 2/29th was being moved off, away from the area where the fighting was, to the west coast-just when they were about to have their first taste of action.

"It's like we're leaving the Thirtieth in the lurch," Jim Kennedy persisted.

"No, we're not," Shep put in. "I think the 2/26th is coming across from Gemas and Batu Anam to relieve them and we're leaving D Company here to give the Thirtieth a hand. According to 'the mouse', the Japs might be trying to break through on the coast road also. There's an Indian unit down there but they don't think it can hold them. That's why they're sending us down there-to stop them."

"Well, I bloody hope so. The way they've buggered us around, I wouldn't be surprised if we never get to meet any Japs."

"I wouldn't have any bloody fears about that, mate," Bomber laughed. "You'll get yer chance. Don't worry about it. And when it comes, you'll probably be wishin' they could have kept jugglin' us around a good bit longer."

Although the men of Arthur Shephard's platoon didn't know the details or the real strategy behind their latest orders, there were a few, including Arthur and Bomber Wainright, who sensed that the sudden and unexpected move was more of a knee-jerk reaction to some new Japanese threat than part of a well-ordered defence. The movement of the 2/29th to the Muar area was only one of a series of what seemed to be increasingly frantic attempts on the part of the Allied commanders entrusted with the defence of Malaya to stop the steamroller rush of the 25th Japanese Army southward towards its ultimate goal, the supposedly impregnable fortress of Singapore. In the forty days since December 8th when General Tomoyuki Yamashita's army had landed at Kota Bharu on the northeastern coast of Malaya, and at Singora and Patani in southern Thailand, it had literally crushed all opposition. Once the Japanese Army had established a beachhead, it had swept inland and south at a terrifying pace, routing one Allied army unit after another.

The defence of northern Malaya had been in the hands of the III Indian Corps, two divisions (the 9th and the 11th) comprising some eighteen battalions of around fifteen thousand men in all. The Indian Army at the time was a product of Britain's colonial rule in India; in effect, only an extension of the British Army. It was commanded and largely led by regular British Army officers and within any Indian Army brigade of three battalions (each of about eight hundred and fifty men), it was general practice, prior to World War II, to include one regular British Army battalion. But due to the rapid expansion of the Indian Army since the outbreak of hostilities in Europe two years previously, this had not been possible. Consequently, amongst the Indian Army units thrown up against the Japanese in Malaya, there were only three British Army battalions: the 2nd Surrey, the 1st Leicesters, and the 2nd Argyle and Sutherland Highlanders.

The Indian units consisted of a bewildering array of different Indian regional and ethnic groups such as the 5th/1st Sikhs, 5th/18th Garhwals, 3rd/16th Punjabis, 2nd/1st Gurkhas, 4th/19th Hydrabads, 3rd/17th Dogras and the 2nd/10th Baluch regiments. Many of the units proved to be poorly trained and not properly equipped or prepared for the type of jungle warfare that the Japanese initiated.

Nor, for that matter, were several of the British units being sent in as reinforcements. They were not up to the standard that was necessary to halt Yamashita and push his army off the peninsula. The 5th Norfolk Regiment was a case in point. Sent in to relieve an Australian battalion at Jemaluang before either had gone into action, they seemed, as one war diarist recorded, "...almost dazed by the position in which they found themselves. In all that mud, the officers' personal gear included trunks, valises and baths. They were a fine body of men, but their training had been in open warfare and not the very close warfare of the Malayan countryside. They demonstrated the unreality of their approach to the situation by lighting up all the buildings in the area and stringing out all of their transport along highly vulnerable and prominent crossroads and by the commanding officer telling his second in command, 'Our first job is to get the mess going'."

In addition, once the fighting was underway, there were unmistakable signs amongst some of the Indian regiments of dissatisfaction, resentment...even hostility towards their white colonial leaders and this was a factor which the Japanese Army propagandists lost no time in exploiting as they moved southward.

Some of the Indian Army units made valiant stands against the Japanese, and elite corps like the Gurkhas and the British 2nd Battalion Argyle and Sutherland Highlanders inflicted heavy losses on Yamashita's forces at Slim River. But through-out the whole campaign to try to save Malaya, the Allies had never been able to establish the air superiority which was crucial to victory. Their air forces in Malaya consisted mainly of Brewster Buffalo and Wirraway aircraft which were outdated, underarmed, slower and less manoeuvrable than the Japanese Zeros which dominated the skies of Malaya.

The air attacks also had a dramatic effect on the civil government and the bureaucratic fabric of the country: the institutions that provided services like gas, electricity, water, council waste disposal and sanitation facilities. In many instances these began to fall apart at the seams, not only as a direct result of Japanese air attacks, but often because of the underlying friction that sometimes existed between the indigenous occupants--Malays, Indians and Chinese--and the British colonial administrators, who were seen by some as occupiers.

The British had been running Penang and Malacca in Malaya and the island of Singapore as the 'Straits Settlements' since the early 1800s, after Stamford Raffles had snatched Singapore from the Dutch, in order, he said, 'to secure to the British flag the maritime superiority of the Eastern seas'. There had always been a body of people who resented and resisted this rule. For these anti-colonialists, although the Japanese invasion might result in another form of colonial rule, it also presented an opportunity to get rid of the British. And if the Japanese did prove to be colonialist, then at least they would be Asian, like the bulk of the Malayan population, instead of European.

Very few of the men in the 2/29th slept well during the night of the 16th January. The preparations for their move were not complete. The rest of the transport required to carry the troops did not arrive at their position between Segamat and Buloh Kasap until the early hours of the morning of the 17th. During the night they had heard the dull, faraway sounds of heavy artillery fire which they knew was coming from the Gemas area, about ten miles further north. In more peaceful times, the irregular 'thump, thump, thump' could easily have been mistaken for distant thunder.

Arthur Shephard lay awake at 2am listening to the sounds and wondering about his compatriots, members of another battalion who, although only a short distance further along the road, were right in the midst of it. He wanted to believe that the 2/30th were sending those shells out to the Japanese, but he felt certain it was more the other way. There was a strange feeling of unreality about the whole thing. He and his men were uncomfortable on the ground but at least they were safe, while a few miles away men were dying.

He heard the low murmur of voices off to one side, several yards away by a low bush. Then he saw the soft red glow of a cigarette illuminating the face of his friend Jack Roxburgh. He knew he must be talking to Jim Kennedy. They, too, were finding it difficult to get any sleep. His immediate reaction was to call out to Roxburgh to tell him to put out the cigarette, but he hesitated. He felt he wanted to join them, to talk with them, to share the burden of dread with others and thereby help make the night pass more quickly.

Until recently, the 2/29th had been sleeping a little more comfortably. During the five months since their arrival in Singapore, they had been shifted to a number of different locations. First they had been in huts in Segamat, a town of several thousand inhabitants, where, prior to the Japanese invasion, they had been in training. After the Japanese landings, they had been given the task of defending the airports at Kahang and Kluang on the road between Mersing on the east coast and Batu Pahat on the west. Here they had slept in small tents under the cover of the surrounding rubber plantations. Now they were positioned around Buloh Kasap, a small village halfway between Segamat and Gemas, where the first contact between Japanese and Australians had been made. In this new defensive position, they were sleeping, or trying to sleep, on the ground in slit trenches with only their groundsheets to protect them from any rain. The ground was sodden but, if the weather held to the pattern of the past few days, they could at least anticipate little or no rain during the night.

In each platoon, every soldier's slit-trench position had been carefully sited by the section leader, usually a corporal under the direction of the platoon commander and sergeant, to give clear lines of defensive fire which would fit into the overall position plans for the site which had been worked out by the company commanders and the battalion commander. In theory, the interlocking fire of each section would form an effective barrier for the platoon; the combined fire of several platoons would present a company's defensive 'wall' and the correct placing of the various companies would hopefully constitute a successful defensive position for the whole battalion. It was thought that more of the enemy would be seen during an attack in daylight as they advanced on the section and platoon positions and could be fired at, either as directed or at will, depending on the circumstances. In the case of a night attack each soldier was supposed to have one or more fixed lines of fire down which he could shoot, virtually blind, so that any enemy advancing under cover of darkness would be caught in well planned and deadly crossfire. At least that was the way it was supposed to work.

During the months prior to the invasion, the men of the 2/29th had done it all before, over and over again, in training. They knew the routine backwards and could almost fall into their correct positions on any site with little direction from their officers. They had developed into a team, as good a team of men as could be found on the Malayan peninsula. They operated automatically in almost all of the important basic functions of soldiers in the field. If there was any one weak point in their performance, it was perhaps their reluctance to dig their slit trenches deep enough. It had seemed a waste of time when, in the early days, they knew there weren't any enemies around.

But during the past few weeks things had changed. From the time of the Japanese landings, they had been based on and around the airfields at Kluang and Kahang. The ground was dry and hard and, prior to the invasion, there hadn't been any real war so the trenches were hardly trenches at all. Once hostilities were underway, however, even though the action was hundreds of miles to the north, the military airfields at Kluang and Kahang suddenly came under air attack from Japanese fighters and bombers and it was there, at Kluang, some weeks before it came into physical contact with the Japanese Army, that the 2/29th suffered its first war casualty.

Arthur Shephard's platoon of signallers had been laying new telephone lines linking the various battalion positions around the field when they suddenly heard the sound of planes coming in low and fast. There was practically no warning. The Zeros had roared in at tree-top level so the sound of their coming had been lost until the very last moment.

"Zeros! Zeros!" everyone had yelled. "Run! Get down! Get down!" and there had been a mad scramble for the slit trenches--what there was of them--with men diving headlong and tumbling on top of each other as the first harsh stutter of machine-gun fire from the leading plane tore up the tarmac and ripped through the fuselage of a stationary Wirraway aircraft less than twenty yards away.

A second Zero tore across the field, strafing everything in front of it. As it passed over and began to climb into the sky behind the lead plane, 'Grumpy' Olsen, one of the men in Arthur's platoon, suddenly leapt out of the trench, muttering, "I left the bloody phone out there."

"Christ Grumpy," Arthur called, "get back, you bloody fool. Get back!"

But before anyone could stop him, he had dashed across the few yards of tarmac to retrieve the instrument he had dropped and the connecting phone line. Suddenly, a third Zero was screaming down the field. Horrified, the men of 1 Platoon cried out to Grumpy, "Run! Run!" Grumpy was running, but not fast enough. With a terrible roar, the Zero's machine-guns tore Grumpy apart before he was halfway back.

His death came as a major shock to the unit. Although they had all trained and trained, learning to shoot their rifles accurately at targets and to plunge their bayonets into stuffed dummies, many of them had never seen a dead man before. Now, suddenly, Grumpy--a live, walking, talking human being, a close friend to many, including Arthur, who had known him since the battalion first formed-was just a chopped-up piece of meat lying on the airfield.

In the weeks since that incident, the image of Grumpy's gruesome end had dimmed slightly in the minds of Arthur and the other men who had seen it, partly because there had been many more bombing raids and more casualties although, fortunately none from the 2/29th. Nevertheless, their trenches had somehow become considerably deeper than they had been at first.

Now, on that last night before they moved off towards Muar, Arthur had had no trouble in getting his men to dig in well. But smoking at night was something else. He watched the glow of the cigarette in the darkness for a few seconds. He could have done with one himself, he thought.

"Put it out Jack," he called softly but firmly into the darkness. The glow disappeared and there was silence. Moments later, one of their own patrols came moving back through the lines, quietly checking with him as they went past. Shortly afterwards, another patrol moved by on its way out. Arthur drifted into a fitful sleep.

2

AT FIRST LIGHT THE WHOLE battalion was on the move. The trucks, which were to shift all the men and equipment, were spread for more than half a mile back down the road-not on the road itself, but under the trees, in the rubber plantations which grew up to the edge of the road. It was the best they could do to avoid possible detection and attack from the air. As each truck was filled with either stores, food, or a variety of weapons and ammunition, it would drive off to wait under the trees until the convoy was ready to move off together.

The road was not a bad one. It was well-surfaced, reasonably flat and straight, although only wide enough for two vehicles. It ran, for nearly the whole distance, between dense rubber, palm-oil plantations, or jungle.

The only trouble for the 2/29th when they got underway was that the road was often clogged with Allied military traffic moving constantly in both directions. Streaming southwards were hundreds of Chinese and Malay refugees, either walking or on bicycles, carrying heavy loads, pushing or pulling carts containing their possessions. Smashed cars and trucks, the victims of previous Japanese aerial attacks, had been pushed to the sides of the road. Crawling along that narrow ribbon of tar, through such a melee, the convoy provided an easy target for any Japanese aircraft that might come along, and every member of the battalion knew it.

They sat crowded together in the back of the transport trucks in their full combat gear, including their rifles, tin helmets and webbing, to which was strapped a water bottle and bayonet as well as two basic pouches containing several clips of ammunition. On their backs they each carried a small backpack containing groundsheet, messing gear and other small articles of clothing. They were hot and sweaty most of the time as the trucks crawled along slowly and they would revel in the occasional coolness of the breeze when the trucks reached fifteen or twenty miles per hour, but that was a rare pleasure.

In the morning, while they were still loading up, a flight of Zeros had roared over their position, heading south. Later, on the section of road between Segamat and Labis, they were held up for almost two hours by the confusion and chaos caused by the same Zeros attacking a convoy of trucks coming north. They all felt the tension of being so vulnerable.

"I wish they'd get a bloody move on," Frank Fox muttered. "Sitting around like this is for the birds. I wouldn't feel so bloody bad if there were a few of our own bloody planes around the joint but we never see any!"

"They're no flamin' good even when they are around," Bomber Wainright added sarcastically. "What use are bloody Buffaloes and Wirraways against Zeros? Damn Zeros can beat the pants off our lot. What we want are a few Hurricanes or Spitfires. We'd run rings around the bloody Nips then."

Although Bomber Wainright didn't know it, a naval convoy carrying, among other war materiel and troop reinforcements, fifty-one Hurricane fighters, had arrived only four days previously in Singapore. But time was needed to assemble and condition the aircraft and to train the pilots. Only twenty-four pilots had come with the convoy which had spent eleven weeks at sea. The Hurricanes would eventually appear for the first time in the skies over Johore less than a week later. But whatever small difference they were to make to the air war, it would be too late for the men of the 2/29th.

By two in the afternoon, the convoy of trucks carrying the battalion had reached Yong Peng and turned off the main trunk road to head west, through Parit Sulong towards Muar.

"Look at the sky." Arthur Shephard pointed through the gap between the canvas roof and the top of the truck's cabin. "We're heading for a real storm...a beauty."

The sun had suddenly gone behind a huge thunderhead and the landscape was growing ominously dark. Within moments, the first fat drops of rain began splashing onto the roof and onto the road receding behind them. As it hit the roadway, which was oven-hot, the rain turned instantly to steam and rose like a fog a few feet above the ground. With the day becoming quickly darker and the rain heavier, the men at the front of the trucks scrambled to untie the straps holding up the front canvas awnings, lowering them so the rain would not pour in.

A tremendous flash of lightning bathed the road and the surrounding jungle in purple-white light for a second, followed almost immediately by a deafening crack of thunder. Then the rain came down in torrents. The trucks slowed again to a crawl as their drivers struggled to see more than a few yards ahead. The convoy was like a great grey snake crawling cautiously through the jungle. The rain became a solid wall, finding the holes and weaknesses in the canvas roofs to drip, trickle and sometimes pour in on the men who shuffled and shifted their positions as best they could to avoid being soaked.

For half an hour the downpour went on and then slowed to a steady rain, then a drizzle, until, within minutes, it had stopped completely and the sky before them to the west began to clear. The trucks moved on at more of a pace. They passed over the narrow bridge spanning the Simpang Kiri River and through the little village of Parit Sulong on the other side only to be blocked, a few miles on, by floodwaters on the road. One of the lead trucks attempted to drive through, but the water was deep enough to soak the distributor and stall the vehicle.

Fortunately, the water began to subside quickly, although there had been a half-hour of tense anticipation as the line of trucks was held up. An air attack at such a time would have been disastrous. Eventually, the convoy rolled forward again, passing a small crossroads marked on the map as Bakri shortly before 4 pm.

The Battalion Commander, Colonel John Robertson, gave orders for the 2/29th to stop and to adopt a defensive position along the road about a mile and a half west of Bakri. His intention was to rest the men for the night, then attack and capture the small settlement of Simpang Jeram in the morning. There was no definite information but Colonel Robertson believed the village to be in the hands of the Japanese.

Earlier in the day, while the trucks had been rumbling along on their slow journey, Colonel Robertson and his company commanders had attended a conference with General Gordon Bennett near the town of Labis. Bennett was the Commander of all of the Australian Army forces in Malaya--but was also in over-all command of a larger group known as 'Westforce' which, in addition to the Australian troops, included the 9th Indian Division, the 45th Indian Brigade Group, an Indian Pioneer Battalion and most of the British Loyal Regiment as well as various artillery, engineer and administrative units. Westforce was charged with preventing the Japanese from taking Malaya's southernmost province, Johore. It was hoped they could stem the tide until reinforcements of Australian and British troops, already at sea, could be landed in Singapore and brought up to Johore.

Bennett, a World War I officer now fifty-four years old, was a dynamic man who had been at the centre of controversy in Australia in the years immediately prior to the outbreak of war. As a civilian, but a senior officer in the Australian Militia Forces, he had written a series of scathing articles criticising Australia's military preparedness and the tendency of the army to bypass highly qualified citizen military officers, with experience from World War I, in favour of permanent officers when allocating positions of higher command. The articles had left him very much out of favour with the regular military hierarchy, yet Bennett's reputation was such that, after a period in the doldrums after World War II began, he was finally given command of the Australian 8th Division.

During World War I, Bennett had served in Gallipoli with conspicuous bravery and, by the age of twenty-nine, had been promoted to brigadier-general, the youngest in any army in the British Empire at the time. Between the wars, in civilian life, he was appointed President of the New South Wales Chamber of Manufactures and then President of the federal body, the Associated Chamber of Manufactures. He was a man of medium build, with a dark, military-style moustache and sad eyes. He had great drive and energy and, when it came to military tactics, a very aggressive philosophy.

When Colonel Robertson and his company commanders entered the General's temporary headquarters in a plantation house along the Labis road on the afternoon of the 17th, Bennett and his Chief of Staff were leaning over a large situation-map. Several other officers stood by peering over his shoulder as he explained the latest movements of Allied troops. He was in summer uniform of shorts, long socks and a short-sleeved shirt. Robertson noticed that the General's shirt was soaked with sweat. A large fan swirled slowly above their heads but did little to alleviate the intense humidity which seemed to be growing more and more oppressive as the day went on.

Bennett greeted the officers of the 2/29th and directed them to find positions for themselves around the map table. He launched immediately into an outline of the current tactical situation and gave them details of the Japanese movements that had led him to so precipitously switch Colonel Robertson's battalion from its intended role as backup for the 2/30th to the new one nearer the coast.

"The original intelligence I received," he told them, "was that a number of Japanese troops...not sure how many, a couple of companies perhaps...had crossed the Muar River some distance above the town of Muar yesterday. We had the 7/6th Rajputna Rifles at various points along the southern bank of the Muar, but they were taken by surprise when the Japs came around behind them and they were overcome. So was the Australian artillery battery, the 65th, which had been at the mouth of the river."

Major Olliff, Colonel Robertson's second in command, looked up from the map. "Overcome, sir? You mean...?"

"No, the 65th, most of it, was able to withdraw down the road toward Bakri, where you're going. The Indians weren't so lucky. What's left of them, the ones that aren't in Japanese hands, are apparently in the jungle trying to make their way back. Hopefully they can also meet up with you somewhere near Bakri." He pointed at the map, which was studded with little flags of different colours and patterned with arrows indicating the movements of Allied troops and the positioning of various units, as well as whatever they knew of the enemy force's locations and movements.

"My first intention, or rather, what was suggested to me by Brigadier Duncan of the 45th Indian Brigade, was to send only a company of Australians to stabilise the situation. But it's quite clear now that the enemy force is larger than company size." "How much larger, sir?" Robertson asked. "Not quite certain at this stage, could be more than a battalion, although I don't think so. Probably just a fairly strong probe. That's why it's important we hit back here as hard and fast as possible. Let them know they've got some real opposition and that they can't just walk through."

"So what's left of the Indian units now?" Robertson asked, running his eyes over the flags. "How have the rest of them come through this lot?"

"Not too badly, not too badly." Bennett straightened up and spoke directly to Robertson. "As I said, the ones on the river were chopped about a bit, particularly the ones on the far side, two companies of Rajputs. Lost them, plus the ones closest to Muar itself on this side, also Rajputs. But there're the Jats, almost a battalion of them, and the Garhwals, both of whom are not in too bad a shape. The Garhwals are moving back towards Simpang Jeram and I'm told the Jats are pulling back towards Bakri where we should be able to consolidate. There's no other way through, except the coast road--or the jungle."

Robertson nodded, but said nothing.

"Now," General Bennett moved back to the table, picking up a couple of small coloured flags, "you won't be there alone. I'm giving you a troop of armoured cars and Lieutenant McCure here with the 13th Battery of the 2/4th Anti-tank Regiment."

Colonel Robertson's body, leaning over the map again, visibly relaxed slightly. "Ah, I see," he said. "That should make things a little easier."

"I don't know about easier," the General's eyes continued to rove over the map. "I have a feeling you're going to need them. It's absolutely essential we contain any movement down this flank, otherwise we'll be in real trouble with the rest of our forces at Gemas and Segamat."

"What's happening with the Thirtieth, sir? I feel we've left them a bit in the lurch."

Bennett tightened his lips and nodded. "Nothing else we can do about it, I'm afraid. I can tell you it's been a very difficult decision for me to make. I know they've been three days without a break and they desperately need relief, especially as we're expecting further Jap offensives around Gemas, but they'll be relieved as soon as we can possibly do it."

He picked up a long pointer and circled the area immediately behind Muar, as if to change to a less unpalatable topic. "Now," he said firmly, "the first thing you'll have to do is consolidate your position around here, or as far down the road to Muar as you can get, probably around Simpang Jeram. Then, as quickly as possible, you should endeavour to push the enemy back to the river and across it in order to restore the position. The river, if it's defended properly, could be a pretty formidable barrier for them, but if they continue to control both sides of it, they can bring their reinforcements across at will. If they get tanks across, it'll be like throwing the door open for them to outflank us and cut off the rest of Westforce at Yong Peng or Ayer Hitam." He waved the pointer over two towns much further south in Johore.

Colonel Robertson nodded, but with a degree of confidence that indicated that there was no doubt in his mind that the 2/29th could perform this task. For a further twenty minutes the men studied the map in more detail and discussed the movement with an eye to developments that might occur when contact with the Japanese was made.

Shortly after this meeting, when the 2/29th officers had left to rejoin their battalion, General Bennett attended another conference, this time with three British officers: Brigadier Fawcett of the III Indian Corps, Major General Key, Commander of the 11th Indian Division and Lieutenant General Percival, the Officer in Command of all Allied Forces in Malaya.

The situation for the Allies, as it was now developing, appeared to be little short of a massive juggling exercise. Whole battalions of men were being frantically shifted around like pawns on some huge chessboard, in desperate attempts to stop the opponent's inexorable advance and entrapment of the 'king'-- in this game, Singapore. The only trouble was that the Japanese

21

seemed to have their queen and other major pieces intact, while the Allies had nothing left but pawns.

General Percival had suggested to Bennett earlier by phone that the III Indian Corps under General Key should take control of the operations in the Muar area, but Bennett had resisted this strongly.

"If we can continue to hold them at Gemas with the 30th," Bennett had said to Percival, "I feel I want to keep a close personal eye on Muar also, because it represents a possible threat to my rear. It's clear that if the Japs break through at Muar, Westforce could be cut off."

Percival had concurred, but at their early afternoon conference Bennett pressed the point further. It was as if he sensed the great danger developing in the Muar sector, even though at that stage there had been no indication of the size of the Japanese forces that had crossed the river, other than the fact that there were more than two hundred men.

"I think there's a chance they might be going to try a major flanking attack at Muar," Bennett said, "and I'd like to hit them now, as hard as we can, to forestall any push in that direction. Consequently, I'd also like to get the 2/19th across here to back up the 29th at Muar."

The 2/19th Battalion was the other infantry battalion that, together with the 2/18th and the 2/20th, made up the 22nd Australian Infantry Brigade. It had been sitting at Jemaluang, on the east coast of Malaya, in a waiting, defensive position, intending to prevent any Japanese move down that side of the peninsula. The 2/19th had already made contact with Japanese patrols coming south, so if General Percival approved General Bennett's request to move them clear across to the opposite side of the country to back up the 2/29th, he would leave a large hole in the defences of the east coast of Malaya. But he gave the approval and, at the same time, issued orders for the 5th Norfolks, a newly arrived reinforcement regiment, to replace the Australian battalion at Jemaluang. As has been mentioned, the Norfolks, although a fine body of men, had no jungle training whatsoever.

"There's still the problem of the main trunk road and the defence of Gemas and Segamat," Percival said to the other generals and officers. "As much as I am loathe to raise the subject,

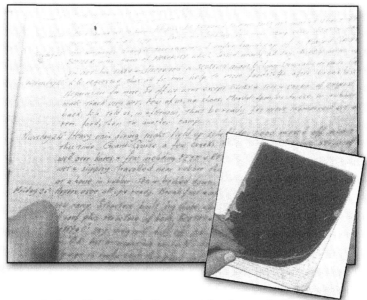

1. *Arthur Shephard's diary; a school exercise book which survived his long sojurn in the jungle, 1942 to 1945.*

2. *Arthur Shephard aged 23. Photograph taken in Melbourne prior to his departure for Singapore.*

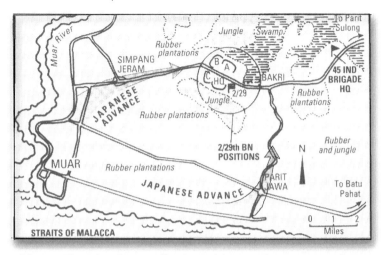

Map 3. The 2/29th Battalion's position on the Muar road at the time of contact with the Japanese Imperial Guards.

3. Gunners of the 13thBattery, 2/4th Antyi-Tank Regiment, shooting over open sights at Japanese tanks advancing along the Muar road. *(Australian War Memorial, negative no. 11302)*

we have to consider the prospect of a further withdrawal from the Segamat area."

"It would be very bad for morale at this stage, sir," Bennett commented. "Our chaps have been waiting for their chance to have a crack at the Nips for several weeks. Another withdrawal at this stage would be hard to explain, unless it was really forced on us."

"But what about the 2/30th?" General Key asked. "Surely they're badly in need of relief?"

"Absolutely," Percival nodded, "but we've the 9th Indian Division and the 22nd Australian Brigade who'll relieve them.

Although the battle front across the peninsula appeared very fluid at this stage, General Bennett left the meeting with his Commander in Chief that afternoon feeling he had made the right decision as far as the deployment of his troops in the Bakri area was concerned. After all, he reasoned, the original suggestion from Brigadier Duncan (45th Independent Brigade) was for a company of some one hundred and fifty men. Bennett was sending instead two battalions, and although they were not up to their full strengths of around eight hundred and fifty men each, with a troop each of armoured cars and anti-tank guns attached, they represented a significant force.

Shortly after five that afternoon, he stood in his head-quarters operations room during a brief respite from the stream of officers and men who had been coming and going all day. An orderly had brought him a mug of scalding hot tea and he stood sipping at it gingerly as he gazed at the situation-map laid out in front of him. He nodded slowly to himself but said nothing to the two staff officers who stood on the far side of the table. He felt growing confidence that the 2/29th, with the 2/19th coming up in reserve, could handle the situation in the Muar area. It was not until the following morning that he learnt that the enemy units pressing down on Muar and beyond were not of company or battalion strength, but the advance elements of the Konoe Imperial Guards Division-the elite fighting force of the Japanese Army, a body of more than ten thousand men.

Up until 17 January, the Japanese 25th Army's thrust south-ward through Malaya had involved a complex force of two infantry divisions (the 5th and the Imperial Guards) totalling around twenty-eight thousand men and a host of other units including tank regiments, anti-tank battalions, mountain artillery, heavy field artillery, mortar battalions, anti-aircraft battalions, engineer regiments, river-crossing companies, heavy bridging companies, railway units...even a balloon company! The total strength of the invasion force up to this time was about forty-seven thousand men. A third infantry division, the 18th, consisting of a further twenty-two thousand men was to land in Malaya on 23 January and take an active part in the eventual capture of Singapore, but up to this point the 5th Division, under Lieutenant General Takuro Matsui and the Imperial Guards Division, commanded by Lieutenant General Takumo Nishimura had alone been responsible for the stunning series of defeats inflicted on the Allied defenders.

It had been the 5th Division, advancing down the main trunk road which had first met and then been stopped by the Australian 2/30th Battalion at Gemas. At the same time, the thirteen thousand men of the Guards Division had been rapidly progressing down the west coast, sweeping through Selangor and Port Swettenham to take Malacca on 14 January. General Nishimura had originally intended to rest his troops briefly in the coastal town of Malacca, but the incredible pace and success of their advance, coupled with the fact that there was an element of rivalry between him and General Matsui of the 5th Division, prompted him to press his forces on almost immediately. He reasoned that if he could quickly overcome any resistance between Muar and Batu Pahat on the coast, he might be able to completely cut off any line of retreat for the Allied forces on the trunk road at Gemas and Segamat. This would be a triumph for his division and for him personally. Nishimura gave orders, two days prior to the 2/29th's move, for his 4th and 5th Guards Regiments to move immediately to take Muar without resting in Malacca.

Nishimura's strategy was to make a two-pronged attack on Muar, with one force attacking directly and another bypassing it to make a seaborne landing near Batu Pahat, well south of Muar. One battalion of the 4th Guards Regiment would undertake the sea landings while the other two battalions were to make what appeared to be a frontal attack on the Indian units defending the town of Muar across the wide, muddy expanse of the Muar River. But while the defenders were kept occupied there, around the town, three more battalions of the 5th Guards Regiment would make a wide, circling movement to the west to attempt a crossing of the river, well upstream.

Nishimura was concerned with the problem of how to cross the river, as the Muar remains wide and deep for many miles inland. But the Japanese soldiers managed to collect, or seize, large numbers of small boats from nearby rice paddies which they used to ferry the 5th Regiment units across during the night of 16 January. The untried Indian troops in and around Muar proved no match for the elite forces of the Japanese Army which bore down on them shortly after dawn on the 17th.

The small craft used in the upriver crossing were then brought down to Muar to carry the remainder of the Japanese forces across later in the morning. During the previous evening, Nishimura's seaborne forces had also made a successful landing further down the coast near Batu Pahat. The way now seemed clear for the Guards to continue their advance southward, heading for the town of Yong Peng where they could hope to cut off the main supply route and line of possible retreat of the Allied forces further north.

During the day, the Imperial Guards consolidated their position in Muar and then, in the afternoon, infantry units of the Iwaguro Regiment began to advance on foot and on bicycles, either their own or ones taken from locals along the way, down the road heading eastward and inland towards a couple of small settlements called Simpang Jeram and Bakri.

Unlike the Japanese soldiers of the 5th Division attacking Gemas, who wore khaki uniforms, the Imperial Guards' uniform, though also of tropical-weight cotton, was a darker, olive-drab colour. On their caps, instead of the simple five-pointed star, these soldiers wore the distinctive Imperial Guards emblem: a star surrounded by a cluster of oak leaves. In addition to their Meiji .38 long rifles, they were carrying standard combat equipment, which included a rubberised fabric belt on which was slung a bayonet and three ammunition pouches containing a total of one hundred and twenty rounds. They also carried a canvas holdall which was slung diagonally across the back and contained a groundsheet, mess-kit, rations and an entrenching tool. A small haversack and water-bottle were carried on a separate diagonal strap.

Although for the most part the men in the Guards were only young, from eighteen to their mid-twenties, they were, as the 2/29th were soon to note, considerably taller than the average Japanese soldier. As a significant number of the Guards were from peasant stock, they were tough and healthy, their fitness and alertness having been further honed by training in judo and ju-jitsu. Many of them had proven themselves formidable adversaries in several theatres of war. They were well disciplined and had revealed themselves in attack, as one commentator observed, 'to be full of determination and courage, with a readiness to push on regardless, when committed to an assault, even when sustaining heavy or sometimes sacrificial casualties'. The supreme honour was to die for the Emperor and, consequently, surrender by a soldier was considered a terrible disgrace both to himself and his family. "If you are afraid of dying," the soldiers of the Imperial Guard were told, "you will die in battle. If you are not afraid, you will not die." These were the men marching to meet Arthur Shephard and the 2/29th Battalion.

At first, as they left the immediate environs of Muar, the soldiers of the Iwaguro Regiment travelled on a flat, straight road. The land around them on either side was agricultural, cleared for rice-paddies and general farming. There was not a soul in sight as they moved, quietly but confidently, along the road. It was almost as if they were passing through a land in which all of the inhabitants had died of some terrible disease, or perhaps been spirited away in the night.

Soon, a mile or so after passing through Simpang Jeram, the flat fields gave way to gently rolling hills which were covered, on both sides of the road, by dense rubber plantations. By about four in the afternoon, the first elements of the Iwaguro Regiment were nearing the area where Arthur Shephard's platoon and the rest of the 2/29th Australian Infantry Battalion were just digging in for the night. The unit commander ordered a halt for the night also, directing that a roadblock be set up and that patrols be sent out to scout ahead.

.

3

WHEN THE 2/29TH ARRIVED AT the position they were to occupy for the night, just over a mile past Bakri, there was a brief change-over process with Indian soldiers of the 5/18th Garhwals. The Garhwals, who were part of the 45th Indian Brigade Group, had established a defensive position there some thirty-six hours earlier. They were now to move back through Bakri and as far as possible down the road to Parit Jawa on the coast to take up a similar defensive stand there.

The 2/29th, which was a company short, having left D Company in the Gemas area to help the 2/30th, now spread themselves out quickly along the road, both sides of which were closely timbered with well-established rubber plantations. Lieutenant Sheldon, in command of 1Platoon, directed his men to the left of the road, with the rest of the Headquarters Company, onto a small embankment which rose eight or ten feet above the level of the roadway, leaving Arthur Shephard to supervise the allocation of positions amongst the trees. Athough no-one wasted any time, neither were any of the men unduly hurried. There was still an air of unreality about the whole thing. They'd seen plenty of the enemy in the air, but so far they had yet to meet any on the ground. They had heard no gunfire during the day so, amongst some of them, a false sense of security had developed. It may also have been wishful thinking.

Not all of 1 Platoon, once they had established their positions for the night, had a clear view of the road. In accordance with the Company's defensive layout, some were sited well to the left, away from the road and facing into rows of rubber trees which stretched off into the distance like reflections in a hall of mirrors. Also visible to their left, through the rubber trees, was

29

an open stretch of paddy fields and an old, deserted Malay house. The trees and undergrowth around them were still wet and dripping from the afternoon's downpour and the ground was damp and soggy. In a few cases, the positions individual soldiers were to occupy happened to coincide with the defensive plan which had been chosen by the Indian unit which had just left. There were a number of small slit trenches which had been dug by them, but they were invariably full of water and the men of the 2/29th were reluctant to use them. Although it required more effort to dig, somehow a fresh trench was less muddy, even in such damp conditions.

"Gawd, what a bloody business," Frank Fox mumbled as he dug away at the base of a tree. "What I wouldn't give to be downing a nice cold bottle of Carlton right now, instead of this."

"Yeah," Bomber Wainright was in the process of laying out his groundsheet in the narrow and shallow trench he had dug. "But don't bank on it bein' too soon, mate. I reckon we're goin' to be stuck here doin' this sort of thing for quite a while."

"What, right here in this spot?"

"No, no, of course not," Bomber said derisively. "I mean in Malaya."

"When do you think we'll front the Japs then? Tomorrow?"

There was a forced air of casualness about the way Frankie Fox asked the question, but it was something that no-one really wanted to have answered.

"Who'd bloody know," Bomber laughed. "Tomorrow, the next day, next week. No-one tells you, a bloody thing around here." He turned to Arthur, who was finishing off his own trench a few yards away. "What do you reckon, Shep? 'The mouse' told you anything?"

"Not much. He doesn't know much himself. He's gone off for a pow-wow with the Count. Maybe we'll get something from that. But apparently the Japs crossed some river, the Muar River, a few miles further on and we're likely to bump into them pretty soon."

Even at this late stage there was still no real awareness of just how imminent contact with the Japanese Army was. The closeness of the trees around them seemed to confirm their misplaced sense of security and, because of the confining nature of the ground, the men themselves were positioned closer to each other than they had been in all of their training back in Australia. There they had trained for much more open warfare, in open country where you could virtually take in the whole of a platoon's position with the sweep of an eye. Here, in the rubber, although in most cases only three or four yards separated each man, no one member of the platoon could see all of the others. .

Nevertheless, by about 5.30 in the afternoon of 17 January, Arthur Shephard, Jim Kennedy, Jack Roxburgh, Frankie Fox, Bomber and the other members of 1 Platoon, Headquarters Company, felt reasonably happy with their set-up...all things being relative. There was some satisfaction in the fact that they were not the most forward company. C Company was ahead of them on the same side of the road, and B Company was on the right. A Company was behind them, also on the right side of the road, roughly opposite their position in Headquarter Company. Battalion Headquarters, the Regimental Aid Post, and the other support groups for the battalion were also in the rubber trees on the left of the road. It was nice to think briefly that being somewhere in the middle was at least marginally more secure, even if, in their heart of hearts, they knew it really wasn't true.

While the battalion had been organising itself, two ammunition trucks had arrived and been directed under the trees away from the road. One of them had brought two Australian war correspondents from Brigade Headquarters near Bakri crossroads, where they had arrived with one other colleague, late in the afternoon. The two who came forward to the 2/29th's position were Hedley Metcalfe, the official photographer for the Australian Ministry of Information and Frank Bagnall, a newsreel cinematographer for the Australian Photographic Unit. They made themselves known to Colonel Robertson who, after briefly explaining the company positions, directed them to do as everyone else was doing: to dig themselves a foxhole each, close to the Battalion Headquarters.

About this time, Colonel Robertson ordered one of the three armoured cars in the troop that General Bennett had assigned to him to reconnoitre the road ahead. The vehicle, manned by soldiers from the British 2nd Loyals Regiment, the main part of which had remained in the Segamat area, was just about to move out from the cover of the rubber trees when a motorcycle roared past from the direction of Bakri, heading down the road towards Simpang Jeram and what, for the Australians, was 'no- man's-land'.

"Jesus! That's Borrie Wiles!" Jack Roxburgh yelled as the motorcyclist sped by and Arthur, Jim Kennedy and several others leapt to their feet shouting to him to stop. To no avail: he heard nothing and roared on.

Tom, or as he was better known, Borrie Wiles was one of the 2/29th Battalion's despatch riders. He had been sent back to the Bakri crossroads in order to lead two mess trucks along the road to the unit's position with the evening meals. But with the battalion so well concealed on either side of the road, he had continued straight on past it, the first mess truck following close behind. Almost immediately they heard the sound of the second mess truck coming along behind, so several men slid down the embankment onto the road waving their arms to intercept it. The truck shuddered to a halt and then hastily turned around to eventually find a parking place a couple of hundred yards back along the road, a safe distance to the rear of the battalion's position, to set up in the rubber trees for the evening meal.

"What the hell's going to happen to Borrie?" Frank Fox voiced everyone's fear. "The stupid bastard sailed right past us."

"Probably just goin' into town to get some beer, if I know 'im," Bomber Wainright commented dryly and there was some laughter. "Anyway, at least we stopped the second truck, otherwise the bloody Nips would've had all our bloody food for tonight."

The distant sound of small-arms fire came to them from down the road and they all fell silent trying to catch the sound more clearly.

"Oh, Christ," Frank Fox said softly, "that'll be Borrie. Poor bugger. Poor bloody bugger... Jesus!" He flung his tin hat to the ground.

Moments later, the armoured car moved off down the road, but it returned barely seven or eight minutes later, having met a roadblock of felled trees and considerable automatic weapons fire only a couple of miles down the road. The mess truck was wrecked in a ditch, with no sign of its driver, or of Wiles and his motorbike.

It is a standard infantry tactic when settling into a new situation, either defensive or offensive, to immediately organise a number of coordinated patrols which generally continue throughout the night. These patrols, sometimes consisting of as few as three men, sometimes ten or more, will stay out for an hour longer to cover large areas beyond the defensive perimeter of the unit, probing into what is loosely called 'no-man's-land'. Two such patrols were just setting out when Borrie Wiles and the armoured car made contact with the Japanese so it was only a very short while later that a patrol from A Company met with a Japanese patrol coming from the opposite direction through the rubber trees by the side of the road. Both sides went to ground amongst the trees and began firing at each other.

As it is generally not the main purpose of patrols to fight extended battles, both sides withdrew shortly to report back to their headquarters and to prepare for the more serious clashes that would inevitably follow.

By this time, the men of the 2/29th were fully aware of just how close the enemy was. First there had been the distant firing that had erupted when Wiles and the armoured car had ventured down the road, but now the sounds of rifle and automatic weapons fire was coming sharp and clear from only half a mile or so away. Every man was digging just a little deeper and rechecking, for the tenth time, his weapon and ammunition.

"Well, this is it, mate," Frank Fox called across the small gap separating him from Jack Roxburgh. "Now it's our turn to show the little bastards a thing or two."

"Too right, and it's about bloody time, too."

There were several similar staccato conversations going on right through the platoon as they waited for the fighting to reach them. An outside observer would have picked the false bravado in their comments, but for most of them it was simply a necessary part of the process of keeping their morale high. Virtually all of them were tense, nervous and afraid, but none of them would have been prepared to admit it. Only occasional quick queries like "Which way do you think they'll come?" betrayed the real concern that lay beneath everybody's confident exterior.

Arthur knew that the others were frightened. He was frightened himself. It felt like a tight ball sitting in his guts. He felt if he could throw up, maybe it would be better. The waiting made it worse. Bomber had told them time and time again, "Once it all starts, you forget your fear. You're too bloody busy shooting back and doing what has to be done to be afraid." They'd heard it all, but only half believed it.

For a few minutes, maybe ten, there had been a lull with only sporadic firing, but then, just as the sun set around 7 pm, mortars started exploding around the most forward positions. A Company took the brunt of the barrage which continued, very heavily, for about twenty-five minutes. Fortunately, as the men were well dug-in and most of the Japanese mortars fell either just in front of or just behind C Company's positions, only one soldier was killed and there were few other casualties from the exploding shells.

But then, almost immediately after the mortar bombardment had finished, members of C Company closest to the front heard a strange sound--a sort of metallic 'clicking'. For a few moments they exchanged puzzled glances with each other, then, through the serried rows of rubber trees filtering the last rays of the setting sun, they saw the enemy. A force of Japanese soldiers came charging onto their position, screaming and hurling hand grenades. Several of the officers and NCOs were wielding Samurai swords and their scabbards rattling against their other equipment had been the source of the strange sound.

The Australians met the attack with a hail of .303 bullets from their rifles and Bren-gun positions, killing many of the charging soldiers in the front of the wave, and forcing the remainder to go to ground. In the midst of this melee, Arthur's mind registered a small, seemingly unimportant fact: the Japanese rifles made a different sound to their own Lee Enfield .303 rifles. It was a short, sharp crack, whereas the .303s had a somewhat deeper, fuller report. Arthur could never have guessed how often he would hear and recognise those sounds in the months to come. The fierce exchange of fire continued for some minutes during which time there were casualties on both sides, although there were many more amongst the Japanese because the Australians were firing from protected positions. Then the Japanese suddenly launched a bayonet charge.

Something was wrong. Although the men from A Company didn't really have a chance to work it out, as they struggled to survive this new onslaught, things weren't quite what they'd expected. The men with whom they were now confronted somehow didn't fit the image they'd been given of the Japanese soldier. These men were big. Not the scrawny little monkey-like types with glasses they'd been told they'd be up against, but full-sized men, as large and well-built as any in their own battalion. And they seemed to be without fear as they ran screaming through the rubber trees towards them, soldiers with bayonets fixed to their rifles and the officers wildly swinging their Samurai swords. An almost electric charge of adrenalin surged through the Australian soldiers as they waited, also with fixed bayonets, to meet the assault. Once again, from their protected positions, they fired directly at the attacking Japanese, stopping many of them in their tracks. Those Japanese who did penetrate into the Australian lines were met in close combat, finding a measure of resistance in the Australians' fierce bayonet fighting that they had not expected.

Surprised at the level of casualties they sustained during the several sanguinary minutes of the bayonet attack, the Japanese withdrew into the gathering darkness, carrying and dragging as many of their dead and wounded as possible. The Australians, too, were surprised, not only by the ferocity of the Japanese attack, but by their own impressive performance in the face of such a terrifying experience. The battalion's casualties after the engagement were only three men killed, all from C Company, and a dozen wounded. They estimated the Japanese losses at between seventy and eighty.

Arthur, and he knew the others felt it too, now experienced a wave of relief sweep through him. They had survived their first real engagement. Bomber was right, Arthur thought, as he tried to go back over the dramatic events in his mind-the fear had disappeared during the heat of the action.

He laughed.

But although the results appeared to have favoured the Australians, they all knew there was more to come and, as time passed, their nerves went back on edge and virtually every man in the 2/29th spent a sleepless night anticipating, at any moment, a sudden new charge from the rubber trees by hundreds of Japanese.

"Funny how, when you stare out into the dark for a while, you start imagining things," Jim Kennedy whispered to Arthur at one stage during the night.

"Right," Arthur replied softly. "I could swear I've seen dozens of bloody Nips floating from tree to tree, getting closer all the time. But it's just your imagination. The worst part of it all is that they're probably miles away and we could be getting a good night's sleep instead of staring out into the flamin' darkness like this."

The 2/29th saw no more of the Japanese during the night. Nevertheless, the enemy forces were on the move, initiating situations which would have a profound effect on the Australians the following day. The Ogaki Battalion of the Imperial Guards was directed to move up the road from Parit Jawa on the coast towards Bakri crossroads, a manoeuvre which threatened to cut the Australians off from the rear. Around midnight, word reached the 45th Brigade Headquarters near the Bakri crossroads that the 5/18th Garhwals, who had been moving down towards Parit Jawa after having been relieved by the 2/29th, had run into strong Japanese forces and been badly mauled by them. They had then retreated to another area near the Bakri crossroads.

When he learnt of the advances being made by the Japanese forces, Major W. W. Julius, the Officer in Charge of the 65th Australian Artillery Battery near Bakri, sent an urgent signal to Colonel Robertson asking him for additional protection for his '25-pounder' guns. Robertson, although reluctant to weaken his own battalion, which was already one company short and now in contact with the enemy, nevertheless decided, at about 1 am, to send A Company, under Captain A. B. Sumner, back to the crossroads to help prepare for the new Japanese threat.

Robertson was a veteran of World War I, having risen through the ranks to become a commissioned officer in the 23rd Battalion. He was wounded during the battle for Broodseine Ridge in France, in October 1917, and won the Military Cross there. He'd served as a part-time soldier in the Australian Militia in the years between the wars and on the outbreak of World War II, had become Commanding Officer of the 2/21st Battalion. Then, in October 1940, he had been given the task of forming the 2/29th Battalion.

He was a big man, with a round, clean-shaven and jovial face, who was universally liked by his battalion. But none of his men, not even his second in command, knew that a recent medical examination had found John Robertson technically unfit to command a front-line battalion. He had been diagnosed as having a heart condition and was under orders to return home to Australia. In an earlier meeting with the commander of the Australian forces, General Gordon Bennett, he had pleaded not to be sent home and to be allowed to lead his battalion into battle for the first time. Bennett had granted his request on the understanding that he would relinquish his command and be relieved within twenty-four hours of going in to action. There seemed little chance of that now.

Meeting with his second in command, Major Jock Olliff and other company commanders in the early hours of 18 January, Robertson had to report to them that already the Allied units at the crossroads, behind their own position, were under pressure from the Japanese forces and that the artillery fire they could hear was not only the 65th battery, but also Japanese guns. The enemy artillery attack, it was later learnt, was so intense and accurate that one of the Australian guns was disabled and an ammunition truck set on fire. Although Robertson was not aware of the exact details of the Japanese movements at this stage, he fully realised the danger.

"I'm sure I don't have to tell you," he said, "how important it is for us that the crossroads be held. We could very easily be cut off if these Japs coming up from the coast, push past the crossroads." There was a moment's silence.

"How big is the Jap force, sir?" Captain Maher, the B Company commander, asked.

"At least company strength," Robertson replied, "but it could be a battalion."

Maher nodded. "And what's there at the crossroads for us at the moment? Just the artillery battery, our own A Company and the remnants of the Garhwals." He paused and then whispered, "Jesus!"

"It's not quite as bad as it looks." Robertson straightened some creases on the map laid out before them. They were in a dugout, the open top of which had been covered over with a tent top. A single hurricane lamp illuminated their faces and tllt map. "If they don't force the issue, Colonel Anderson will be there with the 2/19th by early morning. That'll even things up a bit. But in the meantime we're a bit thin on the ground here until A Company gets back."

"When will that be, sir?" Jock Olliff asked.

"I've told Major Julius to release Captain Sumner and A Company just as soon as the 2/19th have settled in, so, hopefully, they'll be back here with us by late morning."

Robertson then directed that two guns of the anti-tank battery be positioned in the cutting in the road beside the area occupied jointly by B Company (which had spread itself back somewhat to partly fill the area vacated by A Company) and Headquarters Company of which 1 Platoon and Arthur Shephard were a part. Robertson wasn't exactly expecting tanks, but he felt the guns would be a good deterrent to any vehicles on the road-or troops, for that matter. It was a decision that could hardly have been more fortuitous.

The night had been warm, but as usual, in the brief period before dawn there was a pleasant coolness and freshness in the air. At other times it might have been more appreciated by the men standing by the anti-tank guns in the cutting or by Arthur Shephard and his platoon, positioned just above them. As it was, all of the men were beginning to feel the effects of more than twenty-four hours without sleep and they were more than a little irritated with the endless drone of the mosquitoes which had plagued them during the night. Most of them were wearing shorts, knee-length tropical issue, which were cooler than long pants during the sweltering heat of the day, but left inviting openings for mosquitoes during the night.

As the deep darkness of the night gradually changed to a soft greyness, it was apparent that the morning sky was overcast, not with heavy rain clouds, but sufficient cloud cover to hide any sign of the sun.

For some time there had been no sound of gunfire. The heavy barrages of artillery fire from a mile or so behind them in the Bakri crossroads region had ended in the early hours of the morning, apparently with no success for the Japanese, and there had been no sign of more Japanese from along the Muar Road since they had been repulsed from A Company's position just after dusk the previous evening.

But now, in the dim grey light, the silence of the dawn was broken by the distant sound of throbbing motors, faint at first but growing steadily louder. Then, as the sound became clearer, it was possible to discern the clanking noise of tracks on the roadway.

'Tanks!"

4

THE WORD THAT TANKS WERE coming spread rapidly through the rubber trees and once again everyone experienced a heightened pitch of expectation. In the cutting, the three-man crews of the 13th Battery, 2/4th Anti-tank Regiment were standing by their guns, strange-looking devices with a box-like armour-plated protective shield and wheels which collapsed outward to form a stable base for the weapon. The shells stacked in boxes immediately behind the weapons were two-pound projectiles which, because of the high velocity at which they were fired, had armour-piercing capabilities.

The early use of tanks by the Japanese invasion forces in Malaya had taken the Allies by surprise. British tacticians had considered Malaya unsuitable for tank warfare, so there were simply no Allied tanks available in Malaya. The Japanese, however, proved that light and medium tanks could be used to their advantage and on several occasions, further to the north, they had routed Allied infantry formations with their tanks. The unit now advancing on the 2/29th Battalion's position was a company of ten medium tanks under the command of Japanese Guard Major Gotanda.

Seconds after the Australian lines realised that tanks were advancing on them, Japanese mortars started exploding in amongst the rubber trees, and the forward areas of the Australian position began to come under heavy automatic weapons fire.

Every man in the battalion was in his slit trench, either waiting until he could see something to fire at or, like those on the outer perimeters, already returning fire at Japanese soldiers moving through the trees. As far as the tanks advancing down the

40

road were concerned, the anti-tank guns sited on the roadside would have to be the main defence, but in addition to these weapons, each company also had on issue a much smaller, yet still very lethal weapon for dealing with armoured vehicles. It was called simply an anti-tank rifle. It was a good deal bigger than a rifle, with a supporting tripod near the front of the weapon. The firer would lie behind it on the ground, with the butt pulled into his shoulder. It had a tremendous kick which could break a shoulder if not held properly, but it fired a .50 calibre, high-velocity shell which could pierce light armour, and also inflict serious damage to a tank's unprotected tracks, quickly immobilising it. On this occasion tanks had not been expected, so the anti-tank rifles had not been issued or properly sited in advance.

"Where's the bloody anti-tank rifles?"

Arthur Shephard, who had been peering through the trees trying to catch a glimpse of the tanks, looked up to see a tall, thin figure running towards him yelling. "There's a whole line of bloody tanks comin' down the road. Where's the anti-tank rifles, Sarge?" It was Signalman Muir, who everybody called 'Woof'.

Arthur leapt to his feet. "Follow me," he shouted. "They're back here in the ute."

A utility truck was parked well back in the trees under cover. It had a large camouflaged canvas canopy over its back tray. The two men reached the vehicle and Arthur jumped immediately into the back of the truck intending to hand the weapons out to Muir. He bent down on one knee for a moment to pick up the first of three weapons and at that instant a sustained burst of machine-gun fire tore the whole top of the canopy and the cabin roof of the truck clear away. One moment Arthur had been under the cover of the canvas canopy-the next, it had almost completely disappeared, leaving only tattered shreds on the sides.

"Jesus Christ!" he yelled as he dived headlong from the truck's tray to the ground beside Signalman Muir who had also immediately fallen flat on his face to avoid the hail of bullets coming from a Japanese machine-gun.

"Struth!" Arthur gasped. "Did you see that?"

"Yeah. Bloody lucky!"

"Lucky's right, mate," Arthur said, "and I'll tell you something else. I'm intending to stay that way. If you want those flamin' guns you'll have to get 'em yourself!"

Woof nodded as they lay in the grass beside each other, sheltering behind the wheels of the truck. "But we've got to get them, Sarge. We need them real bad."

In the meantime, the area from which the Japanese fire had come was now being raked by heavy fire from two or three Australian positions and, after a minute or so, the two men felt they could risk trying to get the weapons again. They hastily unloaded the weapons and some boxes of ammunition from the truck and made their way as quickly as possible back to the platoon's position overlooking the road, just in time to see the first three tanks rounding a slight bend in the road and moving steadily towards them.

The two larger weapons of the anti-tank battery were ready by the side of the road, one at the head of the cutting and one at the rear. Once the tanks came into range, both guns began firing their solid, two-pound shells at the tanks as fast as they could be loaded into the breech. The only problem, one hardly expected by the gunners, was that the first few rounds of 37 mm, armour-piercing shells not only pierced the tanks' armour, but went straight through and out the other side, apparently leaving the occupants miraculously still alive and the tanks still advancing, firing all their guns as they came.

For a moment the Australian gun crews, crouching behind the armoured shields of their weapons, were nonplussed. It was as if the Japanese tanks were somehow indestructible, invincible...they could not be stopped. From all around, the infantry in the trees were pouring a hail of small-arms fire into the tanks, but they were of no use, just bouncing off the armour.

"H-E! H-E!" Sergeant Clarrie Thornton, in charge of the foremost anti-tank crew, yelled above the din of the battle. Gunner Jimmy Flowers tore open another ammunition box and rapidly loaded AP/HE shells into the breech. These were also armour-piercing shells, but contained a small high-explosive charge which detonated the instant the shell had penetrated the tank's armour, exploding inside the body of the tank.

By this time the first tank, which was travelling at speed, had passed Thornton's position so that to fire on it the gun-layer, Claude Brown, had to rotate the weapon almost 180 degrees, thereby exposing themselves to fire from the oncoming tanks. They fired their first high-explosive shell into the back of the lead tank as it tore down the road away from them. It literally lifted off the ground with the force of the shell's impact, but continued moving forward. Thornton then directed another round into the vehicle's tracks, stopping it dead. But before they could turn their gun back, the second and third tanks had also passed their position. Now, with both anti-tank guns...Thornton's at the front of the cutting and the other at the far end of it...pouring fire into them, these first three tanks were quickly disabled.

Thornton immediately ordered Brown to rotate the gun back towards the front, where three more tanks were now rumbling quickly down towards them. Although Thornton was wounded in this first action, the crew continued firing, stopping a total of seven more tanks, all of which were attempting to blast their way through, but now found that the way was blocked by the leading tanks and fallen rubber trees which had been cut down by heavy machine-gun fire from all directions. Once they realised they were trapped, a couple of the Japanese tank commanders tried to turn their tanks around in a desperate attempt to get away, but the narrowness of the road and the steepness of the cutting prevented any possibility of manoeuvring.

Several of the tanks, although immobilised, were still capable of firing their weapons, medium-calibre canons and heavy machine-guns, and they became, in effect, miniature pillboxes that had suddenly been dumped into the battalion area. This, plus a strong Japanese infantry attack, prolonged the battle for some time. When they first approached the 2/29th's position, the tanks had been accompanied by several Japanese infantry units on foot, but they had met such withering fire that they had been forced to go to ground outside the battalion's defensive perimeter while their tanks were now trapped inside it. The noise was deafening...a dreadful cacophony of sound from all of the Australian weapons, including the anti-tank rifles, that could be brought to bear on the stranded tanks filled the air, as did the choking smell of cordite and smoke.

As well as the anti-tank fire that was being poured into them, grenades and 'Molotov cocktails' were also hurled at the tanks from the embankments above them. Then, as the vehicles burnt and the ammunition in them began to explode with sharp bursts, the hatches of a couple of tanks were flung open and the surviving Japanese crews scrambled out, shooting wildly as they leapt from the burning vehicles. They were cut down almost immediately in the general hail of fire that continued until there was quite obviously no-one alive, either inside or outside any of the ten tanks.

When the firing stopped, there was a brief respite from the sounds of battle and a feeling of general elation swept through the Australian lines. They had won a victory. They had stopped the Japanese juggernaut. There was laughter and back-slapping all around.

Hedley Metcalfe and Frank Bagnall, the two war correspondents, had filmed the action and now took movies and still photographs of the triumphant gun crews, the wrecked tanks and the bodies of the hapless Japanese crew members who had jumped from the vehicles when they had been set alight.

Claude Brown, the gun-layer on the forward weapon, was ecstatic. "I feel so proud," he told the correspondents. "We did what we were trained to do. I always had a nagging doubt that somehow we mightn't be able to do it, but we did. We upheld the name of the old diggers, the ANZACS."

Arthur Shephard, on seeing the bodies, was struck by a momentary flash of pity, but found that he quickly thrust the emotion aside. This was not a time for sympathy or sorrow. This was war. In the engagement they had just been through, it had clearly been a case of 'them' or 'us', and most of the men were fully aware of the fact that while this time it was 'them' who had lost out, next time it could just as easily be 'us'.

As a group of men from B Company began searching the bodies of the Japanese soldiers in order to salvage what maps and papers they could, one of the men was stunned, as he rolled a body over, to see two blue eyes staring vacantly back at him. Pulling the man's helmet off revealed a mop of blond hair.

"Hey, look at this!" he shouted. "A whitey."

Several others rushed up to look at the dead man, who would have been about five feet nine inches tall and around thirty years old. "Must be a bloody German," one of them said.

"But what would he be doing here?"

"Probably an adviser, or observer of some kind."

"Well, he sure as hell didn't give them the right bloody advice this time," someone muttered from the back of the crowd that had gathered. They all laughed.

But there was a bigger, perhaps more important shock in store for them. When the rest of the bodies were searched and any papers they had were examined, they realised that the tank unit was part of the Imperial Guards Division. Up until that time, the British and Indian Army forces had only identified the Japanese 5th Division as being involved. When the news that the elite force of the entire Japanese Army had now joined in the struggle for Malaya eventually reached Brigade Headquarters, the Commander, Brigadier Duncan, received a nasty shock. He immediately realised that the force with whom they were contending in the Muar area must be far greater in size than had been anticipated.

He directed that the battalion of Indian troops, the 4/9th Jats, who had been spread out along the Muar River when the Japanese crossed it, should now attempt to join up with the 2/29th and then, when the Australian 2/19th Battalion, under Colonel Anderson, arrived later in the morning, the three battalions should be able to go onto the offensive.

But it was not as simple as that. The 4/9th Jats had first come into contact with the Japanese on 15 January. It was now the morning of the 18th. During those three days, they had been fighting desperate battles in an effort to get back through to the Allied lines, and they had been cut to pieces in the process. The few that were left were now trying to tear their way through dense jungle to avoid the Japanese who were both behind and in front of them.

As for the 2/29th, their brief moment of glory had passed only too quickly and they were moving inexorably now towards their real moment of truth. Unbeknown to the Australians, during the frenzied firefight with the tanks, Japanese sniper units had circled through the rubber plantations and marksmen had climbed into tall rubber and coconut trees where they found positions from which they could take irregular pot shots at the Australian troops when the occasion presented.

So, as the morning wore on, the men of the 2/29th found themselves subjected to increasing harassing fire from these hidden snipers, fire which, although it succeeded in killing only a couple of men and wounding three or four others, also produced an unsettling and unnerving effect on the Australians. In addition, neither they nor the Brigade Headquarters, were aware that elements of the Japanese Ogaki Battalion, the one which had met the 5/18th Garhwals the night before on the Parit Jawa Road, had also begun to infiltrate the jungle and was about to cut the road behind the 2/29th, breaking its link back to Bakri and beyond to its Brigade Headquarters. It was not until some time later in the morning that the Japanese move was discovered and the danger to the 2/29th realised.

Meanwhile, the Japanese infantry of the Iwaguro Regiment, although deprived of the support of its armour, now began to step up its attempt to break through the 2/29th's defences on the Muar Road. By mid-morning, as a result of a wide, flanking movement through the rubber trees, they had all but surrounded the three Australian companies, some five hundred men, setting the stage for a vicious and decisive battle.

The 2/29th Commander, Colonel Robertson, soon realised that the forces building up around him were considerably larger than those of his own and that he would need more men to successfully hold up the Japanese force opposing him. He had been promised his own A Company back from the crossroads as soon as reinforcements arrived there, but it now seemed to him that he could not afford to wait. He had just directed his signaller to send a message to Brigade Headquarters informing them that he was in need of A Company immediately, when the first Japanese soldiers from the Iwaguro Regiment came out of the rubber trees about a half a mile behind the 2/29th Battalion and onto the road between it and the Bakri crossroads. A sergeant in charge of the group immediately ordered several of his men to begin searching the roadside and the surrounding shrubs for the Australians' telephone landline.

It was general practice at that stage of the war for all battalion signals and communications to be carried by landline. This was usually laid by the battalion signals unit and although it was naturally intended that the line should be hidden from view, unless it was physically buried beneath the ground, secrecy was often difficult, if not impossible to achieve, particularly if the line had to be laid over a mile or more. Wireless communication was available to fighting units, but it was the prerogative of the signalmen attached to the divisional headquarters to set up and run all radio networks. Because of the complexity of the situation around the Bakri crossroads and the amount of wiring that would be required to link up all the units when Anderson's 2/19th Battalion arrived in the area, a request had already been sent to General Bennett at 8th Division Headquarters at Yong Peng for a wireless signals unit--a radio transmitter and Receiver--to be sent to Bakri, and two young signalmen, Max Robinson and Chris Nielson were already on their way, driving from Mersing in a Ford truck with a Model 101 radio transceiver unit in the back.

Also, at 7 am Colonel Anderson and some seven hundred men of his 2/19th Battalion had arrived with supporting Bren-gun carriers at Yong Peng after a seventy-mile drive from the east coast. At Yong Peng General Bennett ordered a troop of British anti-tank guns to join them for the remaining thirty-mile trip to Bakri.

At 2/29th Battalion headquarters, in a broad but shallow trench under camouflaged canvas, set back from the road in the rubber trees, Signaller Harry Bernard turned to Colonel Robertson. "Can't get through, sir. Been trying for the last few minutes. Line's dead. Must've been cut somewhere."

"Cut? God. Just what we need," Robertson moaned. "What the hell does that mean?" He took a couple of paces around the cramped confines of the headquarters dugout. "Are they bloody well behind us now? Surely not." He turned to his second in command, Major Olliff, "What do you think, Jock?"

"I don't think so, sir. We've had patrols back up the road a fair way. It's clear behind us as far as I know. Could be something gone wrong with the line back at Brigade or Bakri. Someone's probably cut the bloody thing by accident."

Colonel Robertson pondered a moment while the signaller tried to get through again. "We're supposed to have that battalion of Jats meeting up with us, but who knows when they'll turn up, if they do at all. We really must get A Company back here...A Company at the very least...or I think we'll be in trouble soon." He turned to the signaller, "Nothing, eh?" "No, sir." "Where's the despatch rider?"

"Bauckham, sir? Just over there." The signaller indicated a small dugout through the trees nearer the road. "Do you want him?"

"Yes. Get him over here as quickly as you can. I want him to go to Brigade."

"I don't think it'll do any good, sir," Olliff said. "We told Major Julius earlier we wanted Sumner and A Company back, but he said Brigade had insisted they stay until the 2/19th arrived there."

"Bloody ridiculous! I'll sort it out with Julius myself and talk to Brigade from there." He picked up a few papers and stuffed them in his shirt. "Even if Anderson hasn't arrived with the 2/19th, I'll bring A Company back with me. We've got to have them. It's as simple as that."

A few minutes later, a little after 11 am, Colonel Robertson set off, heading back towards Bakri crossroads, riding as a pillion passenger on the motorcycle of despatch rider Private Syd Bauckham.

In the meantime, C and B Companies and Arthur Shephard's Headquarters Company were coming under increasing fire from snipers as well as frequent mortar barrages. Only the fact that they were well dug-in by this stage prevented them from experiencing greater casualties. Once or twice, a Zero had swooped in low over their positions, but fortunately they had not been subjected to any serious aerial attacks, largely because their positions under the dense foliage of the rubber plantation made it impossible for the Japanese to have attempted anything but indiscriminate bombing.

All of the men, including those in 1 Platoon, were feeling the effects of their cramped, static and dangerous positions. They were very much pinned down and on the defensive.

"I thought we were supposed to be attacking them," complained Bomber Wainright who, like everyone else, was crouched in his foxhole. "But here we are, stuck in these flamin' ditches, waitin' for them to come and get us. We should be out gettin' them."

"We're supposed to wait until the 2/19th arrives," Arthur put in from his trench about half a dozen yards away. "Without them we haven't got the numbers to take the Nips on. They reckon there's at least a battalion of them out there, maybe more."

As he finished speaking, a bullet whistled into the ground between the two men. All heads turned in the direction from which it came. "Did you see it?" Arthur shouted. "Anybody see where it came from?" Ever since the snipers had begun taking pot shots at them, they had been desperately trying to pinpoint their hidden positions in the trees, so far without much success.

"Then what about these little bastards?" Bomber said to Arthur. "We don't need numbers for them. I don't see why we can't get out and clean up this little lot. They just keep taking a few shots every now and then and it keeps us all pinned down like rats in a hole."

"I don't reckon we should worry about them," Frankie Fox commented. "They're such lousy shots, they're really no harm to anyone."

"Yeah," Arthur agreed, moving his position slightly, "but you don't exactly feel happy about just wandering around looking for them. They might just be lucky enough to get you."

Another shot whistled into the ground, only inches away from the edge of Arthur's trench. ,

"I saw him! I saw him!" Jim Kennedy called from a short distance away. "I'm sure I saw him that time."

"Where? Where?" several of the men asked, and Jim pointed in the direction of a large rubber tree in front and slightly to the left of them. The tree's foliage was completely joined with that of the other trees surrounding it, and it was difficult to imagine how any sniper could find a clear line of sight from it into the Australian positions.

"I saw the leaves move," Jim Kennedy insisted, "and I'm sure I saw some smoke."

Bomber Wainright jumped out of his trench and ran to join Jim Kennedy. Jim pointed at the tree and they both studied it intently. Others in their trenches called to Jim to point out the tree more accurately.

"Put a shot into it," Arthur called to him, "so we can all see which one it is." Jim Kennedy aimed his rifle and fired a shot into the part of the tree he felt concealed the sniper. A few leaves were blown apart as the bullet whistled into the foliage, but there was no other movement.

"Did everyone see that?" Arthur called to the half-dozen or so who could see the tree "All right. Fire two rounds each into that spot. If he's there, we'll see how the little bugger likes being on the receiving end."

"Okay, all at once," Bomber yelled, sighting his rifle on the tree, "fire!" Six weapons fired almost simultaneously into the same tree, but nothing happened. Disappointment all round. "Are you sure you saw him move there?" Bomber said softly to Jim. "That tree?"

"Positive! He's in there. I guarantee it."

"One more round," Arthur called, lining up his own .303 on the area of foliage Jim Kennedy had indicated. "When you're ready, fire."

This time, after the volley had been fired, there was only a slight pause before the leaves of the tree began to shake violently and then, without another sound, the body of a Japanese soldier plummeted headfirst to the ground. A great cheer erupted from the little group of men. "That'll teach the bastard," Bomber shouted triumphantly. "Now, where's the next one?"

When Colonel Robertson had left the battalion area for the Bakri crossroads, the young despatch rider had acted on his commanding officer's directive, "Don't waste any time, Bauckham," and opened the bike's throttle so wide and accelerated down the road so quickly that Colonel Robertson was forced to grab him around the waist to prevent himself from being left behind. The road was well-surfaced and clear, so the bike quickly reached sixty miles an hour, at which speed Bauckham eased up slightly. Between the battalion position and the Bakri crossroads, a distance of under two miles, there was no break in the solid band of rubber trees growing densely right up to the edge of the road on both sides, and there were only two or three slight bends along the whole distance that separated the forward Australian battalion from their compatriots at the crossroads.

The two men on the motorcycle had travelled little more than half a mile when, rounding a small bend in the road, they were confronted with two trees which had fallen from either side of the road into the centre, completely blocking it only a hundred yards in front of them.

"Jesus Christ!" Bauckham shouted, throttling back immediately and applying the brakes.

"What the hell's happened here?" Colonel Robertson said, looking over Bauckham's shoulder. For a moment, there was no sign of movement, or any human involvement about the barricade. But then a flash of olive uniform and a brief glimpse of steel helmets behind the trees and on the roadside near them revealed the true nature of the roadblock. A hail of bullets began flying past them.

Bauckham had already locked both wheels of the bike into a dangerous sideways skid, and only a miracle prevented both men and the machine from tumbling into a heap as they desperately screamed to a stop and then tore off again back in the direction from which they had come.

"Hang on!" Bauckham yelled as he swung the bike around wildly and skidded in the gravel on the edge of the road, then accelerated off at a terrific pace, with bullets whistling around them. ,

"Good lad," Colonel Robertson laughed in Bauckham's ear, "Good—uggh!"

Bauckham felt the Colonel's chest pushed momentarily harder into his back as if he, too, had been pushed from behind. A bullet had struck Robertson in the back. And then, at the last moment before they rounded the bend that would have taken them out of sight of the Japanese, Bauckham felt a terrific blow to his upper left arm as a bullet tore through his biceps. His left hand flew from the handlebar and flopped useless to his side. He struggled to control the bike with his right hand as it slewed to one side and straightened up again. He felt the Colonel's grip around him loosen, but he dared not slow down.

"Are you all right, sir?" he shouted. Robertson said nothing. "Sir? Hang on, sir. We'll be back in the lines in a moment." A low moan escaped from the Colonel's lips and Bauckham felt his body begin to relax behind him.

Oh, Jesus, he cried to himself, and then, "Hang on, sir, hang on! We're almost there."

He slowed the bike down but, as the Colonel began to go limp, Bauckham could not do anything to hold him onto the bike and, when they were only a hundred yards from the battalion's lines, within sight of the rear foxholes, the Colonel's body just collapsed and fell from the back of the motorbike.

Bauckham stopped the bike and tried, futilely, to drag his dying battalion commander back towards the lines but, on the point of collapse himself, he realised it was impossible and began to wave and shout for assistance.

One of the platoon commanders, Captain Gahan, seeing what had happened, leapt into a Bren-gun carrier and roared off down the road in it to pick up the wounded Robertson and rush him back to the relative safety of the battalion perimeter. The unit's Medical Officer, Captain Victor Brand, gave what help he could to the Colonel, but there was no hope. Within twenty minutes, he was dead from shock and loss of blood.

Captain Brand, who had been leaning over him when he died, looked up at Captain Gahan. "He's gone."

Gahan turned his back. "Jesus!" he whispered. He stood for a few moments staring into the trees, then moved off quickly to detail some men from the mortar platoon to dig a shallow grave for the CO.

Several men came across to begin digging.

The battalion's chaplain, Padre Macneil, shocked and sorrowful, read a brief burial service. The sergeant in charge of the men who had dug the grave stood looking down at the Colonel's body and suddenly burst into tears. For a few moments he sobbed uncontrollably. The faces of the other men were also streaked with tears.

5

THE NEWS OF THEIR COMMANDING officer's death spread rapidly through the lines of the 2/29th Battalion and, although it did not cause any massive collapse in the battalion's morale, it came as a terrible shock. Robertson had been respected and revered by virtually every man in the battalion, so it was a serious blow. What was of greater concern to the men, though, were the details of his death. The idea that any possible line of retreat for them, and also their lines of support from the rear, were now cut off by a Japanese force behind them, was cause for alarm.

Major Olliff, the battalion's second in command, now took over the leadership of the beleaguered unit. Olliff was a pleasant, round-faced man of thirty-six. He was a company manager from Armadale, in Victoria, who had spent time in the army reserve and joined up, first with the 2/21st, and then transferred to the 2/29th when it was formed at the end of 1940. He was the commanding officer of Headquarters Company. He had a great sense of humour and a kindly nature, as those members of his company who ever got into trouble could testify, but he was also a stern disciplinarian. His company nicknamed him 'The Count'.

Olliff naturally realised the precariousness of their position, but what to do? There had been no orders for them to retreat. In fact, the 2/29th's last directive from Brigade Headquarters indicated that when the Indian battalion and the 2/19th Battalion arrived in the area, they would be going onto the offensive. This was clearly not possible. Olliff was now faced with the same dilemma as Colonel Robertson-not knowing what was happening and not being able to tell anyone outside about their own situation.

At 45 Brigade Headquarters, just beyond Bakri, there had also been mounting concern, as the morning wore on, about the inability to make contact with the 2/29th. The officer in command, Brigadier Duncan, frustrated by his fruitless attempts to get messages to or from the Australians, ordered an armoured car patrol to head down the Muar Road to contact the 2/29th. At about the same time, around noon, the bulk of Colonel Anderson's 2/19th Battalion arrived at Bakri cross- roads (most of its D Company had been directed to stay on the east coast) and began taking up defensive positions. The armoured car patrol returned shortly afterwards to report withering fire from both sides of the road at the point where the roadblock had been set up.

Major Vincent, the 2/19th's second in command, now gave permission for the 2/29th's A Company to return to its own lines. To make sure it could get through the roadblock, he asked for an additional armoured car, with Bren-gun carrier and mortar support, as well as providing two platoons from the 2/19th Battalion. Their initial attack on the Japanese at the roadblock failed, but after a renewed attack and heavy fighting, the Japanese force was routed and the roadblock cleared. The trucks which carried A Company, accompanied by the wireless truck with signallers Robinson and Nielson, finally arrived at the 2/29th's beleaguered position around mid-afternoon.

Major Olliff immediately ordered the signalmen to get to work establishing a wireless link back to Brigade Head-quarters. He also directed that one of the trucks be loaded with wounded and sent back to Bakri. Captain Brand, the Medical Officer, selected about six of the most seriously wounded and put them into the truck. The two Australian war correspondents were also told to leave in an armoured car which had come through with the trucks. The return convoy left as soon as the truck was loaded. They found the roadblock still clear and sped on to Brigade Headquarters, where details of the battalion's parlous position and Colonel Robertson's death were passed on to Brigadier Duncan.

The correspondents, reunited with their colleague,

4. A Japanese tank crewman lies dead beside his tank at the end of the engagement with the 2/29th batallion on 18 January 1942 (Australian War Memorial negative no. 11307)

5. One of the two 2/4th Anti-Tank gun crews relaxes at the end of the battle in which ten Japanese tanks were destroyed. (Australian War Memorial negative no. 11309)

6. *2/29th Batallion medics give emergency aid to a seriously wounded soldier shortly before their withdrawal.*

(*Australian War Memorial negative no. 11308*)

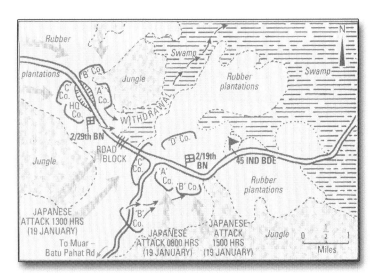

Map 4. 2/19th and 2/29th Batallion positions immediately prior to 2/29th's attempts to break out from the Japanese trap.

newsreel cameraman Cliff Botomley, stayed with the wounded as the truck, now carrying a large Red Cross sign, continued southwards. Although they had no way of knowing, those who travelled in that truck were the last of the 2/29th to be evacuated successfully and the only members of the unit, wounded during the Muar road fighting, to ever reach hospital.

"How's that bloody wireless transmitter going?" Major Olliff asked the Intelligence Officer, Lieutenant Wastell. "They've been at it for an hour."

"Any moment, sir, if we can believe them. They've cleared up the problem apparently, and we should be on the air any time."

But shortly afterwards, Signalman Max Robinson squatted down in the battalion dugout with bad news.

"Sorry, sir, but we're just not getting through. I think the batteries are okay, so it could be that their receiving gear is on the blink. Either that or the jungle is affecting the signal badly. We need a higher aerial."

"Christ!" Olliff muttered. "What a predicament! This is bloody ridiculous. We've got to keep in touch, otherwise we haven't a clue what's happening."

"We're going to chop some long bamboo poles, sir, and tie them to a couple of trees. If we can get the aerial above the general level of the trees, we should be all right."

"Okay, hop to it," Olliff said. "Don't waste any time."

The general attack on the 2/29th had eased slightly and for the remainder of the afternoon there seemed to be a lull in the fighting. The road back to Bakri was kept open and the men of the 2/29th enjoyed a brief respite from sniper and mortar fire. But it was a worrying time. They knew that the Japanese were regrouping and bringing up reinforcements in preparation for a new attack.

At about 4 pm, a British officer from the Indian Jats Battalion reached the Bakri crossroads. He reported to Brigadier Duncan that his battalion, which had been routed at the Muar River two days previously and with whom he had been retreating through dense jungle and rubber plantations, was only about six miles north-west of Bakri and should arrive before long.

At the time of A Company's return to the 2/29th, Major Olliff had been informed that Brigadier Duncan's earlier directive (that when the Jats arrived they should be part of a renewed offensive) still stood. But, because of the lack of communication, and the fact that the Jats still had not arrived, Olliff had no further idea of what was happening. Neither could he know that the British officer's report to Brigade Headquarters now cast serious doubts on the whole plan. The Jats were a much diminished and dispirited force, many of them with no arms or ammunition. The officer told Brigadier Duncan that they had also been without proper food or water for two days and would be in no condition to go into action again.

As the evening drew on, there was no sign of the Jats arrival in the 2/29th's area and by 5 pm it was clear that, even if the Indians were in fighting condition, they would not arrive in time for the combined force to mount any offensive before dark.

Trucks were now despatched to the 'A' and 'B' Echelon areas, beyond Brigade Headquarters, for food, ammunition and other supplies. They also carried more wounded with them as well as an urgent plea for ambulances to take out other wounded. Passing without incident the area where the road- block had been, they drove on through Bakri to arrive safely at Brigade Headquarters. The wounded were given further treatment there and were told they would continue south in the trucks the following morning.

In the 2/29th's position, as the sun set and light gradually faded, Arthur and his companions were amazed to see a distraught young Chinese man suddenly appear in their lines. He had come from what they had all believed to be an empty house, on the far side of a paddy field, to their left. Speaking broken English, he somehow managed to convey to Captain Brand that his wife and son were lying wounded in the house. Captain Brand ran with the man across the paddy field to the house to find the man's wife lying face-down on the floor, her thighs and buttocks torn with large bullet wounds, and the little boy, about eight years old, with a deep laceration of the right arm. He found that the husband had packed the wounds with kapok, which had stopped the bleeding. Brand did what he could to treat the wounds further, but then told the man that, as darkness was approaching, he could not get them out tonight. However, he promised to try to get them out in the morning and back to hospital as soon as possible. He left the man and woman and dashed back to his own lines, expecting to be brought down by Japanese fire.

Just before nightfall, Signaller Nielson reported to Major Olliff that wireless connection back to Brigade Headquarters had been established.

"Thank God for that," Olliff said, directing a string of messages to be sent back immediately.

Once Brigadier Duncan had been made aware of the 2/29th's situation, he postponed his plans for a counterattack until the following day, but Olliff had serious doubts that they would work even then.

As dusk began to close in around the men of the 2/29th, in order to re-establish a 'night perimeter', they drew in on themselves somewhat, taking up previously prepared positions which, for the close conditions of the rubber plantation and darkness, represented a considerably tighter formation than had been adopted during the day. Although they had remained in a defensive posture for most of the time, they had been able to expand outwards slightly in some directions, depending on the conditions and the relative positions of the Japanese.

"I wonder if the little buggers'll try it on tonight?" Jim Kennedy's voice came out of the deepening gloom on Arthur's left. He was talking to Jack Roxburgh.

"They're not so bloody little, from what we've seen so far," Bomber Wainright grunted from his position, also off to the left. "And the bastards aren't all half-blind like they kept telling us back at Segamat."

"No, but they can't see any better than us," Arthur put in. "They can't see in the bloody dark ... at least I hope they can't."

Almost as if the Japanese had heard him speaking and were out to prove him wrong, the night suddenly erupted into a cacophony of whistling mortar shells exploding in the battalion lines, mostly along the left-forward elements of C Company and their own Headquarters Company. There was the chatter of machine- and Bren-gun fire to the front from their own lines, and heavy small-arms fire, which indicated a Japanese attack. Everyone sank a little lower into their slit trenches, adjusted their steel helmets and peered into the night, concentrating and trying harder to see whatever there was to be seen. Within a few minutes, they again heard the distinctive sound of Samurai swords and bayonet scabbards, clinking against grenades and other webbing equipment, coming closer to them through the darkened corridors of rubber trees.

"They're comin' again," Bomber called. "Keep your eyes out."

As he spoke, several grenades exploded close by and rifle fire erupted all around them. Several Australian voices, from Arthur's platoon although he couldn't recognise them, were heard shouting from further to the left. "Here they come! Watch out, Charlie!", followed by more firing and yelling. Then, suddenly, there were figures amongst them in the dark. Bright flashes of fire from the rifles of both sides pierced the blackness for brief instants, leaving the area from which they originated even darker than before, and all accompanied by the sharp cracking of rifles and pistols and the stutter of sub-machine-gun fire, as well as frenzied yelling in both English and Japanese. For a few short minutes, the whole scene had an aura of madness, of a nightmare.

The Japanese had again charged with bayonets fixed, but although the darkness gave them the advantage of surprise and they had the initiative in being on the offensive, they also found the inability to see what they were attacking a serious hindrance. The Australians, too, had their bayonets fixed and were in a good situation to lunge quickly at the Japanese as they came by. After what seemed like an eternity, but was probably only five minutes or so, several loud whistles were heard, followed by much shouting in Japanese and then the attackers withdrew, disappearing into the trees as quickly as they had emerged.

For a few moments, there was silence as the Australians waited to see what might happen next, then voices began to chatter between the trees. "Stopped the bastards again!" someone yelled. "You bloody beauty!"

"Have a look at this, will yer?" Bomber Wainright called out. A Japanese soldier had fallen dead near Bomber's slit trench, having been shot in mid-charge. "He's got a bloody gasmask with him! Don't tell me the little bastards are going to try gas on us?" Bomber was acutely aware of how distasteful gas warfare could be, having survived two gas attacks in northern France in 1917.

It was soon discovered that all of the Japanese soldiers who had been killed during the attack had been carrying gas respirators and it was reasonably assumed that the others who had survived and retreated were also carrying them. The information, when passed on to Battalion Headquarters, surprised Major Olliff and he ordered Signaller Chris Nielson to pass it on immediately to Brigade. At Brigade Headquarters, the news was doubted. They just could not believe that the Japanese were about to initiate gas warfare and yet they were clearly prepared for it, which was more than could be said for the Allied troops.

The attacks on the 2/29th during that evening of 18 January were conventional infantry attacks in which some one hundred and fifty Japanese had come into close combat with the Australians. Although the Australians realised they were still on the defensive, the fact that they had once again repulsed what they now knew to be an elite element of the Japanese Army was a great boost to their morale. In addition, the almost mad fearlessness the Imperial Guards displayed in their charges and close-quarter fighting had not deterred the Australians on this occasion.

The experience of the previous evening and a growing understanding of the Japanese techniques had prepared the Australians somewhat. The Japanese clanking of their weapons and shouting as they came had been intended to frighten their adversaries, but once the Australians were aware of what the Japanese were doing, they used it to their own advantage. Waiting quietly in the dark, either in their shallow trenches, beside them, or behind a tree, they were able to use the Japanese shouting to pinpoint the target and to shoot or bayonet the attacking soldier with ease.

Each Japanese attack on various parts of the Australian lines had been thrown back with severe losses which were increased when the Australians laid down heavy mortar barrage into the area through which the Japanese were retiring.

Although the 2/29th felt justifiable satisfaction in having turned the Japanese back on their heels once again, there was still the unpleasant sensation that the opposing forces were building up and that they now had a reasonably good idea of the layout of the Australian battalion and the positions and strength of the various platoons and companies. This was borne out during the night as the Japanese were able to direct a number of accurate mortar barrages of their own onto the Australians. The thick foliage of the rubber plantation provided some cover, but it was a mixed blessing. Some of the mortars exploded on contact with the branches of the trees and, while this sometimes dissipated the blast, in others it sent showers of shrapnel screaming down into the dugout positions, inflicting several casualties during the night.

Arthur Shephard and the rest of 1 Platoon, along with virtually everyone else in the battalion, had now been almost forty hours without proper sleep. Some, including Arthur, had managed to doze briefly during the afternoon, whenever there was a moment's respite. But now, in the pitch blackness of the rubber plantation, the desperate need to sleep crept over the men, even though they could not escape the feeling that their lives might depend on staying awake. There was a 'watch' system in operation whereby men would take turns in sleeping and standing watch during the night, but even those who dropped off to sleep legitimately found themselves shuddering awake with a start at the sound of machine-gun fire in the distance, an explosion or occasional ear-splitting yells from the Japanese in the jungle beyond their lines.

"Hey, Joe!" one of them would call in English. "We coming to get you." Or perhaps, "Surrender now, or you die!" Or several of them might laugh, or produce a series of fiendish cackles which were simply designed to unnerve the Australians.

The tactics had their effect on some but, for the most part, the men of the 2/29th, after listening in surprised silence for a while, gave back as good as they received, although unfortunately not in Japanese.

"Pull yer flamin' head in, you little yellow bastards," Bomber Wainright yelled back early in the night, much to the delight of those around him. "If you step over here again, you'll end up with a bayonet up yer bum!"

Arthur managed a total of about four hours of intermittent sleep during the night, but by dawn he felt it had done him no good at all. His body was tingling with tiredness and, like the rest of his men, his brain felt numb with fatigue.

As dawn broke, the young Chinese man appeared in the lines again, begging the Medical Officer to help get his wife out. A small group of men, including a couple of stretcher bearers, was sent off with the man to bring the wounded woman and boy back. They quickly returned, carrying the woman to the Aid Post area where she and the boy were treated by Captain Brand, given a meal of bread and jam, and told they would be leaving before long in one of the ambulances that had got through to them during the night.

With the grey light of morning spreading through the rubber trees, and more movement in the battalion area, the men seemed to brighten up. Not that there was much to feel bright about. The situation around them was obviously deteriorating rapidly. It was now estimated that the strength of the Japanese forces surrounding the Australian unit, still one company short of battalion strength, was at least two infantry regiments: the Kunishi Pursuit Unit and the Iwaguro Pursuit Unit as the Japanese called them. These were the 4th and 5th Infantry Regiments of the Imperial Guards--a total of almost four thousand men. Four thousand against the 2/29th's six hundred and the seven hundred of the 2/l9th. And to make matters worse, a patrol had reported that the Japanese roadblock between the 2/29th and Bakri crossroads had been reestablished at greater strength during the night, once again effectively isolating the 2/29th from any support from the Allied forces at Bakri and beyond. It was now impossible to get any more wounded out and there were no supplies or food coming in.

"We could probably fight our way out, sir," the Adjutant, Captain Morgan, said to Major Olliff as they discussed the situation in the morning. "But we'd have to do it soon. The longer they are allowed to stay there, the more likely it is they'll be reinforced."

"Right," Olliff agreed, "but we've got no orders for that. We have to wait. See if Captain Maher can spare a couple of platoons from B Company to go up there and assess the situation." He paused a moment. "If they can't clear it themselves, then they should get back here as quickly as possible with an estimate of what we're dealing with."

Olliff radioed the news of the re-established roadblock, and his moves to deal with it, to Brigadier Duncan at 45 Brigade Headquarters. He told the Brigadier, "If you can keep the road open, we can stay here until hell freezes over." Duncan, who was still working on the possibility of the combined counter-attack, told Olliff to maintain his position, at least until the Jats arrived, or until a decision had been made by higher command.

So, by the morning of 19 January, the 2/29th were facing a potentially disastrous situation. Brigadier Duncan knew it, as did General Gordon Bennett and General Percival. Percival had already directed the Australian 2/30th Battalion, still holding the Japanese at Gemas, to withdraw down the trunk road behind Segamat and to be ready for a further pullback to Yong Peng. It was now also patently clear that the forces in the Muar area, including the 2/29th and the 2/19th should be withdrawn also, perhaps as far as Yong Peng. But no orders were given to this effect during the morning of the 19th.

At 45 Brigade Headquarters they were still waiting for the Indian Jats Battalion to come in from the jungle.

"Where the hell are they?" Colonel Anderson, CO of the 2/19th fumed on several occasions during the morning as he waited for the Jats. He had been ordered to delay his planned mini-offensive until the Indian troops arrived. "We can't do a damn thing until they turn up."

"They've been in the jungle for three days now, sir,"

his second in command, Major Vincent, said quietly. "I don't think they'll be up to much even if they do come in."

Shortly afterwards, Anderson held a brief field-telephone conversation with Brigadier Duncan and, in the absence of the Indian troops and the realisation that they would almost certainly not be able to make any worthwhile contribution to an offensive, Duncan now changed his plans and gave Anderson permission to mount an attack down the Muar road towards the embattled 2/29th position.

Anderson's plan was to send one company advancing down the Muar road to test the enemy strength and also, hopefully, to clear the area for the Jat's arrival through the jungle. If they were still coming, they should be very close by now, he reasoned. However, before his A Company, under Captain Beverly, could begin its advance, it had to wait for a British anti-tank gun unit which would support it. This did not arrive and, while waiting for it, the other companies of the 2/19th Battalion, which were spread out around the Bakri crossroads area, came under rear attack from a Japanese force which had been deployed from the Parit Jawa road eastward through the jungle.

Colonel Anderson responded quickly by sending two platoons from A Company, and all of B Company, to give the Japanese a taste of their own medicine by encircling them. The manoeuvre proved highly successful, catching the Japanese by surprise. They found themselves running around in circles, caught in vicious crossfire from the Australians, who then launched a bayonet charge against the scattering remnants of the Japanese force. At the end of the brief engagement, the ground was littered with corpses. One hundred and forty Japanese dead were counted against ten Australians killed and fifteen wounded.

Not long afterwards, at around 10 am, a truckload of wounded from the 2/29th, one of the last few to get through from the battalion area during the night, prior to the Japanese re-establishing the roadblock, was preparing to leave 45 Brigade Headquarters on the thirty-mile drive to Yong Peng. Additional wounded from the just-completed action were being crowded into the back of the truck, which was parked under the cover of some rubber trees next to a small plantation bungalow that was being used as headquarters. Inside the building, a group of officers, including Brigadier Duncan, stood huddled over a situation-map discussing a signal from Command Headquarters at Yong Peng.

Three Japanese 'Val' dive-bombers came screaming down on the area, strafing several vehicles, including a Bren-gun carrier and an armoured car in the road. Each of them released one 500-pound bomb as they passed. Two of the bombs fell harmlessly in an otherwise empty part of the rubber plantation, but the third came down through the trees, missing the truckload of wounded by hardly more than a dozen yards or so, to make a direct hit on the bungalow that was the Brigade Headquarters. Brigadier Duncan was hurled to the ground unconscious, while all of his staff, except two officers, were killed or seriously wounded.

The carnage was shocking. There were 'bodies lying everywhere', one of the wounded men in the truck, Lieutenant Ben Hackney, later wrote:

Portions of men's stomachs hanging on limbs amongst the leaves of the trees...torn, bloodstained limbs scattered about with only a lump of bloody meat hanging from them to indicate the body from which they were torn. Just beside the road, a naked waist with two twisted legs lay about two yards away from a scarred, bleeding head with a neck, half a chest and one arm...there were some still alive, but bent over, and others crawling with every manner of injury.

Sergeant Clarrie Thornton, the anti-tank gun commander who was amongst the wounded, reported seeing the British Brigade Major rushing about in the chaotic aftermath of the explosion, giving orders for the wounded to be helped, while he himself was in a critical state, having had one of his arms blown off.

The bomb also destroyed all of the vital maps as well as the codes which the signallers needed for communicating with West Force Headquarters, and for some time they were unable to get through at all. When they finally did make contact and the news was passed to General Gordon Bennett, he found the disaster almost impossible to believe.

CHAPTER FIVE

When the extent of the blow was realised, the forces at the Bakri crossroads did what could be done to pull the situation together again. Colonel Anderson, assumed command of the Brigade. Brigadier Duncan was alive and not seriously wounded, but he was incapacitated by shock and concussion. Anderson decided that the 2/29th should be extracted from their perilous position as soon as possible, *if possible*, to join up with his own battalion somewhere behind Bakri crossroads. But the Indian Jats Battalion had still not shown up so, rather than totally abandon them, he opted to hold the 2/29th's attempt at withdrawal until the Jats arrived. The delay proved to be a costly one because, in waiting for the Indians, all of Anderson's own companies now came under renewed attack and heavy fire from the Japanese Iwaguro Regiment which were now pressing in increasing numbers up the road from Parit Jawa. At the same time, other enemy units, either from the Iwaguro Regiment, or the Ogaki-or both--had further infiltrated between the two Australian battalions to strengthen the roadblock on the Muar road and to slowly begin tightening their noose around the 2/29th.

Then, suddenly, around noon, the Jats began arriving through the rubber trees on the right flanks of the 2/29th's position. They were lucky not to have been shot up as they came, but after considerable yelling on their part to identify themselves, a ragged force of about two hundred were quickly allowed to enter the battalion area. The Indians had fought their way through other Japanese forces which had been seeking to extend their grip around the northern side of the 2/29th, but once they had managed to get by the Japanese, they were finally able to link up with the Australians after their long trek through the jungle.

They were in a deplorable condition. Not only were many of them young, insufficiently trained and frightened, but they were desperately tired, hungry and thirsty. Their first reaction upon their arrival in the Australian lines was to charge madly for the water truck which was standing in the trees near the battalion headquarters dugout.

"Stand back! Stand back!" Captain Brand shouted, jumping towards them. "You'll all get a drink." But they continued their wild dash for the truck and began to mill around, fighting for water. A shot rang out. Then another.

Captain Brand and Major Olliff, as well as one of the British officers commanding the Indian group, had all drawn their pistols and were aiming them at the soldiers at the taps.

"Back! Get back, unless you want to be shot," Major Olliff yelled. "Stand in line! You'll all get a drink. And keep down, under the trees, because if we don't shoot you, the Japs will."

Fortunately, the wild scramble quietened down and within a short time all of the Jats had been given water. But while their thirst was slaked, their new situation with the 2/29th was hardly any better than it had been before. They were still well and truly trapped, as was the 2/29th.

Not long after the Jats' arrival, Major Olliff decided to launch an attack on the roadblock behind them to try to open up the way for the battalion's withdrawal. Until then, he had been unable to spare enough men to attempt an attack on the road-block without seriously weakening the battalion's own defensive position in other areas. Now there was the opportunity of using some of the 2/29th and the newly arrived Jats in a joint effort to force a breakthrough.

But, because of their inexperience and also, perhaps, a combination of fatigue, disillusionment and fear, the Jats were not up to the task. They were cut to ribbons by the devastating fire-power of the Japanese, who were now positioned at the road-block in some strength as well as in the surrounding rubber plantations and on both sides of the road for some distance from the roadblock itself. The Jats broke and ran, but were mown down in numbers by heavy machine-gun fire.

The attempt to break the roadblock was called off and the Jats were regrouped into defensive positions at the battalion's rear. At the same time, although they did not know it then, other remnants of the Jats battalion were making a wider circle through the jungle, slightly further to the north, missing the 2/29th's position entirely, to meet up with Colonel Anderson's battalion at Bakri crossroads.

As the day wore on, the 2/29th's position worsened. With no supplies coming in, water and food were running low and the lack of ammunition would soon become critical. And to make matters worse, they now came under heavy bombardment from Japanese artillery. 5.9 inch shells began bursting all around them. They heard, one soldier later recalled, 'the faint reports of the guns firing in the distance, then the crescendo scream of the shells and the ear-splitting crash of the burst'. Everyone took what cover they could. The Jats, who had not dug any slit trenches, were panic-stricken and, despite calls to lie down, ran around hysterically, sustaining even more casualties.

In the meantime, Captain Brand and a couple of assistants continued their herculean task of trying to treat the wounded. Brand was amputating the remains of a soldier's foot with a pair of scissors when given the news that one of the stretcher bearers, Private 'Kanga' Boyd, had been killed while trying to bring other wounded soldiers to the Aid Post. Private Jack Dorward, the other stretcher-bearer, had been severely wounded.

When the barrage finished, Brand rushed to the road, where he had been told there were several more wounded. He found one man lying with his thigh terribly smashed and near death, though conscious and in great pain. Brand administered almost a gram of morphia to the man and passed on to another, an Indian who pointed piteously at his legs, one of which was badly torn and broken. Telling the man to put his arms around his neck, Brand struggled to get him up the embankment. Unable to go any further, he called for help and, after another soldier left his slit trench to crawl to the edge of the cutting, the two were able to lift the Indian into the cover of the rubber trees.

Others now came to the aid station in a flood. Some were affected by 'metal splash', the result of exploding shells and shrapnel. One man, Sergeant Wedlick, had been sprayed by metal splinters across his face and neck, while another showed a line of large metal splinters across his back. But these casualties, as bad as they might have been under normal circumstances, were for the most part sent away, as Captain Brand was almost totally occupied with other, more seriously wounded: those with legs or arms blown off, or serious internal injuries which were life-threatening. One man came up to the aid post with a wound caused by a bullet passing right through his mouth, and out one cheek, tearing half his tongue off on the way. He took one look at the other men being treated by the medical officer and turned away.

At Bakri crossroads, meanwhile, Colonel Anderson, now in charge of what was left of 45 Brigade, was confronted with the news that his own line of retreat was now also cut. A Japanese force had breached the road behind the 2/19th's position and established a second major roadblock between Bakri and Parit Sulong. The Allied forces were being divided up piecemeal. A section of Bren-gun carriers was sent to attempt to force its way through, but was unable to, so heavy was the opposing fire.

Anderson now felt that the only course was to get the withdrawal of the 2/29th and the rest of 45 Brigade underway as soon as possible. But the 2/29th's position looked almost hopeless. The only way they could be given any significant help in their pullback would be to lay down a concentrated, timed barrage of artillery fire which would start close to their own position and move backwards through the Japanese roadblock as the men of the 2/29th followed it back towards Bakri.

The strategy behind this kind of tactic is the same for withdrawal as for an advance--the artillery fire is meant to keep the enemy's heads down until one's own troops are right upon them and in a position to fight their way through. The danger in the strategy is that it requires great accuracy on the part of the gunners, precise timing on the part of the friendly forces on the 'receiving' end, and good communications between the two. It would be difficult, if not impossible, to satisfy all of these conditions under the circumstances, but they had no choice but to try.

Radio signals of the escape plan got through to Major Olliff, but there would have to be a delay of some hours before the artillery barrage, from many miles to the rear, could be arranged. This meant that the withdrawal could not start before 6 pm and, all the while, the Japanese attacks on the battalion were building up.

A force of Japanese machine-gunners, swinging around on the 2/29th's right flank through the rubber trees, launched an attack in mid-afternoon but was beaten off by the Australians who, leaving their foxholes and moving from tree to tree, advanced on the Japanese, forcing them to retreat. Similarly, on the left flank shortly afterwards, a Japanese attack and an Australian counterattack resulted in the Japanese force retiring. But with the weight of numbers building up behind them, the Australians knew that these were only temporary retirements. Just before 5.30 pm, Major Olliff gave the order that word be passed on through the dugouts of the different platoons that the 2/29th was at last to move out, in an attempt to link up with the 2/19th Battalion.

"We're pulling back," Lieutenant Sheldon told Arthur. "Make sure everybody's ready. We're moving in exactly thirty minutes."

"We're all bloody ready, sir," Bomber said from one side. "Don't worry about that." He laughed softly. "We've been bloody ready for three days!"

6

THE WITHDRAWAL WOULD UNAVOIDABLY BE a complicated manoeuvre and, although every man already knew it, they were all made aware once more of the dangers of following one's own artillery barrage. It was planned that the battalion would retire along the line of the road, heading straight back towards the roadblock. They could hopefully break through the block and continue on to Bakri. Timing within the various platoons would be crucial and everybody would have to keep as close an eye as possible on their officers and NCOS who would be attempting to direct the movement of the troops in relation to the expected landing areas of the artillery shells. At the same time, as in all withdrawals, it was critical that the enemy not be aware that a retreat was underway. As the Japanese were now pressing on all sides, they could easily become aware of any weakening of the opposition by the absence of firing from a particular sector and would attack there even more vigorously.

Consequently, Captain Gahan, who commanded the Bren-gun carrier platoon, volunteered to stay behind with three of his carriers to keep some heavy fire-power from his machine-guns pouring into the enemy positions at the front so that the remainder of the 2/29th could begin their move out to the rear.

Captain Brand was directed by Major Olliff to load all of the wounded into whatever trucks were available and to proceed by road when and if the roadblock was broken. Trucks were immediately unloaded. Bed-rolls and all sorts of equipment were thrown out, papers and maps were burnt and the wounded, totalling about fifty Australian and Indian soldiers, were lifted into the trucks which were lined up on the road, nose-to-tail, waiting.

Arthur Shephard, feeling desperately tired, waited silently in his slit trench for the order to come. In the fading light of the early evening, he could see his mates Kennedy and Roxburgh off to one side, and Bomber Wainright a little further away lying on his back with just a bit of his tin helmet showing above the edge of his trench. Bomber could have been asleep, but Arthur knew he wasn't. Bomber was as anxious as everyone else to move. They'd been able to hold the Japanese at bay, but they'd nevertheless been pinned down in the one spot for two days and two nights-which felt more like two weeks-and they were beginning to feel the terrible reality of their position. They were trapped. And they would have to do something to get out.

Sharp on 6 pm, they heard the dull 'CARUMPP! CARUMPP! CARUMPP!' of heavy artillery shells exploding behind them as the expected barrage on the Japanese roadblock to their rear began. At the same time, the command to move out was given and passed on by the waving of hands.

"Come on!" Arthur called in a hoarse whisper, waving his arm to the members of the platoon near him. "We're off. Keep your heads down, shut up, and don't move in front of Lieutenant Sheldon."

They heard the machine guns on the three carriers open up to begin pouring belt after belt of covering fire into the surrounding trees and paddy fields.

Bomber, Kennedy and Roxburgh all slid out of their shallow foxholes and, spreading out through the trees, began to move back through what had been their own lines. They could see men who had been occupying trenches behind them moving now like shadows through the trees. They came up to Captain Brand and his truckloads of wounded. How the hell are these poor bastards going to get out, Arthur wondered as they passed by.

During the past forty-eight hours, except for brief lulls, the noise of battle had been loud and almost continuous and, in order to be heard, communication between the men, whether it was commands being passed down from Battalion Headquarters or just comments or conversations, had been by shouting. Now they were all quiet, moving as silently as was possible under the conditions. The noise of the artillery barrage was loud enough to cover any noise they might make but they slipped through the plantation almost as if their breathing could be heard. They watched and listened intently for any commands or directions, given mainly by hand signals but sometimes by soft calls from one man to the next. As they passed back through the rubber trees on the right-hand side of the road, they involuntarily adopted a half-crouched posture, stepping from the trunk of one rubber tree to the next, seeking the best cover possible.

Dusk was falling rapidly, but there was still sufficient light for the Australians to present good targets for Japanese riflemen as they crossed the road and occasional pieces of open, grassy ground. There was the danger, too, that they might tend to bunch up and make even better targets as they went along, but with frequent exhortations from their officers and NCOS, and quiet signals amongst themselves, they overcame the natural tendency to close up on each other.

The plan was to follow the line of the road until they reached the area of the roadblock to their rear, at which stage, if the British artillery's range and timing was right, the enemy positions should be receiving a heavy pounding. Then, they all felt sure, they would be able to push their way through the Japanese positions.

The artillery bombardment was continuing but now, amongst the din of exploding shells, they heard heavy small-arms fire ahead of them—automatic weapons and rifle fire. In the gloom, Arthur tripped over a body. He stooped to look and saw immediately that it was a Japanese soldier. As they moved on, crouched low, he saw two more dead Japanese, frozen in grotesquely distorted poses, one with his mouth open and eyes staring. A burst of machine-gun fire tore through the trees above them, seeming to come from nowhere. With a shout, Frankie Fox, who was ten or fifteen yards in front of Arthur, hurled a grenade as far as he could over a low line of bushes to his right and all near him went to ground. Within seconds, the sharp 'crack-thump' of the explosion sent a shock wave blasting across them.

"What is it, Foxy?" Arthur and several others called. "Where are they?"

"Just over there, behind those bushes," Frankie answered. "I saw them moving."

But now there was no movement. Everybody lay still,

watching the area that Frankie Fox indicated. Nothing. Two or three men from further back circled carefully around behind the bushes, soon confirming that there were no Japanese there. Frankie had imagined it.

"Better be a bit more careful from now on, Foxy," Arthur said to him as they moved on. "Don't want to give ourselves away, and we gotta keep our eye on the ammo, too."

But every one of them was jittery and, more than once, shots were fired, including one by Arthur, into the trees and bushes at their side, when there was no enemy there.

They had covered about a quarter of a mile without any actual contact with the Japanese. They could hear Captain Gahan's Vickers machine-gun still firing away behind them. There was heavy firing in front of them and sporadic shots off on either side. Now, to their front, as A Company was crossing an open patch of high lalang grass, a sudden and prolonged burst of machine-gun fire from the right ripped into their midst immediately killing two A Company officers, Captain McNaughton and Lieutenant Calvert, and several men, bringing progress to a halt. Fire was returned, but the Japanese gunners continued with heavier, sustained fire.

Major Olliff, moving immediately at the rear of the leading company, had been just about to cross the lalang grass patch when the firing erupted. The majority of A Company had already got across, but now the Headquarters group and the rest of Headquarters Company, including Arthur Shephard's 1 Platoon, were pinned down close to the edge of the road.

"There's a machine-gun nest, sir," one of the remaining A Company men, who had dashed back to Major Olliff, explained. "Somewhere in the trees up ahead."

Olliff turned to Lieutenant Sheldon, who was at the head of 1 Platoon, just behind him. "Come on, Sheldon, let's take a look," he called softly.

Creeping forward through the rubber trees, Olliff, Sheldon and several others came to a point where there was a slight bend in the road beside them.

"Where the hell are they?" Olliff asked the soldier who had come back with the information.

"Somewhere in there, sir...I think." The man vaguely indicated a large area on a small rise by the side of the road about fifty yards ahead of them.

"That's no good," Olliff muttered. "We'll have to pinpoint him before we can have a go at him. And if we don't get a move on, the arty'll be coming down and we won't be in the right position on time."

Suddenly, more deadly machine-gun fire was erupting all around them. Chips of wood from the rubber trees splintered over them. One of the soldiers who had run to change his position was hit in the hail of fire.

"Christ! They're on to us here," Olliff shouted, "but we still can't see the bastards."

A deep trench, a storm-water channel whose sides were overgrown with vegetation, ran alongside the road a few feet to their right.

"Into the ditch...quick!" Olliff yelled. "We'll be better off there."

The five men rolled into the ditch and then, crawling on their hands and knees in the mud, began to make their way back towards the Headquarters Company group which was still pinned down in a low piece of terrain between the road and the open patch of grassy field. But before they could reach the safety provided by a slight bend in the ditch, a long burst of machine-gun fire raked the length of the trench, cutting Olliff, Sheldon and the other three men down before they knew what had happened. '

Several men scrambled from more secure positions nearby to try to pull Olliff and the others to safety. The three soldiers were dead, but Olliff and Sheldon were still alive, though mortally wounded. They were out of the line of fire now, but there was nothing that could be done for them. Within minutes both men were dead.

"The Count and Twitty Mouse have copped it!" Arthur heard someone call back.

"Christ!" he muttered.

"Poor bastard," Bomber said from behind him. "Poor bastard." Arthur knew he was referring to Sheldon, not Major Olliff, for although Bomber had always taken a rise, or made fun of the Lieutenant, he quite liked the young man and would never have wished him harm, not the real harm he had come to now.

Two other attempts were made by members of the Headquarters Company to try to establish exactly where the Japanese machine-gun nest was and how it could best be dealt with, but they met with equally intense fire and only produced more casualties. What remained of the Battalion Headquarters group and Headquarters Company were now stuck in the trees on the edge of the road in almost total darkness, with the new battalion commander dead and most of the lead company, A Company, gone on ahead of them. Behind, there was no sign of B and C Companies which were supposed to be following them. There was some confusion as to what course they should follow.

Arthur and the rest of the men of Headquarters Company could hardly have known that, while they had been pinned down, first C and then B Company had swung around from their rear to the left in an attempt to clear the machine-gun nest, or detour around it through the jungle. At the same time, B and C Companies had been unaware, when they made the move, that a large number of their comrades were pinned down just to the side of them. Moving deeper into the rubber on the edge of the jungle and a large swamp, B and C Companies had come upon the track followed earlier in the day by those remnants of the Indian Jats Battalion which had succeeded in making their way through to Bakri. B and C Companies continued on, following the track, bypassing the Japanese machine-guns to eventually reach Bakri crossroads and Colonel Anderson's 2/19th Battalion. A total of seven officers and one hundred and ninety men made it through.

As the roadblock had not been broken, the trucks carrying the wounded could not get through, so Captain Brand had been forced to make the difficult decision to unload those walking wounded who could travel with him, leaving the rest. The small group of about eight men, including the two signalmen Robinson and Nielson, who had stayed to the last, headed off into the scrub, intending to circle the roadblock and join up with the battalion on the road beyond it. Captain Gahan and several others had also made a break for it when it became impossible for them to continue their rearguard action with the machine-guns, and were also struggling separately through the swamps to the north of the battalion position.

In the meantime, the remaining trapped members of the 2/29th, including Arthur's 1 Platoon, managed to backtrack in the gloom, almost to their own original lines, to attempt the same wide swing to the left, around the Japanese machine-gunners. But even before they were clear of the danger of the machine-gun emplacements, they were hurled into an even worse situation.

Arthur Shephard, now in command of his platoon, was hurrying through the grass and rubber trees, with the rest of his men strung out behind or beside him, when a tremendous blast erupted hardly a dozen feet away, killing two of his men outright. Several other men, including Arthur, were hurled to the ground wounded.

Amazed and terrified, and not really knowing what had happened, Arthur scrambled on all fours trying to get up to run for cover. Close by him, Bomber Wainright was moving to do the same, but within seconds, before they were even on their feet, another shell burst only half a dozen feet away, literally lifting them off the ground in a shower of mud and grass and throwing them to one side. An Indian soldier next to them was blown in two, the torn and bloody halves of his body strewn several yards apart. Arthur had felt a stunning blow to his neck and his right side, but as he continued moving, scrambling desperately back to the shell crater, reasoning instinctively that a shell wouldn't hit the same place twice, the thought flashed through his mind, I'm still conscious. I'm still alive! But his right arm refused to function and, glancing at it, he saw that the whole of the right side of his shirt was soaking in blood...his own blood!

Lying down, he gingerly touched his chest with his left hand. Nothing wrong there. And then, as his hand moved around to his right shoulder, he felt a gaping tear in the back of his neck—a deep hole below and behind his right ear. He let his head fall to the ground and lay stunned for a moment in the muddy shell-hole, staring upwards into the night, trying to collect his wits. Around him more shells were landing in a cacophony of sound. He felt a desperate urge to swallow. He tried, but couldn't. Again he tried, succeeding this time, but only with terrible pain.

The chaos continued. His own actions since the second explosion had taken only a few seconds, during which he had been preoccupied with establishing whether he was alive or dead. But now he was back in the present.

"Jesus Christ!" someone was yelling. "They're our own fucking shells! We're into our own bloody artillery fire!"

And there's no possible way to stop them, Arthur thought vaguely, his mind in a mist.

By a devastating twist of fate, the little band of soldiers was now subjected to a ruinous bombardment by the British artillery. The shells continued to rain around them for several minutes as they huddled as close to the ground as possible. Then, in accordance with the predetermined plan, the artillery fire shifted back a couple of hundred yards before moving further back again.

"You all right, Shep?" someone called from the left.

It was Jim Kennedy.

"I don't know," Arthur replied. "My arm's buggered, bleeding a bit. What about Jack and where's Bomber? He was right beside me."

"I'm here," Bomber called. "Copped something in the side, but I think I'm okay. Jeeze that was close. If we'd been standing up after that first one hit, we'd have been blown to the shithouse!"

Staggering to their feet, the battered group now stumbled towards the swamp as it seemed to offer the greatest degree of safety. Lieutenant Wastell, the battalion's Intelligence Officer, argued that travelling left, right or to their rear would only lead them into contact with the Japanese again. The swamp, straight ahead, was their only alternative.

In the darkness, the men kept close together, so as not to lose sight of each other. There were approximately two hundred men—one hundred and fifty members of the 2/29th, including a few from A Company and their commander, Captain Sumner, and about fifty of the Jats soldiers who'd come into the battalion lines during the afternoon.

There was no clear way to follow as they moved into the swamp. The ground quickly changed from a soft, soggy consistency to a deep mud and then dark, fetid water into which they sank, first to their knees, then thighs, then to their waists. They waded in amongst the mangrove trees growing in the shallows, and while their feet tripped on the tangled roots, the branches scratched and scraped at their faces and bodies. In the darkness of the swamp, their retreat turned into a terrifying shambles.

"Keep together," voices from the blackness called softly. "Keep together or we'll lose each other." They tried to keep in single file, each man hanging onto the bayonet scabbard of the man in front, but this was extremely difficult, particularly for those men who still carried weapons. They had to use one hand to fend off creepers and vines and enveloping undergrowth that grew or hung over the swamp in many places. It was easy to lose balance, and often the line was broken.

"How deep does this bloody water get?" someone muttered as they moved further out into the swamp. "I can't swim."

"Don't worry about the bloody swimming, mate," another disembodied voice replied. "It's the fuckin' alligators you've gotta watch."

"Alligators? They don't have alligators here, do they?"

"My bloody oath. And snakes as well."

"Jesus!"

Since they first entered the swamp, the sound of the artillery barrage had continued, although at a good distance from them, but now machine-gun and rifle fire erupted much closer. Both behind them and to their right they could see streams of tracer bullets cutting through the trees on the edge of the swamp. The group turned away from the firing, with Arthur plunging on blindly amongst them, thinking of nothing but escape and survival. Around him, other dark figures were wading as silently as possible through the black water.

Putting his left hand to the wound on his neck, he felt again the wetness of his own blood and the numb, torn flesh around it. He wondered if the piece of metal that had caused the wound was still in his neck and if he would soon begin to die from loss of blood.

"Try to keep your weapons dry," he heard a voice say off to his left and he became aware that he no longer had his rifle. It's hardly much use to me anyway, he thought, feeling the useless appendage of his right arm hanging limply by his side.

Suddenly, there were shouts to the front, Japanese

voices. More shots rang out and they could hear bullets passing close by. Machine-gun fire and tracer bullets were raking the swamp ahead of them.

"Down! Down! Get down, everybody!" Arthur recognised Jack Roxburgh's voice just ahead of him in a group of three or four men who all shouted at once. They were all much deeper into the swamp now, anyway, with only their heads and shoulders above water.

"Jack?" Arthur called.

Two figures turned in the dark and came back towards him. "That you, Shep?" Jack Roxburgh whispered. Jim Kennedy was with him. We wondered where you got to. How're you going, mate?"

"Not too bad, I suppose. Bloody arm's had it though."

"Need a hand?"

"Dunno. Think I'll be all right."

"Better stick with us. We'll keep an eye on you. Have you seen Bomber?"

"No," Arthur replied. "He was right next to me before."

"Bomber!" Jim Kennedy called softly into the dark. "Hey, Bomber--where are you?"

But there was no reply from the group of dark heads which bobbed like so many bodiless floats on the water around them. Although the men were mostly from the same company, it was as if they were all strangers. In the gloomy blackness of the night, each man seemed to have retreated inside himself, squatting in the swamp water, waiting for something to happen...for someone else to make a decision about what to do next.

When they stopped for a while, as they did now, the unknown terrors of the swamp began to creep in on the edges of their minds. Their feet were sunk deep into the warm, slimy ooze of the bottom, and each had the dread feeling that, if he stayed in the one place for too long, he would just keep sinking deeper and deeper into the dark morass. When they tried to move, it was a slow, laborious process to pull one foot out of the muck and place it in again a little further forward.

A whispered piece of information came back through the darkened collection of heads around Arthur.

"They can hear us when we move. The Japs are on the

edge of the swamp. They know we're in here somewhere and whenever we move, they can pinpoint us. We gotta stay still."

When they were still and completely silent, they could hear the sounds from groups of Japanese soldiers to their right and to the rear. At one stage, a mortar barrage was laid down in the swamp but, fortunately, the bombs fell into an area on their right. Several of the projectiles landed very close to the Australians but, as far as anyone could tell, caused few, if any, casualties. The concussion of the explosions could be felt under the water but was dissipated considerably by their distance from them.

The little band took advantage of the sounds of the barrage to move further away into the swamp and then, at the end of the mortar attack, to listen quietly to the sounds of the Japanese moving in the darkened jungle on the fringes of the swamp-sounds which, thankfully, seemed to be a greater distance away than they had previously.

At one point, as they rested briefly, Arthur was conscious of a sudden relaxation of his body. They had been in the swamp for what seemed like hours. The water and the mud made it feel like a warm bath. The bombing and the machine-gun fire had stopped some time ago, and Arthur's mind had drifted subconsciously to other things. If this really was a nice warm bath, he thought, and I was just lying back, enjoying it, I could go to sleep. He felt like lying back and going to sleep, to just let everything float away. He could just sink into the nice warm water and sleep. He felt a great tiredness sweep over him. He could think of nothing but sleep. The thought passed vaguely across his mind that perhaps he was dying. This is what it must be like. Loss of blood. Just go to sleep. Not really so bad after all.

"Shep! Shep!" A voice broke through and Arthur jumped. Someone was whispering and touching his left arm. "Come on, Shep, we're moving on." It was Jim Kennedy.

Arthur blinked his eyes and shook his head and, without replying, began to move slowly through the water behind the others.

"What's the time?" he heard someone say. "My watch is buggered."

"Half past two."

They had been in the swamp for almost seven hours and

neither Arthur, nor any of the men around him, knew where they were, how much of the swamp they had traversed, which direction they were heading, or how much swamp still remained to be crossed. Someone was leading, though, someone up ahead, and almost two hundred men were following.

At least, Arthur thought, the firing had stopped and there was no longer any sound of the enemy moving around them. As they waded through the water, it became gradually more shallow and, for the first time, the mud on the bottom seemed only two or three inches deep. Their progress became somewhat easier although, in the shallower water, they were once again in amongst the tangled roots of the mangrove trees and were constantly tripping over them. Within minutes, however, they came out onto firmer ground and began weaving their way out of the mangroves into thick, long grass.

The group stopped and began to bunch up as they waited for the last stragglers to come out of the swamp.

"Is everybody out? Any more to come?" the voices were saying. Arthur could hear them, but felt incredibly remote from it all. How the hell would anyone know, he thought. How many went into the swamp and how many came out would be anyone's guess. They were just a confused mob of wet, muddy, tired and wounded men trying desperately to save themselves by following directions which someone else believed to be right. But how did the leader, whoever he was, know? And anyway, what did it matter? What else was there to do?

The group now began to move off into the darkness towards a low line of trees just visible in the soft starlight on the far side of the open ground.

"We're keeping moving," Jim Kennedy muttered beside him. "Gotta put some distance between us and the Nips."

"When are we going to stop?" Arthur asked. "I've got to sleep...or something. I don't think I can go far."

"Come on, mate," Kennedy said, taking Arthur's left arm. "You'll be right. If we keep going, we can rest in a little while."

When they reached the trees, the going became easier. They were once again in a rubber plantation and, although it was much darker under the dense foliage of the trees, the ground was clear and free of obstacles and undergrowth. Even so, Arthur found it impossible to keep up with the rest. He felt unbearably weary. Every pace forward was an effort. He felt weighted down by wet clothes and boots, and his webbing and equipment. He wanted nothing more than to just lie down where he was and go to sleep. But Kennedy and Roxburgh, who had hung back to remain with Arthur, kept urging him on. "Come on, Shep. Not much longer," they said. "We'll be stopping soon. You'll be right then."

"Where are we going ?" Arthur asked.

"We're heading north-east," Jim Kennedy said softly. "Lieutenant Wastell has a compass. I thought before that we would be trying to circle around the Japs to get past Bakri, but I think we're going to try something else now."

For roughly an hour and a half, the group plodded silently on through the rubber trees, sticking as closely as possible to a general north-easterly bearing. They moved without speaking, in a long single file, dark, zombie-like shadows trudging through the trees until finally, about two hours before dawn, a halt was called and word was passed back, that, apart from a number of volunteer sentries at various points along the column, all could rest.

Arthur dropped soundlessly to the ground beside a large rubber tree and, resting his head against the trunk, closed his eyes and instantly fell asleep.

When he was awakened by Jack Roxburgh, a pale light was suffusing the plantation and he could see, spread out through the trees, men beginning to rise from their sleep. Several officers were now walking back down the line, counting men and taking stock of what ammunition had survived the night.

Arthur noticed that Lieutenant Wastell, who had apparently led the group through the swamp, was now accompanied by the Adjutant, Captain Morgan, Captain West of C Company, A Company's commander, Captain Sumner and Lieutenant McCure of the 4th Anti-tank Company.

The officers held a brief conference not far from where Arthur sat quietly on the ground. They then passed the word along the line confirming what Jim Kennedy had said about avoiding Bakri. The plan would now be to try to head across country roughly parallel with the main road, and try to link up with the rest of the battalion and the 2/19th at Parit Sulong.

As Arthur was getting to his feet and wincing with the pain he felt in his right shoulder, he heard a voice behind him. "Gidday, Shep. How are yer?"

"Bomber! What the hell happened to you? I thought we'd lost you in the swamp."

"Hah! I thought we'd lost youl How's yer arm?"

"It's my neck. Got a bloody hole in it."

"Jesus...that's nasty," Bomber grimaced, inspecting the wound. "Been any bigger, it'd've taken yer block off."

"Thanks a lot. Is it still bleeding?"

"Yeah, a bit. Not much. Looks as if you lost a fair bit, though." Bomber examined Arthur's shirt.

Most of the blood that had drenched Arthur's shirt and pants had been washed out in the swamp, but during the trek through the trees after they had left the swamp, the bleeding had continued, and the right side of his shirt, both front and back, was covered in dried blood.

"You look a bloody mess, mate. They won't let you on parade like that!"

They both laughed. "You're not so bloody hot yourself," Arthur said.

Bomber's shirt and pants were equally bloody. He had been injured badly by shrapnel, in the rear of his right thigh, in the upper right arm and in his back, just above his right kidney. All of the wounds had bled heavily.

"I can't tell if there's anything still inside," Arthur said of his own wound. "Is Aspro Jack around?"

"He's not with us. Must have copped it, I suppose," Jack Roxburgh replied. "There's a couple of other wounded blokes down the line a bit who could use him too. Both got head wounds. Pretty bad, I think."

"You all right to walk, Bomber? Your leg looks pretty crook." Arthur noticed that Bomber moved with a pronounced and obviously painful limp.

"Yeah, she'll be right, mate. I'll just take it easy as we go along."

They all set off shortly afterwards, moving in a more open formation through the rubber trees and Arthur found that, although he was in considerable pain and his muscles were stiff, the few hours rest seemed to have done some good. He could move along at almost the same pace as the rest.

He and Bomber walked together, with Jack Roxburgh and Jim Kennedy accompanying them and lending a hand whenever necessary. The two other badly wounded men whom Roxburgh had mentioned soon dropped back to where the little band from 1 Platoon was walking. Arthur recognised the two men. One of them was from C Company, Leo Boyle, while the other was Claude Brown, the gun-layer from the forward anti-tank gun which, only two mornings previously, had blasted the Japanese tanks to pieces. Arthur remembered the young man's happy face beaming out from under his steel helmet as he stood with his fellow gunners in front of the shattered tanks, posing for photographs and talking to the war correspondents who had been there during the action.

Now this young gunner was stumbling along on another soldier's arm, his face ashen and his eyes staring blankly to the front. A dreadful wound, the hair around it matted with blood, covered the back of his head. Somehow, although the group had started off with some medical supplies, there were none now. They had been lost during the night so there were no surgical dressings for any of the wounded.

Around mid-morning, after they had travelled several miles, the party, which was now being led by Captain Morgan, came upon a dirt road, one of the many feeder roads by which the rubber plantations in the area were supplied and along which tapped rubber was carried to central locations for eventual transportation to processing plants. Even though the sun had only been up a few hours, the temperature and humidity were rising rapidly and as they walked along the road, sweat began running down Arthur's face and his shirt was soon soaked.

Shortly after they began following the dirt road, they rounded a bend and suddenly came upon three Australian soldiers walking ahead of them. For a few moments, there was fear on both sides that the other was a Japanese group, but that quickly passed and then a shout went up as one of the three men was recognised as Tom Wiles, the despatch rider who had mistakenly ridden his motorbike into the Japanese lines on the first night when he was leading the mess truck down the road from Bakri.

Almost everyone had heard how Wiles had driven through the battalion's position and into the forward elements of the Japanese force, and he had been thought either captured or dead--the 2/29th's first action casualty. Now, as if by a miracle, here he was again, alive and well. He had just finished telling the story of his encounter with the Japanese for the second time, when Arthur, Bomber, Jack Roxburgh and Jim Kennedy, who were amongst Tom's closest friends, arrived with the rear of the column. So he began his story for the third time, accompanied by much laughter.

"Well, I'm burning down the road, you see," he said, "and I know the mess truck is right behind me, and I'm thinking about what's on the menu, what's for tea. I'm feeling a bit peckish, I suppose, and not concentrating too well. Then I come round this bend and I think, I don't remember this bit, but then, with all this rubber, the whole bloody place looks exactly the same from one end of the road to the next, so on I go. But then I suddenly see a bunch of blokes in khaki uniforms by the side of the road ahead of me. I thought, that's not our uniform. It's not the Brits or the bloody Indians. Shit! I thought-and I'm still riding along-it's the fucking Japs!!

"Anyway, I'm just hitting the flamin' brakes as hard as I can and they're starting to open up on me with everything they've got, when suddenly there's one of these side-roads right beside me on the right. I swing the bike in and bore off up the road hell-for-leather. Not a scratch. Just as well they're bloody lousy shots."

"But what happened then?" Bomber asked. "Where've you been the last couple of days?"

"Well, I travelled for a while on the bike, but the road didn't lead anywhere. It was one of those roads which go round in a big circle for the rubber tappers. I knew roughly the direction I should be going, but the road wouldn't take me there. I tried riding through the rubber for a while, but I kept getting stuck in the ditches and eventually I had to leave the bike. Then I met a Chinese bloke who gave me a meal and put me up for the night. In the morning he gave me directions for getting back to our own lines, but I could hear all sorts of fighting going on in the distance so I tried to skirt around it to come in to the battalion from behind, but wherever I went there seemed to be Japanese. A couple of times I nearly got caught. Anyway, I just kept going towards where I thought I'd meet up with our own forces-and here I am!" He laughed and held out his hands as if he had just performed a feat of magic. "And what about you?" he asked. "Where's the rest of our blokes?"

Several voices answered, beginning to explain what had happened to them over the past forty-eight hours, but they were interrupted by Captain Morgan and the other officers who wanted to question Wiles about the information he had been given by the Chinese man on the direction he should travel and whether or not he might expect any help along the way.

They were soon all on the move again, still on the rough dirt road which seemed to be maintaining the general north-easterly direction they wanted to follow. A group of six cyclists suddenly appeared on the road ahead of them. They seemed to be Chinese, but they stopped in their tracks at the sight of the Australians, turned sharply around and pedalled off in the opposite direction as fast as they could. After a hasty conference between the officers, Captain Morgan directed that the group should now leave the road and head once more through the rubber plantations towards a jungled mountain ridge slightly to the north of their former route. He felt that the risk of continuing along the road after the encounter with the cyclists was too great to take. They might well be just innocent, scared plantation workers, but they could also have been Japanese, or even unfriendly Chinese or Malays who might report to the Japanese what they had seen.

As they trekked through the rubber towards the mountain, they caught glimpses through the trees near the edge of the jungle of what appeared to be army trucks. They paused and then proceeded more carefully until it became clear that the trucks-there were two of them-were abandoned military vehicles, Indian Army by their markings. Captain Morgan ordered that the trucks not be approached until the group had reached the jungle verge and what he considered a more secure position. Then, at about 4 pm, while the whole party rested just inside the cover provided by the thick foliage along the edge of the plantation, a small group of men was sent back to investigate the trucks and to see if there was any tinned food or ammunition in them. They came back with a small quantity of flour and tinned pineapple. Some of the other men had also been carrying supplies of bully beef and hard biscuits, so it was all collected up and divided equally amongst the company of men. Their first meal in two days. One small tin of bully beef for each eight men and two biscuits and a piece of pineapple each. The wounded were each given a swig of whisky which had been confiscated from a drunken Tamil rubber tapper earlier in the day.

Arthur, whose neck wound was making it difficult for him to swallow anyway, coughed and spluttered painfully as the whisky seared his throat. It felt like fire, but it seemed to do something for him, dulling the pain in his right shoulder slightly.

After half an hour they moved off once again, but only for a mile or so, to find a safer position, hidden just inside the jungle's edge. There, when the order to halt and permission to rest was given, Arthur once again allowed himself to collapse onto the ground and fall immediately into a deep sleep.

The night was quiet and, for the first time in four nights, the men were able to have an uninterrupted sleep. Apart from the distant sound of artillery fire and the occasional noises of jungle animals, there was no sound to disturb them. All of the tired and battered little group, except those who took their turn on four-hour sentry shifts, slept as if they had been drugged. Arthur, who was asleep well before darkness fell, knew nothing until he was awoken by Jim Kennedy and Jack Roxburgh more than twelve hours later. He had lain flat on his back without moving for the entire time.

As he tried to rise, his body was racked with terrible pains. His neck and shoulder felt huge and heavy and they throbbed as if being pounded by a hammer. It was again painful for him to swallow and, now, even breathing was difficult. He had begun to feel slightly encouraged during the previous day that his condition might be improving. On one occasion when he had gone to make an involuntary gesture with his right arm, it had moved forward. Surprised, he had tried again and found that, although it had hurt, he could bend his elbow and lift his forearm. He could also move his fingers. But now his whole arm hung slack again beside him and the pain when he tried to repeat the previous day's performance was too great to bear.

Fortunately, it took time to organise the whole company of men before they moved off. The unexpected luxury of such an extended sleep in an atmosphere of relative quiet and security had slowed the men down. For the past few days they had been living on their adrenalin. Now, if Morgan had said, 'All right, men, we're staying here for another twenty-four hours,' there would probably have been little dissent and more than half of the men would have gone straight back to sleep.

So it was not until 9 am that the party was once more on the move, walking through the cleared spaces between the trees of the rubber plantations, but still staying close to the edge of the jungle. There was an eerie, empty feeling about the rows of trees. Under more normal circumstances, they would probably have met quite a number of people along the way-rubber tappers and other plantation workers going about their daily chores-but now they met no-one. It was as if they were the only people in the world, although that feeling was complicated by the fact that there was often the sensation of being watched. Arthur found that, on several occasions, he was looking around to the rear and off to the sides with the distinct impression that there were other people nearby. He and Bomber Wainright and the two men with head wounds were now all together at the rear of the group with Jim Kennedy and Jack Roxburgh. They had started off the morning near the head of the column as it advanced through the trees, but gradually, as their pace was slower, they had begun to fall back through the rest of the men until eventually they were trailing well behind the main body. Although they had started slowly, the rest seemed to have given the fitter members of the band new vigour and the pace they set was considerably faster than on the previous day.

After a couple of hours the company came to a halt and Arthur and the others caught up again. The leading men had been stopped by an old Chinese woodcutter who lived nearby. He informed Captain Morgan and the others that the Japanese were many miles away and that, if they wished, he would cook up some rice and feed as many of the men as possible. His offer was accepted readily and several men were detailed to help him prepare it as it was no small task. He lived in a small shack nearby, on the edge of a bamboo forest, and from there he produced a couple of bags of rice and three large pots. Separate fires were lit and within a short while, every man had been given a small plate of rice and a few slices of canned pineapple which had been left over from the stores taken from the Indian trucks.

The old woodcutter now spoke to Captain Morgan about what the group planned to do. He offered to provide a guide to lead the way to Parit Sulong. Morgan and Wastell reasoned that Allied forces should still be holding Parit Sulong and that they would be able to reach it more quickly than Yong Peng, where Westforce had set up temporary headquarters.

"But the way we go in jungle very rough," the old man warned in broken English. "Difficult for some men." He glanced around at some of the men who still showed signs of exhaustion.

"We have some badly wounded men," Captain Morgan said. "Could they make it?" He knew the answer before he asked the question. '

"Show me," the old man said.

He was taken to where Arthur and the others lay stretched out on the grass. The woodcutter turned away and spoke softly to the adjutant and they walked back towards his shack together.

Shortly afterwards, another of the officers came back to where the wounded were lying. It was Lieutenant Bill McCure, the commander of the battery of anti-tank guns which had been with the 2/29th on the Muar road. McCure sat down beside Arthur, clearly embarrassed and upset. He was a tall, thin man in his late twenties with curly, sandy hair and a pointed nose.

"Look, er, Sergeant Shephard. . ." He glanced across at the semi-comatose forms of Brown and Boyle. He began slowly, then spoke in rapid bursts. "This Chinese bloke says he can get us through to Parit Sulong. He knows a track through the jungle, but it's pretty rough. It'll be tough going, he says, and. . ."

"He doesn't think we'll make it," Bomber Wainright put in.

"Well, no. That's right. He says he can get you through later, at your own pace, but not now, with the rest of them."

"So what's going to happen?" Arthur asked. "We're to stay here?"

"Yes, that's right. There'll be the four of you--yourself, Wainright, Brown and Boyle. We'll leave as much food as we can and he says he'll be able to feed and hide you until you're rested up enough to make the trip, perhaps in a day or two."

None of the four men concerned spoke. Neither of the men with head wounds were well enough to say anything at all, and both Bomber and Arthur felt so weary as to be almost unaware of the implications. It was almost a relief not to have to face the prospect of struggling on any more, although in the back of their minds there lingered the dread feeling that this was the end of the road.

The extra supplies were brought to them, almost like offerings to be included in some sacrifice being left for the dragon. Several men came to say goodbye including, of course, Jim Kennedy and Jack Roxburgh who had stuck by Bomber and Arthur since the swamp. But now there was a terrible air of embarrassment about their parting. Of the two hundred men, these four were to be left alone, to survive as best they could. Although Captain Morgan and the others who were going on could rationalise the move on the basis that the four wounded men had to be left behind for the good of the majority, it was not a pleasant taste that was left in the mouths of the men as they moved off once again. Several of them glanced back and waved at the four who remained seated underneath two rubber trees. "Goodbye, Shep...goodbye, Bomber," Jim Kennedy called as the last of the men trooped off through the trees. "We'll see you in Parit Sulong, mate."

But each of them knew--the departing and the departed from--that there was little chance they would ever see each other alive again. Arthur continued leaning back against the trunk of the tree as he watched the last man in the group disappear through the lines of rubber trees. For a few more minutes, he and his three companions could still hear the sounds of the party moving away. Then there was silence, complete silence. He looked around at Bomber and the other two lonely figures, also each leaning against a tree and facing in the direction taken by the departing men. Here we are, Arthur thought, four wounded men, sitting on the ground alone in a rubber plantation, surrounded on all sides by bloody Nips and eight thousand miles from home. Fat bloody chance we've got!

7

"ARTHUR! COME ON ARTHUR, WAKE up or you'll never get to work."

His mother's voice seemed detached, a part of the dream. He knew he was dreaming, but he wanted to keep the dream going as long as possible. He was running...running along the beach at South Melbourne. It was a sort of race, with some of his friends from school, but they were also being chased by Mr Wilson from the mills. What was really extraordinary was the fact that, on every second or third step he took, he could leap forty or fifty yards at a time, almost flying, leaving his friends and Mr Wilson far behind. Now he was striding and gliding along through some back streets near his old junior school, Moreland Primary. He turned into the old street that ran behind it, the one that was just a dirt road. In his dream, it was years since he'd been there. And he remembered that, as a little boy, he used to pick the small flowers that grew along the edge of the road. They had seeds in them and he would eat them. He wanted the dream to go on and on, it was such a wonderful feeling. He stopped now to pick some of the flowers, but as he bent over, Mr Wilson caught up to him, his heavy hand suddenly grabbing Arthur by the shoulder and shaking him.

"Arthur! Arthur! I'm not going to do this for you every morning. You've just got to learn to get up at the right time." The blankets were pulled back and his face was given a squeeze. He felt the cold through his pyjamas.

"Oh, all right, Mum," he grumbled as he sat up on the edge of the bed, making sure his bare feet didn't touch the cold floor.

"Mr Wilson will sack you if you don't get there on time."

"But I'm always on time. I'm never late."

"Only because I wake you and badger you to get out of bed."

His younger brother Jack stirred in the other bed, turned over and continued sleeping.

Lucky little bugger, Arthur thought, as he stumbled into the bathroom to stand, still dazed, over the toilet relieving himself.

He looked in the mirror and stroked some of the blond hairs that were growing, quite long now, on his upper lip. He'd thought about growing a moustache, but it was taking too long. Perhaps he should shave it off. He was thirteen and it either had to be one or the other. But not this morning. Too bloody cold. He splashed cold water over his face, dried it and returned to his room to dress.

He could hear the older girls, Laurel and Myrtle, both moving about in the next room, also getting ready for work. The young ones, the lucky ones--Jack, Lucy, Joan, Frank and Bobby --could all stay in bed until six-thirty, another hour, before they had to get up: Lucy, Joan and Jack to go to school, Frank to kindergarten and Bobby, who was only two, to stay with Arthur's aunt, while his mother went to work.

Five-thirty in the morning wasn't such a bad time to get up in the summer, when it was light and warm. But five-thirty on a mid-winter's morning in Melbourne, when it was cold and dark and wet, was no way to start the day.

"No, Shephard, no." Mr Wilson elbowed Arthur aside and grabbed the bale he'd been working on. "You still haven't got it. You've got to do them much tighter than that, otherwise, when they're being carted around the country, they'll fall apart." He took the big needle and twine from Arthur's hand and deftly folded the hessian over as he stitched the bale of noil wool up one side. He pulled it tighter and tighter as he moved up to the last corner, so that its shape became a large, rough cube. Then he tied it off and cut the twine. "There," he said, handing the needle back to Arthur, "get on with it, and don't let me see any loose ones."

He's not such a bad bloke, Arthur thought. At least he shows you what he wants. But Arthur also knew that Wilson could be tough, if not downright mean, if he didn't like you. Since he'd started work as a 'noil boy' at the Lincoln Spinning Mills at the beginning of the year, he'd seen people sacked by Wilson for what Arthur thought were very minor incidents, including one for the sin (that his mother kept warning him about) of regularly turning up late for work.

But so far, in the six months he'd been working there, he had managed to keep on the right side of Mr Wilson, probably because he showed a healthy respect for him and, except for times when Wilson had to show Arthur something twice, as with sewing the bales, Arthur had not incurred his displeasure. Arthur had been late once but, fortunately, Wilson had been ill that day, so it had passed unnoticed. Arthur knew, though, that it was something he would have to watch.

Still, it was a difficult adjustment to make: from school-boy to noil boy almost overnight. The noil boys were responsible for dealing with the noil on the raw wool that came in from wool sales all over Victoria. As Arthur very quickly found out, even after the wool was graded, it still contained burrs and thorns, small twigs and other small bits of vegetable matter. And when the wool was combed out on a big machine, and the 'noil' containing all this debris cut away, the noil boys' job was to collect the refuse from the floor and bale it up again for sale. Arthur didn't know who bought the adulterated wool, or what they might do with it- all he knew was that it was always sold.

To begin with, Arthur's work at the mills only involved labour: shifting the big bales around, helping prepare the wool for the noiling machine, and picking up the cut-off material from the floor for baling. But recently he had been given the task of sewing up the bales. He was an exceptionally fit young man, already about five feet four inches tall, stockily built and very strong. And he needed strength. It was tough work at the mills and by 5 pm, at the end of a ten-hour day, his back really knew he'd been working. At the end of a seventy-hour week- ten hours a day, seven days a week-Arthur would collect his pay-packet of twenty-nine shillings and ninepence ($2.97).

Every week he would go home and, taking the ninepence (seven cents) out for himself, give the rest to his mother to help pay for food and clothing for the family.

Ever since Arthur's father had died of a heart attack four years previously, life had been a struggle for the Shephard family. Frederick, a large, powerful man, had come home from work one afternoon and was standing in the living room talking to the baby, Frank. He was showing him a rubber-band trick, called 'dead-man's-finger', when he suddenly collapsed and died in front of the child. Arthur had only been nine years old at the time and he and his older sisters Laurel and Myrtle, had been heart-broken. His mother had been pregnant with Bobby. Frank, who was only two, didn't really understand what had happened, while the twins Jack and Joan, who were four, were also still a bit young to grasp it all. Lucy, who was six, was terribly upset, but, as with all children of that age, life and all its diversions soon dulled the pain of her father's death.

Arthur found that, now his father had gone, he wanted to know more about him. His mother, who was a farm girl from Tasmania, the daughter of a policeman, told him that she had met Frederick when he had come out to Australia as a skipper of one of the clipper ships: the great sailing vessels that carried tea out to Australia and wool back to Europe. After several trips out to Australia, Frederick decided he wanted to stay, so he took a job that the Port of Melbourne Authority had offered him as skipper of a tug. He and Rhoda Shepherd (they had almost the same sur-names) were married in 1912.

Arthur, the third child, had been born in 1917, when they were living in South Melbourne. But, so his mother told him, the great dock strikes of 1920 had crippled the family financially and they had had to move to Brunswick, another suburb of Mel-bourne. And there, over a period of years during which Lucy, Jack, Joan and Frank were born, the family pulled itself up again, so that life, as Arthur remembered it, was good and the family was happy. It was a big old house they lived in on Prowse Street, not far from the tram sheds on Sydney Road. His mother never told him whether they had owned the house or rented it, but for

Arthur, it was the ideal house. There was a pond in which several ducks swam and a fowl coop from which he and the other children would daily collect their breakfast eggs.

Frederick's death plunged the family into another financial crisis. His mother found it impossible to claim any sort of pension, so she began taking in 'piecework' for Christies, a local silk stocking manufacturer. At the time, it was fashionable for stockings to have small decorative stitching, in the form of a clock, or a flower or something similar, on the side. Working from home, Rhoda began sewing these tiny decorations on the stockings. She was paid a small fee for every dozen pairs completed.

Laurel, who was thirteen at the time, soon went out to work in a milliner's shop, while Myrtle went to work in another stocking factory, a year or so later. In that way Rhoda was able to hold her family together.

Having finished primary school, Arthur started at Brunswick Technical College, with ideas of becoming an architect, but very soon it became clear that he, too, would be needed to supplement the family income so, after his thirteenth birthday, he put his age up two years and was taken on by the Lincoln Mills to train as a noil boy.

It was also during this difficult period that the family was forced to leave the big house in Brunswick. They moved to a smaller house, less than two miles away, in Victoria Street, West Coburg where Arthur lived the rest of his teenage years.

"Don't you be late now," his mother said as he raced out the door. "Don't hang around when you've finished there," she shouted after him. "You come straight home."

"All right, Mum," he shouted back, and immediately pushed the thought of coming home right out of his head. All he wanted to do now was be at the Scout Hall on time. Scouting had become a minor obsession with Arthur since he'd joined at the age of fifteen. He liked everything about it, particularly making things. They were taught how to make simple everyday objects and tools, even camp furniture, like a stool, out of wood. They were taught how to work with rope, how to tie knots and how to make things with rope and twine. And how to use a compass and to read a map, to be able to navigate through unknown areas.

Arthur liked the idea of being an explorer and travelling through distant lands where no-one had been before. He read of Robert Falcon Scott's epic voyages to the Antarctic and of Fawcett's explorations in South America and dreamed of making similar journeys one day.

Scouting became a major commitment for Arthur although for him, more than for many of the other young people in the troop, the effort of belonging and participating was considerable. Scouts met one night a week, on Tuesdays, from 6 pm. But he didn't finish work until 5 pm, so it was always a mad rush for him to get home, change into his uniform and be at the hall on time. Also unlike his young companions, several of whom were still at school, by the time Arthur reached the hall he had already put in a gruelling ten hours work at the mills, labouring with heavy bales of wool.

The times Arthur liked most in scouting were when they went on weekend bivouacs in the mountains. They weren't really big mountains. The Dandenongs, just outside of Melbourne, were, and still are, hardly more than large hills, but there was plenty of bush there and, to the boys from the Coburg Scout Troop, they were 'the mountains'. Arthur loved all the things about setting up camp: picking up firewood, lighting fires, cooking their own meals and sleeping under canvas--especially when it rained. To be in the tent, warm and dry in his makeshift sleeping-bag, while it was pouring rain outside, was his idea of heaven.

The bivouacs were usually on a long weekend when they could spend two nights and two and a half days away camping. The days would be spent learning more bushcraft skills as well as identifying various forms of flora and fauna in the bush: lizards, birds, bugs, spiders. They often saw wallabies, plenty of rabbits, an occasional goanna and even an echidna. They were shown how to find yabbies in ponds and creeks and how to cook them up for dinner. When it came time to pack up and go home, Arthur often felt he wanted to stay.

After he had been Scouting for about a year, Arthur decided to move from his job at the Lincoln Mills. With Bobby, the youngest in the family, now seven years old, his mother had gone to work on a full-time basis at the Prestige stocking factory, the company for which she had been doing piecework for so long.

She had told him of an opportunity that was soon coming up in her factory and Arthur decided to try for it.

He was sixteen at this stage, but he put his age up to eighteen in order to get the position, a highly sought-after job, as a 'topper'. With the introduction of the new 'flat' knitting machines in the late 1920s and early 1930s, the so-called 'fully- fashioned' hosiery process had taken over in most factories. A topper's job was to take the stocking from the 'legger' machine, after the half-hour knitting process had finished and then fit them onto a bar which transferred the stockings onto the 'footer' part of the machine.

Although the topper's job was relatively lowly when compared to the 'operator', they were paid on piecework rates, which were tied to the operator's output, so everything they produced above the quota meant a bonus at the end of the week. If the operator was doing well, the toppers were too. In 1933, Arthur's pay-packet of £3 a week made him the envy of all of his young friends.

Arthur stayed working and learning the trade as a topper for two years and then decided to try for a job as assistant operator. By this time, he understood much more of life on the shop floor and how the stocking business operated generally. He realised that by changing his job, that is moving from one stocking factory to another, he could leap-frog to assistant operator much faster than if he stayed with Prestige, where there were other, more senior, toppers. In the early part of 1936, when he was still eighteen, although his employers thought he was twenty, he managed to get a job as assistant operator at the Beaumonde Stocking company, which was also in Brunswick. His earnings there climbed to £7 a week. At that rate, Arthur was by far the best paid of all his friends. '

Then, in late 1938, he made another move, this time to a company called Mignon, not far from Beaumonde, which also manufactured stockings. At last, with this move, he made the grade to 'operator'. His pay now averaged between £13 and £14 a week, a huge amount when the basic wage was less than £4 a week. He still lived at home and, as his salary had grown, his contributions to the running of the house had grown also, so that with his mother's and the rest of the family's earnings, they were able to live quite comfortably.

Arthur's mother, anxious to keep her children off the streets, had enrolled them one-by-one in the local Salvation Army band. Arthur had been learning music at school and, since joining the Salvation Army band at sixteen, had been playing the big E flat tuba.

Every minute of Arthur's time, every day from morning till night, seemed to be occupied. In addition to the Salvation Army band, he had joined a running club-the Carlton Harrier-a cycling club and a gymnasium where he boxed and wrestled. Up until he was eighteen, he also remained a member of the Scouts. He left them only after starting work at Beaumonde, because it became too difficult for him to attend the weekly meetings. However, in early 1938, partly because he missed the comradeship of Scouting, he decided to join the army reserve or, as it was known at the time, the militia.

His first attempt to join was at the drill hall of the Victorian Scottish Regiment in South Melbourne, a somewhat elite infantry militia unit with a high reputation. Entering the hall and making a few enquiries, Arthur was directed to the office of the Regimental Sergeant Major, a tall, red-haired, florid-faced man in his late thirties or early forties, who interviewed him, but only briefly--the man's Scottish brogue was so broad that Arthur couldn't understand what he was saying.

"I beg your pardon?" he said. The man repeated what he had just said. Arthur paused a moment, desperately trying to decipher what seemed to him a foreign language. "I beg your pardon," he repeated. The Sergeant Major's face grew even more red.

"Look, I'm sorry," Arthur said, "but I can't understand you." '

The man's face now went almost purple as he exploded in a tirade of abuse, the only bits of which Arthur understood were when he pointed to the door yelling, "Git oot and stay oot!"

Arthur was somewhat crestfallen over this unfortunate confrontation, but was pleased to find out shortly afterwards that another militia unit, the 3rd Division Signals, held weekly parades, on a Monday night, in the main hall of the South Melbourne Football Ground, not too far away from his home in West Coburg.

The unit held a weekend bivouac every couple of months, where the young soldiers were able to undergo more intensive training. For Arthur, although these outings involved considerable hard work and were not quite the relaxed fun that his Scouting bivouacs had been, they were a reminder of the good times he had had in the past as a Scout and he generally enjoyed them immensely. The unit also held an annual camp at Seymour, about fifty miles north of Melbourne, where the training was even more intense and members of the unit were exposed to situations that were more like life in the regular army.

When his first camp came around at Easter, 1938, Arthur was unable to get the time off work for the full two weeks that the camp was to run. So, with the unit commander's permission, Arthur turned up at Seymour railway station, having travelled by train from Melbourne, one week after the camp had started. He was met by a corporal and driven to the camp and directed to the area where his platoon had set themselves up in large, camouflaged bell-tents, each of which contained six metal-frame camp beds on a wooden floor. As he had arrived in the early afternoon and the rest of his companions were out on training exercises, the day was almost over by the time Arthur finally met up with them.

At four the following morning, an artillery weapon fired a deafening round from a position not more than a hundred yards from Arthur's tent. As no-one had warned Arthur that this was the standard wake-up call, he leapt from his bed with a startled yell and ran out of the tent, much to the amusement of his comrades.

"What's the matter, Shep?" Bert Dyson laughed. "Not scared of a little gunfire are you?" Bert, who worked as a butcher not far from Arthur's home in Coburg, had been in the militia for three years and this was his third camp at Seymour. He knew the ropes, but although he and Arthur got on well together, he wasn't going to make anything easy for Arthur.

"Course I'm not," Arthur scoffed. "Just wasn't expecting it, that's all."

The artillery shot was not only the morning wake-up call, it was also the signal for everyone to be dressed and out on parade in front of their tents within five minutes. It was Arthur's first parade and, although he was wide awake at five past four in the morning, in the pitch dark and cold, he found he didn't quite have his wits about him. '

The platoon sergeant walked up and down the line of men, looking at their faces but saying nothing. "Hands up all those who haven't done cookhouse fatigue?" he suddenly said.

Cookhouse fatigue? Arthur thought. What's that? He didn't know the word 'fatigue'. Probably means learning how to cook, he thought. He put his hand up. Several people sniggered. Bert Dyson behind him whispered, "I knew he was mad. Must have shell shock."

"Right!" the platoon sergeant said, "Report to the cookhouse in ten minutes."

From the time he arrived at the cookhouse, shortly after 4.20 am, until ten that night, Arthur did nothing but wash dishes, stopping only three times for a fifteen-minute break for breakfast, lunch and dinner. He staggered back to his tent to collapse into bed, swearing to himself that he would never again volunteer for anything.

Despite this inauspicious start to Arthur's first military camp, the rest of his time went relatively smoothly and Arthur enjoyed what he was doing, both at the camp and in the weekly meetings and weekend bivouacs that continued throughout the rest of 1938 and into 1939. The unit was training in all the field communications technology used by an army at war. Arthur began to learn the finer details of field signals equipment: for example, how to lay landlines and set up phone connections for an infantry battalion. There were established guidelines of standard procedure and requirements for all sorts of units, right up to brigade and division level. He began to develop expertise in morse code, which was still a requirement for anyone connected with signals and communication in the army. Although the wireless side of signals was a separate one, in which he had not yet had an opportunity to specialise, he underwent considerable training in wireless procedures and equipment, stripping and reassembing radio transmitters and receivers as well as being required to pass rudimentary exams on radio telegraphy.

Until the early part of 1939, Arthur had not had a regular girlfriend. Then in April, he met Clara. She was twenty-two years old, a few months older than Arthur, but, like him, she was interested in physical culture and fitness. She was a runner and also a member of the gymnasium. They seemed to have a great deal in common and after going out together on a few occasions, to the cinema and to dinner, they settled readily into what looked like being a longer-term relationship.

For months the newspapers had been full of Hitler's aggressive posturing in Europe, the German Army's march into the Rhineland and Czechoslovakia and now, in September, he was moving against Poland. Up until then, Arthur had believed that somehow war would be avoided in Europe, but now all the signs seemed to indicate that it was inevitable. On September 1st, everyone's worst fears came true. Hitler had invaded Poland. Two days later came the announcement by Britain's Prime Minister, Neville Chamberlain, that Britain was at war with Germany and, within hours, Prime Minister Robert Menzies declared, in a radio broadcast to the nation, Australia's support for Britain and war against Germany.

At the outbreak of war, Arthur's militia unit, the 3rd Division Signals, was called up for full-time duty in the permanent army, to be based at Mount Martha, south of Melbourne. Arthur, who, like many of his young comrades, wanted to get into the war against Hitler as quickly as possible, immediately resigned from Beaumonde and hurried off to join his unit. Although he didn't really have much choice at the time, he found that he had made something of a mistake in sticking with his militia unit.

3rd Division Signals was already earmarked as one unit that would provide knowledge and training for the newly forming elements of the 2nd AIF, the Australian Imperial Forces. It would not, however, be going overseas itself. Within two months, in November 1939, a new unit called 'Signals Southern Command' was formed and Arthur was transferred into it as an instructor with the rank of Corporal of Signals. Their immediate task was to train signals units in the newly formed 6th Australian Division. A couple of months later, as the first AIF contingent embarked for the Middle East, Signals Southern Command and Arthur were absorbed into a new body known as the AIC, the Australian Instructional Corps, based at Melbourne's Caulfield racecourse. Arthur's posting there carried the rank of sergeant. Officers and NCOS were billeted in rooms underneath the stands, while other ranks slept in the stands on mattresses laid out on the seats.

The AIC's sole job was to train different instructors in specialist units that were sent to them from the various AIF regiments that were being formed. The AIC unit at Caulfield had instructors in many fields of military activity of which Arthur's signals unit was only a minor part. The facility provided training for instructors from anti-aircraft units and anti-tank gun units as well as giving specialist instruction on mortars, machine-guns, transport, messing, medicine, electrical and mechanical engineering, maintenance and a host of other activities.

But, while everyone kept telling Arthur and the other members of the AIC that they were doing an essential job, and that the war effort couldn't be sustained without them, as the months passed by, they saw unit after unit form up, train and leave to fight the war in Europe or the Middle East. All they could do was sit on Caulfield racecourse and watch.

Arthur applied for a transfer to a combat unit.

"Sorry, Sergeant," the Commanding Officer said to Arthur, "It's out of the question."

"But, sir, we'll never get to the war," Arthur said. "Everybody we're training is going off and getting a crack at it while we have to stay home."

"I know that, Sergeant Shephard. But don't flatter yourself you're going to make any difference to the war if you get over there. You're far more valuable here. We just haven't got enough instructors with the right know-how to go around. We need everyone here. This is where you can do the most good."

"Do you think it will change as we get more instructors trained, sir?"

"I shouldn't think so. Not in the foreseeable future. The policy stands: No transfers out of here, unless there is a specific request for you by another unit. If you're really desperate to go, you'll have to get someone to 'claim' you. But it'll have to come from the commanding officer."

For Arthur, 1940 wore on slowly. All eyes were on Europe. The Germans invaded Holland and Belgium. The epic battle and the escape of thousands of Allied troops from Dunkirk captured the world's headlines and imagination. Italy joined with Germany to form the 'Axis' powers and declare war on Britain and its allies, including Australia. France signed an armistice with Germany and, by July, the Battle of Britain had begun.

In September, while Arthur kept teaching signals procedures, the Italian Army invaded Egypt. The Japanese, who were not at war with the Allies at this stage, nevertheless began to occupy bases in Indo-China. In October, the Italian Army invaded Greece. Arthur saw a chance.

The 8th Australian Division had been forming since July. It consisted of three infantry brigades, but suddenly one of the brigades was transferred to the 9th Division. A decision to form a new brigade to take its place meant that three new battalions would be raised. One in Queensland, one in New South Wales and one, the 2/29th, in Victoria. By chance, Arthur knew the man who was to be the Signals Sergeant in the new battalion, Sergeant Phil Simmons.

"Can you get me in, Phil?" he asked as they sat over a couple of beers one late October evening in the sergeants' mess at Caulfield.

"I can talk to the CO," he said. "His name's Robertson. I don't know if there's any chance really, because there's only one signal sergeant on the establishment list for the battalion— that's me—and we've already got a corporal."

Arthur sat for a moment staring moodily into his beer. "I'll drop my stripes if they'll take me," he said. "Tell the CO that."

But nothing happened. The 2/29th had a full complement of signallers and there was no room for Arthur. December and Christmas 1940 came and went. The war in North Africa grew more fierce as the battle of Sidi Barrani raged. Throughout January and February, Australian soldiers were fighting the Italians and the Germans right along the North African coast-line, at Bardia, Tobruk, Derna and Benghazi. In February, the first Australian troops disembarked at Singapore.

Meanwhile, the training work of the AIC continued at the Caulfield racecourse and Arthur became more and more frustrated. He even found he was giving signals training to people from the new 2/29th Battalion in the jobs he wanted for himself.

In early February 1941, Arthur suddenly had another chance to join the 2/29th. Sergeant Simmons contacted him to tell him that one of the men from his signals unit had been invalided out with meningitis. Arthur told Simmons that he was still interested.

"Even if it means losing your stripes?"

"Yes."

Arthur's friends in the AIC training unit thought he was crazy. They sat him down to try to talk him out of it.

"You're leaving one of the highest formations, signals, to go to one of the bloody lowest--the infantry," Bert Dyson said to him. "Do you know what it's like fighting a bloody war in the infantry? It's all blood and guts. You're right up front where the fuckin' bullets are flying. You won't have a bloody chance. At least in signals you're a bit out of the way."

But Arthur's mind was made up. And in the middle of the month, word came through to his commanding officer at the AIC that Arthur had been 'claimed' as a signaller for the 2/29th Battalion. Arthur packed his bags and headed off to join the battalion at its training camp at Bonegilla, near Albury, on the New South Wales-Victoria border. At the time, he thought he would be able to spend frequent weekends and leave breaks with his friends in Melbourne. Although Melbourne was some 150 miles from Bonegilla, it could be reached by bus, or hitch-hiking, within about four hours.

But he had only been with the 2/29th at Bonegilla for a week before they were told that the battalion was moving to Bathurst, which would separate him from his family and friends in Melbourne by a distance of almost 600 miles. Nevertheless, he and all the other members of the battalion adjusted to the move without great difficulty. The main problem was the weather. Although in many ways Bathurst had much the same sort of rolling, open country as Bonegilla, the climate was very different. At some 2500 feet above sea level, the nights, even in late summer and early autumn, were cold.

The battalion now became part of the 27th Brigade, which consisted of three battalions: the 2/26th from Queensland, the 2/30th from New South Wales and the 2/29th from Victoria. They launched immediately into a concerted training programme designed to accustom everyone to operations at every level. These involved manoeuvres utilising the smallest formations-ten-man sections and platoons of approximately thirty men-right through company-and battalion-strength operations, to brigade manoeuvres in which between four and five thousand men might take part.

They knew they would soon be going overseas, but no-one knew where they were heading or when they would be leaving. In the meantime, they were given home leave of several days, roughly once every four weeks, and for Arthur and the rest of the 2/29th, this included a train trip back to Melbourne.

It was just before one of these leave trips to Melbourne that Arthur and some of his friends were told of a place called Delmenicos in Glenhuntley, a suburb not far from Caulfield racecourse, where Arthur had been billeted for so long with the Training Corps. Delmenicos was apparently a place where servicemen were given free food and drinks in their off-duty hours or when on leave.

"They make the best spaghetti you've ever tasted," Jack Roxburgh told Arthur, describing a feast he'd had there.

"But what is it--a restaurant?" Arthur asked. "And how come it's free?"

"It's just a private house, owned by an Italian couple," Jack had said. "They've been in Australia for twenty-five years. Their kids have all grown up. They say they're ashamed that Italy has gone to war against the Allies and that they want to put something back into the country that has given them so much."

On one of these visits to Delmenicos, at the end of March 1941, Arthur met Nancy Muller. Nancy, a vivacious twenty-two-year-old, lived at 90 Grange Road, the house directly opposite the Delmenicos, with her parents, four other sisters and a brother. One older sister had already left home. Her father, William-an accountant with the Vacuum Oil Company-and her mother, Margaret, both disapproved of the Delmenicos.

"There's too much drinking and carrying-on over there," Mrs Muller had said to Nancy and her younger sister Bette when they had first said they were going across the road to join one of the Delmenico parties.

Nancy and Bette, who was two years her junior, had seen the activities across the road develop into regular parties at which up to thirty young servicemen and women, including officers and other ranks, would turn up for lunch or dinner, then spend afternoons and evenings singing around the piano and dancing into the night. It was like a magnet for the young Muller girls.

"But, Mum," Bette had protested, "there's nothing wrong with it. They're just having fun. And the Delmenicos are there all the time."

"It's the drinking I don't like," Margaret Muller said. "I just don't want you girls getting involved in that sort of thing."

"Oh, Mum, it's not like that," Nancy had said. "You should come across and see for yourself. Mrs Delmenico cooks up great meals for the boys and then there's just singing and a bit of dancing. There's not much drinking. They're just doing something to make the boys feel a bit happy. After all, most of them are being sent away to the war."

Mrs Muller knew she was fighting an uphill battle to keep Nancy and Bette from the Delmenicos, and before long the two young girls became regular visitors there.

On the day of Arthur's first visit, he had been handed a glass of Victoria Bitter as he came through the door. He drank one more before lunch and a third after he had finished his second large plate of spaghetti bolognese. Arthur had never been anything but a very light drinker. He found that a few beers generally affected him much more quickly than it did his friends. On this occasion, it simply put him to sleep. He had stayed up all of the previous night, on the train from Bathurst, playing cards with his friends and now, after a big meal and three glasses of beer, all he wanted to do was lie down and sleep.

"What's this?" Bette Muller exclaimed as she and Nancy came into the lounge-room of the Delmenicos on that afternoon and caught sight of Arthur, sound asleep on the sofa while all around him there was conversation, music and several couples dancing.

"No-one's allowed to sleep at Delmenicos," she said, shaking Arthur awake and pulling him to his feet. "Now's the time for dancing."

"But, uh. . . ah. . .that is--" Arthur struggled to wake up. "Look, I can't dance."

"That doesn't matter," Nancy laughed. "Bette can teach you."

"No, no. Listen," Arthur protested, "I really can't dance."

But Bette took no notice. A Tommy Dorsey record was playing, 'Maple Leaf Rag'. She grasped Arthur in the dancing position and began leading him around the floor. Arthur stumbled, his friends cheered and laughed. Bette laughed and then Arthur laughed and then Bette gave up. Arthur sat back down on the sofa next to Nancy.

"I don't know why, but I never learnt to dance. I suppose I should have really," he said to her.

"What about your girlfriends, don't they dance?" Nancy asked.

"Well, I've only really had one girlfriend, a regular one...a steady, that is. And she was into body-building."

"Body-building!?" Nancy looked amazed.

"Well, not really muscle-building, but working-out...keeping fit, in the gym, you know, athletics, that sort of thing."

"And, er, are you still going round with her?"

"No, no," Arthur said. "That was a fair while ago, before the war started. I haven't seen her for ages. Don't know what she's doing."

"So, maybe I could teach you to dance," Nancy smiled.

"No," Arthur laughed. "Not dancing." He looked away for a moment and then back at Nancy with a smile. "But maybe we could go to the pictures, or out to dinner."

On a Friday evening, one month later, Nancy stood waiting outside the main Bourke Street entrance to the Myer Emporium, where she worked in the lingerie department. She had finished work and the store had closed. The last of her friends from the store had gone home and now she was left on her own, looking for Arthur through the crowds of rush-hour people. He was late.

On the day following their meeting at Delmonicos, they had done what he had suggested and gone to the movies together, and both found that they enjoyed each other's company. But that had been all they had had time for on that brief, first leave of Arthur's. He and she both had family commitments that prevented them from seeing each other again. However, Arthur had written to Nancy from the camp at Bathurst and they had arranged to go out for dinner on his next leave. He was to pick her up outside the department store and they would walk to the Hotel Australia in Collins Street to have a few drinks, and then dinner at the rather exclusive Narvoretti's restaurant across the road. But he was late, ten minutes-Nancy looked at her watch-fifteen minutes late. She began to feel a little angry. She was wearing her best dress. She had on a new silver necklace and some beautiful perfume she had bought in the store only that afternoon.

You better turn up soon, Arthur my boy, she thought, or you'll be in trouble. And then she saw him. Swaying through the crowd towards her. He's been drinking, she thought.

"G'day Nance," Arthur smiled. "I bought you these." He handed her a beautiful spray of orchids.

"You've been drinking," she said.

"Just a couple, with the boys."

"Is that why you're late?"

"Late? Oh no, that's because I went to buy the orchids."

Nancy smiled and kissed him on the cheek. "All right," she said, "you win. And thanks for the orchids. They're lovely."

Nancy put her arm through Arthur's and they walked together around to Collins Street, looking in all of the shop windows on the way. Although Australia was at war with Germany, the more drastic effects that would come from the war with Japan had yet to have their impact on Australian society and the economy. 'Blackouts' had not yet been inflicted on the public, so the streets were still well-lit. The shops were also full of light and plenty of consumer goods. There was no rationing, apart from petrol, tobacco and newsprint and, although more and more people were in uniform, nobody really yet felt that the war was close to home.

Nancy enjoyed the dinner at Narvoretti's that night more than Arthur. She had eggplant parmigiano and cannelloni with green peppers, followed by a tartufo, while Arthur had beef consommé, spaghetti marinara and chocolate gelato. The only problem, an embarrassing one from Arthur's point of view, was that he hadn't brought enough money to cover the bill, so Nancy had to dig into her purse to help pay for it. "The Delmenicos' spaghetti is much better anyway," Arthur kept muttering on the train ride back to Glenhuntley.

Arthur had only two more home leaves from the training camp at Bathurst before the 2/29th sailed for an undisclosed overseas destination. On each of them he spent as much time as possible with Nancy. On the last occasion, after another all-night train trip in which Arthur had again stayed up, without sleep, playing cards, he turned up at her department in the Myer Emporium to see her, only to find that she had gone out for her afternoon tea-break.

"She won't be long," one of the other assistants said to him. "Why don't you take a seat." She gestured to a hard-backed chair next to the big glass showcase that formed part of the lingerie department.

"Thanks very much," Arthur said, seating himself in the chair. Within moments, he began to nod off to sleep.

The particular section of the lingerie department where Nancy worked was one of the most exclusive in Melbourne. The glass showcase against which Arthur was now leaning, fast asleep, carried frilly underwear, nightgowns and negligees, which were supposedly the best and most expensive in Australia. Handmade by nuns in Italy and France, according to the accompanying publicity, they sold for up to £70 and £80 an item.

"I think that's your boyfriend over there," one of Nancy's co-workers said as she returned from the afternoon tea-break. She pointed at the uniformed figure slumped against the display case, attracting disapproving glances from some of the presumably more affluent customers who patronised this corner of the store.

"Oh, my God," Nancy gasped in embarrassment. "It's Arthur." She ran across and began shaking him. "Arthur! Arthur! Wake up!"

8

FOR FIFTEEN MINUTES, THE FOUR men remained sitting where they were, each leaning against a tree, staring silently towards the maze of other trees through which the last of their comrades had disappeared. Arthur Shephard had been swept with a feeling of utter desolation and loneliness. The air was warm and humid, but as it was still relatively early in the day, the heat had not penetrated the shade of the plantation rows. There was no movement and no sound. Arthur thought of his mother and of the house in Coburg. He thought of Nancy and of the good times they'd had before he left, and of life going on in Melbourne as it had been before the war. Of course, he realised that everything had been changed by the war, even back home, but he felt a desperate wave of homesickness sweep over him. And worst of all was the feeling that he would never see any of it again. For a while, he remained in a sort of limbo, until something brought him out of it: a bird in the trees, or an animal moving in the jungle nearby. As he looked around at his companions, who were also lost in their own thoughts, Arthur realised that his face was wet with tears. He wiped them away and broke the silence.

"Well..." He paused a moment. His voice sounded strangely detached and out of place. "The old bloke said that as soon as he got the other guide and set them all on the right track, he'd be back for us. If we get a few days clear rest here, we should be able to follow the others."

Bomber turned and smiled and then struggled painfully to stand up. "Yeah, I suppose so, but I reckon we oughta get ourselves out of sight, somewhere over by the old fella's hut, in the long grass."

The two other men, Brown and Boyle, slumped motionless against a couple of trees, were awake, but they said nothing. It was clear that they were both in bad shape and when Arthur went to try to help Brown, the anti-tank gunner, he saw close-up, for the first time, the massive wound the man had sustained on the left side of his head. The sight sent a hot flush and a shudder through Arthur and he nearly fainted. In amongst the matted blood and hair, a hole about two inches in diameter had been torn in the man's skull. In the centre of the wound, Arthur could see a mass of soft and bloody tissue which moved rhythmically up and down. He averted his eyes and, kneeling beside Brown, paused for a few moments to collect his senses. He could not imagine how the man was still alive, let alone conscious.

"Come on, Claude," he said eventually, "we're going to move across to the old bloke's hut, about a hundred yards or so over there."

Neither Arthur nor Bomber were in a position to be of much physical help to Brown and Boyle as their own wounds prevented them from using their right arms, but somehow they managed to get the two more seriously wounded men to their feet, one at a time, and to support them as they staggered the short distance to the long grass and the shade of a large banyan tree close by the woodcutter's hut where they would be shielded from view. Here they lay down once more to rest.

As both Brown and Boyle drifted off into a coma-like sleep, Arthur leant across to Bomber, who lay near him, propped up against the trunk of the big tree. "Jesus, Bomber, have you seen the gunner's head? It's bloody terrible. You can see his brain!"

"The other bloke's the same," Bomber grimaced. "By rights the poor buggers shouldn't be alive. Bloody amazing." He shook his head slowly.

"But what can we do?" Arthur whispered. "We haven't even got any field dressings."

"I think we've got a little disinfectant," Bomber said. "They left some with the tins of bully."

Strangely, the sight of the frightful wounds of the other two made both Arthur and Bomber forget their own injuries and to feel almost fit and healthy by comparison. They now considered themselves to be quite fortunate. Their own wounds were bad enough of course, but they had at least stopped bleeding and, with a bit of luck and time, might heal up. Arthur's neck wound, however, seemed as though it might cause him permanent disability. He could still barely move his right arm.

"Hello?!" A voice calling out from the direction of the wood-cutter's hut startled them. "Hello, Australians. You are here?"

It was not the old man's voice. Arthur and Bomber looked at each other with some apprehension and remained silent, sinking lower into the long grass beside the tree.

Bomber and Arthur looked at each other again and then Arthur called out, "Over here." It was an act of faith that neither of them would have allowed themselves during the months to follow.

The stranger walked across through the long grass to where the men lay in the shade. "Good afternoon," he said. "My name is Lee Kim Swee."

He was a young man, in his mid-twenties, perhaps, quite small, but stockily built with a flat, open face. He had a pleasing smile which revealed large white teeth. Over his left shoulder he had slung a hessian sack and in his right hand he carried a large machete, the sight of which prompted a few momentary qualms on the part of Arthur and Bomber. The machete seemed out of place as he did not appear to be a manual worker. He was dressed in a clean, white, short-sleeved shirt, well-pressed khaki shorts and a pair of good leather sandals.

He passed a quick, appraising eye over the men, pausing for a moment on Leo Boyle and Claude Brown, who lay asleep to one side. "Ah Seng has asked me to look after you," he went on. "He said to tell you that he will not be back until after dark."

"Do you live around here?" Bomber asked, his earlier caution and suspicion fading as a result of the obvious openness and apparent trustworthiness of the young Chinese.

"Yes, some miles from here. I work on a rubber estate, in the office. I do the accounts."

"What's happened to the estate? It's not working with all this fighting going on around here, is it?" Arthur asked.

"No, the manager and his family have gone to Singapore."

"He was European, the manager?"

"Of course, English. So now nothing is happening. We just wait and see. The Japanese have passed us by. Already they are at Parit Sulong."

"Parit Sulong?" Bomber said in surprise. "But that's where the others are going."

"'No. It has been changed. Now they are heading for Yong Peng."

"Are there any Japs around here?" Bomber studied the man's face intently.

"No, not yet. But once they have established themselves along the main roads, they will spread out to check on all plantations and villages." He bent to open the small sack he had been carrying with him. "Here," he said, "I have brought you some fruit. Papaya and coconut."

Both Arthur and Bomber whistled softly with pleasure and anticipation, and even Leo Boyle stirred and began to rouse himself on hearing the young Chinese man's words. Raising himself slightly, he watched expectantly as the newcomer deftly cut off the top of one of the coconuts with the machete without spilling more than a few drops of the cool, clear milk inside the husk.

"Give it to the others first," Arthur said, indicating Leo and Claude, and then he and Bomber moved to prop up the other two as Lee Kim Swee poured the precious liquid between their lips. They both drank eagerly and then ate some of the pieces of papaya and the soft, white meat of the coconut which had been cut up. But they said nothing.

Arthur and Bomber shared the juice from another coconut and then sat chomping on its sweet meat as they continued to ply the man with questions.

"If the Japanese are already at Parit Sulong," Arthur asked, "how long before they get to Yong Peng?"

As he spoke, he realised it was hardly a question he could expect Lee Kim Swee to answer. Both Bomber and he had had first-hand experience of the Japanese onslaught. They were almost certainly in a better position to answer the question than a young accountant. And yet, somehow, it was as if he, a local, would have an inside line on the Japanese movements. As it happened, this was almost true. The Malayan version of the 'bush telegraph', where news is passed by word of mouth from one person to another over astonishing distances at equally astonishing speed, was often very effective. In this instance, Lee Kim Swee had known that the Japanese were already at Parit Sulong only a very short while after the fact.

"I am not sure," he replied to Arthur's question, "but it cannot be long. A few days, perhaps only one or two."

"But what'll happen to us? We'll never get back to Singapore if they take Yong Peng. We'll be cut off for good."

"Do you think that Singapore will hold against the Japanese?" It was now his turn to study their faces intently. It was an impossible question at this point of time, one that none of them could reasonably answer but only guess at, with underlying feelings of either hope or despair. But the guesses of both the white men and the Chinese were based on the concept of what had been, until that time, invincible British power-a concept that had received a considerable shake-up over the past month as the Japanese had pushed the white masters of Malaya relentlessly back down the peninsula.

Yet Singapore might hold. Singapore was different...surely Singapore was different? It was 'Fortress Singapore' wasn't it? The last bastion against which the Japanese would struggle in vain. And inside that tiny island fortress, the Allied forces would gradually be resupplied with men and munitions to re-build their strength and then push these 'little yellow invaders' back up, and then off the Malayan peninsula. At least that was the desperate hope, not only of Arthur and Bomber, but also of all the Allied forces now in full retreat towards that so-called 'fortress', and all of the other military personnel and Singapore civilians who were waiting there, on the island itself, for the final cataclysm.

"Oh, yes." It was Bomber who spoke. "Singapore will hold. There are tens of thousands of new soldiers arriving there. The Japs won't take Singapore. It's too strong."

Lee Kim Swee said nothing. The silence seemed to grow. No-one spoke for some moments. They were lost in their own individual thoughts about the unthinkable prospect of the collapse of Singapore and total victory for the Japanese. It was an almost impossible idea to grasp at that stage.

Arthur wanted to ask Lee Kim Swee what he felt about the British going, the fact that those who had been the colonial masters of Malaya were no more, but a low moan from Claude who, with Leo, was lying in a deep sleep a few yards to one side, attracted their attention.

"We must try to dress their wounds," Bomber said. "We've got some Dettol, but we need bandages, or some cloths. And where can we get some water?"

"There is a stream, over there behind the hut," Lee Kim Swee pointed. "It is very clean and fresh. You can get some water there and I will try to find some cloth for you."

Bomber went with Lee Kim Swee to the small river and, with a metal saucepan collected from the hut, scooped some water from the fast-running stream and brought it back to the banyan tree.

In the meantime, Arthur had forced himself to examine the other men's wounds more closely. Leo Boyle's injury was not quite so ugly as Brown's, but they were surprisingly similar in size and shape. A piece of Leo's scalp was missing at the back of his head. Arthur peered intently at the wound without actually touching it and, although he could not see pieces of metal, there were several broken chips of bone amongst the matted blood and hair which surrounded it.

Bomber had torn a piece of material from his shirt and, with some disinfectant mixed with stream water, the three men set about trying to clean the terrible head injuries. Both Leo and Claude lay quietly, flinching occasionally with the sting of the disinfectant. Arthur and Bomber, on the other hand, were slightly in awe of the situation. Both felt a desperate ignorance of how to approach and handle an exposed, living human brain.

"Better be careful not to get any Dettol on the...ah...er, in the middle," Bomber said softly. "just clean around the edges first."

Gradually, over a period of half an hour or so, they managed to clear the congealed mess from around both of the wounds so that they could clearly see the extent of the injuries. Although the wounds now appeared much less ugly with the surrounding blood gone, Arthur and Bomber still felt hopelessly inadequate for the task of caring for them. Neither had the slightest idea about the best treatment for someone who had a piece of their skull missing. The only thing they could think of was a cloth dressing.

"I will bring some clean cloth with me when I come back," Lee Kim Swee said as he prepared to leave shortly afterwards.

"I must go now, but I will return with some food this evening. I think you must stay here, where you are, tonight. If it rains, you should go to the hut, but if the Japanese come, it would be better not to be there."

"But you told us there were no Nips around here," Bomber said.

"That is right. But I am not their commander. He could decide to do anything. It is better to be careful."

When Lee Kim Swee had gone, Arthur and Bomber lay quietly for a while, talking about their situation and their luck in meeting Kim Swee, as he suggested they call him, or 'LKS' as Bomber had dubbed him. After a while they dozed off to sleep.

Lee Kim Swee returned after dark for an hour or so and helped them, in the woodcutter's hut, to prepare some rice mixed with a few pieces of already-cooked chicken and a pot of tea. Both Claude and Leo managed to eat some of the meal when it was fed to them but, again, neither of them spoke.

When they awoke in the morning, there was no-one about. They had expected the old woodcutter to be back, but obviously he wasn't. Lee Kim Swee arrived later in the morning, accompanied by another man. He also carried the news that the old man had continued on with the Australians. As Parit Sulong was now in the hands of the Japanese he felt he would have to stay with them to lead the way through the jungle to Yong Peng.

"He may not return here for some days, now," Kim Swee told them. "So I have brought a man who will build you a shelter in the jungle a little further away from this hut. I think it is too dangerous for you to be so close. Even if the Japanese do not come here, not everyone will be so friendly to you." He hesitated a moment, looking slightly embarrassed. "Do you have any money?"

Bomber and Arthur looked at each other. "A little," Arthur replied.

"Good." Kim Swee smiled. "This man is a coolie. He is very poor. If he builds you a hut, it will take time he could have spent providing food for his family."

"How much should we give him?" Bomber asked.

"He will be very happy with three or four dollars."

"For a hut? Only three or four dollars?"

"Of course. We will finish the shelter first, then move your friends to it from here. I have some cloth for their wounds and supplies for you." He presented another hessian sack containing a pot and some eating utensils as well as quantities of rice, salt, sugar and margarine.

The two Australians were amazed and delighted. "Thank you," Arthur said to Kim Swee. "You are very kind to us."

"It is nothing." The young man shook his head and then motioned to his companion and to Arthur and Bomber to follow him. "Come. First we must find a safe place and then he can build your shelter."

Less than a hundred yards from their banyan tree, they approached what appeared to be an impenetrable wall of thick foliage. Brushing aside some dense, overhanging bamboo, Lee Kim Swee's companion forced his way in ahead of the others, hacking a short path through the vegetation and then, not more than forty or fifty yards further on, set about cutting a small clearing. Of course, if anyone came across the path it would lead them directly to the clearing, but the overhanging bamboo at the entrance would hopefully provide a natural piece of camouflage to conceal it.

There was little that Arthur and Bomber, or Lee Kim Swee for that matter, could do to help the man in his task. He obviously knew what he was doing and set to work like a demon, first cutting down lengths of thick bamboo for a frame and then pieces of rattan to use as cord in binding them together.

It was hard to tell his age. He could have been forty years old, or fifty...or even seventy. He was small, hardly more than five feet two or three inches tall, and thin and wiry. He wore only a pair of torn khaki shorts and a pair of sandals made from an old rubber tyre. His skin was deeply tanned by the sun and had the appearance of polished leather. Long sinews and veins stood out on the muscles of his arms and legs as he worked. His face was only slightly lined, but there were creases around his eyes and mouth which made Arthur feel that, perhaps, on other occasions, he laughed a lot. Now, however, he did not produce even a smile. Nor did he talk. He just worked steadily away at the job in hand.

In almost no time, he had constructed a floor of split bamboo which was elevated about a foot above the ground. By the end of the morning, he was putting the finishing touches to the shelter. It was enclosed on three sides by attap leaves which were woven and tied into the bamboo frame. The roof was also made of attap leaves, but thicker by several layers than the walls. The fourth side of the hut was open and facing eastwards onto the small, new clearing beyond which dense, unbroken jungle continued for many miles. How many, neither Arthur nor Bomber knew.

"I think you will be safer here for a while," Lee Kim Swee assured them. "But you must be careful about noise. You will not be heard talking, even from the old man's hut, but still you must be careful. If you light a fire, burn only dry wood or leaves because they make little smoke--and do not make a fire until after dark."

There was a pause in the conversation as they watched the coolie working diligently. Arthur's unasked question of the previous day returned to him.

"I suppose that, in a way, you must be glad to see the Englishmen go?" Arthur began a little cautiously, looking first at Lee Kim Swee and then up into the branches of the tree. "After all, as an Asian, you and your people must have felt some resentment of the fact that the British have ruled this country as a colony, without the locals having any say."

Lee Kim Swee smiled and then nodded slowly, pausing as if deciding whether to say what he was thinking or not. "Yes, that's true," he eventually said, "but it's a difficult question for us to answer. In some ways we must answer yes and in others no. You see, I was born in Malaya and I have grown up being always aware of the fact that the British were masters of this country. Although they ran the country well--it was a stable country and had an efficient government system, law and order and so on—there is much resentment amongst our people, particularly the younger ones, because we have no opportunity to get good jobs in government, or to control our own lives. There are strong feelings about this, especially among the Malay people, who are even less fortunate than we Chinese."

"So it should be to your advantage to have the Japanese kick the British out," Arthur commented.

"Maybe," Lee Kim Swee smiled. "But it's not so simple. You see, as for myself, being Chinese, I must make the Japanese my enemy. China has been at war with Japan for many years now. Japanese invaders have been raping and killing my countrymen in the thousands for all of that time. If the Japanese win Malaya, the Chinese in Malaya will always fight them. If we allowed them to stay, we would only be replacing a European colonial master with a Japanese one, and that would be far worse."

Both Arthur and Bomber nodded, feeling a degree of relief in the knowledge that, although they were so far behind enemy lines now, they would not necessarily be treated as 'European dogs' by a 'liberated' Asian populace. A significant number of local people might, perhaps, be relied upon to help those who were obviously enemies of their enemies.

While they had been speaking, the coolie had been cutting a new path to a small stream which they could hear tumbling by about thirty or forty yards to one side. When he had finished, he and Lee Kim Swee helped Arthur and Bomber to move Claude and Leo to their new shelter. Arthur then paid the man for his expert building work. Five Malayan dollars. The man's eyes lit up in pleasure and a large grin spread across his tanned face. "Teri mekasi, teri mekasi," he thanked them in Malay several times before nodding goodbye and trotting off on his own.

"And now I, too, must go," Kim Swee said. "I cannot return for two days—that is Saturday. Perhaps the old man will be back by then. But I think you will be all right. You have some

7. *The 2/29th Batallion on a training march through Bathurst in 1941. Arthur Shephard and Lt.A.C. Sheldon* (2nd and 3rd from left) *leading 1 platoon HQ Company.*

8. *Members of 1 Platoon, H.Q. Company at Bathurst training camp. L to R standing: F.W. Fox, T.E Wiles, L.K Dunn, D.M. James, Arthur Shephard, P.J. Harris, H.D. Curtis, C.J. Nichols. Centre Row: A.R. Olsen, J.A. Kennedy, W. Muir. Seated: H. R. Murdoch, W. James, J.R. Carr, J.D. Roxburgh, L.C Kerr, J.V. Welsh*

food now. You can rest and look after your friends." With those words he waved and disappeared through the bushes.

After surveying their new 'instant' house with pride for some minutes, Arthur and Bomber then set about collecting a pile of large leaves which, when spread several layers deep over the bamboo floor of the shelter, made a crude, but comfortable mattress. Later they would come to prefer the harder bamboo because it provided a less inviting environment for the tremendous variety of crawling insects, both large and small, that inhabit the Malayan jungle. Nevertheless, their first night in their new hut was spent more comfortably than any of the previous week. With their stomachs full of rice and the remains of the coconut and papaya, they again slept soundly.

For much of the next day they continued to sleep or rest, without moving at all from their small clearing. They heard no-one come or go from the woodcutter's hut and they hoped that no-one heard them. Bomber and Arthur again did their best to treat the head wounds of the other two men, as well as their own body wounds which, despite their size and ugliness, were showing signs of healing. Although it was difficult to make an appraisal of Claude and Leo's injuries, at least they were now covered with makeshift dressings which gave the wounds some protection from further injuries and from the flies which tended to swarm around the wounds when they were open.

On the following day, after another good night's sleep, they each began to feel their isolation. Although the subject had not been raised for some time, both Arthur and Bomber were thinking about their future plans.

"Do you know what day it is?" Bomber asked.

"It's Saturday, isn't it? LKS said he'd be back on Saturday."

Bomber nodded and smiled. "You know, it was only last Saturday that we left Buloh Kasap to go to Bakri. Jesus. What a week!" '

"Seems more like a bloody month," Arthur muttered.

The sound of someone moving through the bushes and up along their track made them instantly silent and alert. But it was only Lee Kim Swee arriving with some more supplies, including something that Arthur had asked for: a pencil and a small notebook...actually a school exercise book-which he intended to use as a diary.

Kim Swee also carried some disquieting information that there were now Japanese soldiers moving through a number of the rubber plantations set back from the main roads. The Japanese realised that, as many of the Allied units had been dispersed, individuals, or small groups of soldiers, were still in the rubber plantations or the jungle, trying to make their way south to Singapore.

"It will only be a matter of time, perhaps only a day or so, or even less, before they will come here. I am sorry, but I think you must go further into the jungle, at least during the daytime. There is a swamp nearby and there are places in there which are very safe. I think perhaps if you could stay in there during daylight and then sleep here in the hut at night, it would be better."

"But what about Leo?" Arthur asked. "He can't move at all by himself now and we can't carry him backwards and forwards every morning and night."

Kim Swee looked at the prostrate figure of Leo Boyle and nodded slowly, and then looked at Claude Brown who had shown considerable improvement over the past thirty-six hours and was now sitting up against the wall of the hut. He had been up twice that morning and had walked twice without any help from Arthur or Bomber; once to the stream for a drink and once to a small hole which had been dug on one side of the track as their latrine. Arthur and Bomber had been encouraged by his apparently improved condition. He had carried on a rather brief, although vague and disjointed, conversation with them. He seemed to be aware of the reality of his surroundings, but told them he felt as if he had been living in a dream world. His voice had been laboured and slow as he spoke.

"I remember, we started to pull out," he said. "But what happened after that? What are we doing here? Where are the others?"

When the two men had explained the sequence of events to him, he could not believe that so many days had passed. They had been a blank for him.

After a midday meal of rice and some pork which Kim Swee helped them to prepare, there were more sounds heard from the direction of the woodcutter's hut and Kim Swee went out to investigate. It was the old man. He had finally returned from the expedition to guide the remnants of the 2/29th to Yong Peng. He came back to the shelter with Kim Swee and both Arthur and Bomber saw from his downcast and forlorn manner that all had not gone well.

As the old man could not speak English well, he spoke in Chinese and Kim Swee translated his story. The trek to Yong Peng had been a long and arduous one. The party had been unable to find sufficient food along the way. They were all shattered with fatigue and hunger and when, upon reaching the vicinity of Yong Peng, they found that it too, had been taken by the Japanese and that their own forces had retreated even further south, they became dispirited and unsure of what to do. They began throwing away their heavier weapons and equipment and splitting up into small parties which would try to find their way back to Singapore separately. Some thought it would be possible to get a small boat or sampan to try to cross the forty-mile-wide Straits of Malacca to the island of Sumatra in the Dutch West Indies.

'But what about the officers?" Arthur asked through Kim Swee. "What did they say?"

"They agreed," Kim Swee translated. "They all felt that the group was too big to travel secretly through the jungle together, to find food and so on, so they decided that splitting up was the best way."

While they were talking, the sky had darkened as heavy, rain-bearing clouds moved across it. Now, with the jungle still and soundless around them, it began to rain: first a few, fat, heavy drops, then a steady downpour, then a torrent. The five men crowded inside the little shelter beside the still form of Leo, who lay curled up like a foetus in one corner. As the rain bucketed down, Arthur glanced around the inner sides of the attap ceiling and walls, looking for leaks. There were none. He felt a degree of satisfaction in being able to remain dry in so simple a shelter while such a solid wall of water was falling all around them.

The old woodcutter remained with them for a further half hour, apparently thinking that he might be able to avoid getting soaked if he waited, but eventually he realised that he would have a long wait and so, saying goodbye, he stepped out into the rain to make his way back to his hut alone.

"Of course, we can do nothing about going to the swamp today," Kim Swee said, "but I think we may have to build you another place, further into the swamp. You can take your friends in there and be safer, and not have to come backwards and forwards every day."

He left them shortly afterwards, saying that he would return the next day. The idea of living in a swamp did not have much appeal for them. Their previous swamp experience had hardly been pleasant and that had only been for one night. A permanent stay was not really something they wanted to contemplate.

Arthur, whose right arm had improved somewhat, now started writing his diary. Realising that it may have to last some time, he began at the very top of the first page in tiny letters, with the battalion's departure from Buloh Kasap:

JANUARY 1942 Sat. 17th. BN less 2 Coys moved to Bakri. Object was to contactjap forces (approx 200) which had been reported to have landed at Muar. Contact made sundown-much sooner than expected. D/R T. Wiles missing.

He continued writing until he had brought the diary up to date.

The following morning, the old woodcutter arrived early with Kim Swee and his nephew, who was to help construct the new shelter this time. They set off into the jungle, with Arthur and Bomber following close behind, for about half a mile until they came to a large swamp. Skirting the edge of it, they came eventually to a great old tree, another banyan, with a huge network of thick roots at its base and thick vines hanging down from its branches. The woodcutter obviously knew the place well because, unless one knew the way or came upon it by accident, it would have been almost impossible to find. There were no tracks leading to it and the old man instructed the Australians, through Kim Swee, to use several different routes in coming and going from the hideaway, so that no obvious paths would develop.

As the new construction got underway, it was clear that the woodcutter was happy about the Australians shifting here, away from his hut. It would have meant death for him, Kim Swee explained, had the Japanese ever discovered them so close to his home.

The hut which was taking shape now was similar to the first shelter, but it was built into the vines and roots of the enormous tree so that it was completely hidden from view on all sides except from a direct approach across the swamp. It was totally suspended over water and, had the circumstances been less dire, it would have had much of the child-like, adventurous appeal of a 'Swiss Family Robinson' tree-house. Although neither Bomber nor Arthur had been looking forward to the move, when the new shelter was finished, once again after only a few hours work, they both felt quite happy about it.

It was a considerable struggle to shift Claude and Leo to the new hut. Claude was able to walk with frequent rests, but Leo had to be carried the whole way. Kim Swee and his nephew helped and after more than two hours, the move was finally accomplished. Only a short time later, as they were sitting down resting, they were surprised to hear someone coming down the track towards their position.

"It is the woodcutter," Kim Swee told them after peering around the corner of their hut, "but..." he paused. "He has someone else with him."

Arthur and Bomber got up to look.

"G'day!" The greeting came from the man following the old woodcutter as he clambered over the tree roots and into their hut. It was Lieutenant McCure, the young anti-tank officer who had brought them the news, during their flight from Bakri, that they (Arthur, Bomber, Claude and Leo) were to be left behind. "How're you all going? All right?"

Bomber and Arthur were momentarily nonplussed. They sat staring at the man with their mouths open but saying nothing.

"Where the hell did you come from?" Bomber managed to say eventually, adding quickly, "...er, sir?"

McCure confirmed what the old woodcutter had reported the day before, that the remnants of the 2/29th had found Yong Peng occupied by the Japanese and had split up into smaller parties to try to make their own way back to Allied lines. But the trials and disappointments of the past days seemed not to have affected the young officer, who spoke with infectious optimism. "I'm with a bunch of other blokes-there's nine of us altogether. There're waiting down the track a bit. We're going to head down to the coast, to a place called Kisung. There's a bloke who says he can get us a boat there to get over to Sumatra." He looked around at the woodcutter. "We met this old character and he told us you were in here. I thought I'd come and see how Brownie was getting on-and the rest of you, of course." He glanced at Claude, who was sitting in the back of the hut, leaning against one wall. "G'day, Brownie. How are you, mate?"

Claude nodded and smiled. "Not bad, sir, not too bad," he said quietly.

"Any chance of coming along with us?" McCure did the right thing by asking, but it was patently obvious to him that Brown could not go. Arthur and Bomber could have gone, perhaps, but he didn't ask them and if he had, they probably wouldn't have felt like accepting the offer. Although they both realised that their injuries needed more time to heal, the thought passed briefly through Arthur's mind that maybe they should try to make it to the coast with McCure. However, he realised there was no way that Brown and Boyle could go and he and Bomber could hardly abandon them here.

The young officer stayed with them for another half hour, giving them what other news he had, before bidding them goodbye and leaving to meet up with his companions.

Over the next few days, Kim Swee came and went frequently, bringing food supplies and whatever news he had collected. During this period, Arthur and Bomber had been able to feed Leo and Claude, and to bathe and dress their wounds. Claude, whose condition had shown the most improvement, seemed to be reasonably stable and gave at least some cause for hope that he might eventually recover. He could walk and talk, although his conversation remained vague and limited. There were periods of lucidity in which he told them that he had been a barber in the Victorian town of Eaglehawk. At other times he would sit quietly for hours, doing nothing. Leo, on the other hand, made virtually no progress. He was often conscious and seemed, on occasions, to show some awareness of his surroundings and of his three comrades, but he never spoke, except from time to time to utter one word: "Turnout". He would be lying in one corner of the hut, when suddenly he would mutter softly, "Turnout! Turnout!"and that would be that.

"Poor bugger," Bomber whispered on one occasion. "It's as though a whole part of his mind has been shut off. And there's not a bloody thing we can do."

The rains came regularly now, every afternoon, and for many hours they could do nothing but sit and watch the torrents of water breaking the surface of the dark swamp in front of them. Whenever it was dry, usually in the mornings, Bomber and Arthur would take it in turns to wander out to the woodcutter's hut to see that the outside world was still there. Often, Kim Swee or his nephew would be there already and sometimes they would have other Chinese friends with them.

There were now quite a number of people, all Chinese, who knew that the four Australians were living in the swamp not far from the woodcutter's house. Most of the Chinese that they met in the woodcutter's house would look at Bomber or Arthur with interest, perhaps shake their hand and nod, or smile politely, but as they could speak no English, there was rarely any conversation.

Lee Kim Swee was their only translator and source of information. As the days passed, the news he brought back to them was less and less encouraging. The Allied troops were being forced to retreat back onto Singapore Island and the Japanese forces were now beginning to consolidate for a final assault on the so-called 'fortress'. There were also some horrifying stories coming in from surrounding areas of what sort of treatment they might expect from the Japanese if they were caught. Kim Swee reported to them that eighty Australians had been captured nearby and taken to a camp close to Muar where they were being forced to clean the streets while surrounded by Malays armed with big sticks. Later, a friend of Kim Swee's reported that captured Indian troops were being lectured in a school hall in Muar on the principle of Asians combining together against Europeans. The Japanese had apparently also launched a programme aimed at indoctrinating the local populace along similar lines, in an effort to turn them against the British. The whole thrust of the message was evidently geared towards a promised independence for Malaya and India. The lectures seemed to have had some impact, according to the reports, because many of the Indian troops had switched their allegiance to the Japanese and had been put on guard over British and Australian prisoners.

During this period, Lee Kim Swee and his friends kept the four men well supplied with food. Rice was the staple, but there were often biscuits and some meat, usually chicken, or a piece of pig.

Arthur and Bomber found that they could light a fire beside their hut at night without any real fear of detection. It was an unusual fireplace in that it was set in a great pile of wood that had collected in amongst the tangled roots of the banyan tree, which was actually floating on water about eighteen inches below. The fires burned well, except when they would burn down through the layers of twigs to reach the more sodden branches, where they would sputter and die. In some parts, near the edge of the swamp, the floating layers of wood and leaves were so thick that they could walk on them, although sometimes they would sink right through.

The swamp conditions made it very difficult for them to keep their feet dry and both Arthur and Bomber began to develop severe cases of tinea. At the same time, however, the condition of Arthur's arm improved rapidly. He now found that he could move it forward and sideways, although not above chest height, and that he had regained almost the full use of his right hand, with some loss of strength.

During the second and third weeks of their isolation, Claude and Leo both underwent changes. Leo began to brighten up considerably. He started to get some of his speech back and be could stand up and look around for a while, although he appeared to be very shaky on his feet. On the other hand, Claude, who had previously been showing good signs of re-covering, began to complain of severe pains in the head. Bomber thought that perhaps some sort of infection may have set in, although neither he nor Arthur could see any sign whenever they dressed his wound. They felt completely helpless in trying to treat their two comrades without adequate medicine. All they could do was cross their fingers and hope.

Within a day of first complaining of pains, Claude became completely paralysed on his right side. He lay in the hut, staring at the ceiling. Outside, the rain poured down, setting up a continuous roar as it pounded on the dense jungle foliage all around them. Later that evening, Claude slipped into a delirium and Arthur and Bomber could only sit ineffectually to one side as he mumbled and moaned and occasionally moved spasmodically in his corner of the hut.

For all of the next day, Claude remained delirious. Arthur and Bomber gave him water, but there was nothing else they could do. At three the following morning, Wednesday, 4 February, Claude died. It was clearly a release. His tortured movements and groaning slowed and finally stopped. His body relaxed and he lay still.

Arthur and Bomber spent the next morning digging a grave for him in the jungle, just beyond the edge of the swamp, with a small shovel they borrowed from the woodcutter. Neither of the two men were particularly religious, but they felt they should try to hold a small service for Claude before they placed his body and his steel helmet in the grave.

"I'm no good at this sort of stuff," Bomber muttered. "Go on, you say something."

"I can't, Bomber. I don't know anything about funerals, only that 'ashes to ashes, dust to dust' stuff, but I don't know how it goes after that. All I can say is..." Arthur looked down at Claude's body lying in the makeshift grave and closed his eyes for a second or two. "Goodbye, Brownie. We're sorry you didn't make it, mate. I thought for a while you were going to. Maybe, if we could've done a bit more for you, but...well, it just wasn't like that." He moved to one side to pick up the shovel.

"Yeah. Goodbye, Brownie," Bomber said. "Didn't get to know you very well, but, well, if you've got a god, I hope he's with you now."

Arthur pulled some of the damp earth from the small mound at the edge of the hole into the grave and Bomber followed suit. Together they covered the young man's body with earth and then spread the bare patch of ground with leaves and branches so that it virtually disappeared from view. To any but a highly trained eye, the spot which now formed Claude Brown's last resting place was no different from any other part of the surrounding jungle floor.

In the days that followed, Lee Kim Swee came with more news of the impending collapse of Singapore. Although the main action had moved right down to the bottom tip of the Malayan peninsula and the Allied forces had all withdrawn onto the island of Singapore by 31 January, Arthur and Bomber were not aware of this. When they heard what sounded like continuous artillery bombardment to the west and south of them as late as 10 and 11 February, it gave them a false sense of confidence that there was still some significant resistance remaining in Malaya. In fact, these actions were nothing more than mopping-up operations being carried out by the Japanese.

Shortly after Claude's death the little group shifted camp yet again. On Kim Swee's advice they moved from the swamp about half a mile deeper into the jungle, further from the old woodcutter's house, but closer, as it happened, to where Kim Swee's own house was located. Kim Swee had reported to them that the Japanese were now trying to bribe local people into either capturing or giving information about any British or Australian soldiers who might be hiding in the jungle. A reward of fifty Malayan dollars and a bag of rice was being offered for each soldier reported.

During this time, a friend of Kim Swee's, returning from Muar, gave a gruesome picture of what might await the Australians if they were caught. He told of seeing British troops there being tortured by the Japanese. They had tied up a group of men so that each had one arm secured behind his back. They were then offered cups of coffee to drink with their free hand. While they were drinking, they were shot in the thighs, first one, then the other. Then they were shot in both arms. Their ears and noses were cut off, then they were blinded and finally killed. The man reported to Lee Kim Swee, in awed tones, that the whole performance, which was watched by a large crowd of Japanese soldiers, took some considerable time. When passed on to Arthur and Bomber, it left them not only outraged, but with a chill feeling of dread about their prospects should they ever fall into enemy hands.

134

All of this time there seemed to be a gradual improvement in Leo's condition. He was now able to get up and move around somewhat, and his speech began to return slightly. Not so that he could hold a conversation, but he was beginning to be able to make himself understood and it was clear that he had a reasonable idea of what was going on around him. They established, in the occasional coherent periods that Leo began to enjoy, that he came from the small town of Horsham, in Victoria, and that his father ran a butcher's shop there.

The move to the new camp meant that they would have to build yet again. But, having been through the process twice, Bomber and Arthur were beginning to accept that it was probably going to be a regular fact of life that they might as well get used to. Their readiness to move on was more than likely also related to their improving health. Their wounds were healing well and Arthur's arm seemed to be better each day. He was convinced that exercise helped to improve it, so he tried continually to force it beyond its previous limits.

Slowly, the new camp took shape. This time, most of the work was done by Arthur and Bomber. Lee Kim Swee apparently felt that they had seen how it was done, therefore they should be able to do it themselves, although he did bring his nephew along to help during the second day. The first day had been spent cutting bamboo poles and erecting the structure of the shelter. The next was devoted to collecting attap for the roof and putting it up. Once that was complete, they then decided to indulge themselves by making beds. The prospect of such luxury put them in a good humour and they laughed at their own defiance, not only of the elements and the creeping, crawling creatures of the jungle, but of the Japanese--and of fate. To complete their sense of real decadence, Lee Kim Swee managed to supply them with three large, thick, Indian Army blankets.

But these comforts were counterbalanced by the fact that they were running out of food. First their sugar, then butter, then salt ran out, and for a short while Kim Swee found that he was unable to replenish their supplies. For several days they had rice only, and then Kim Swee's nephew arrived with some soup and a small monkey he had just killed for them to cook up. Later the same day, Kim Swee also turned up, accompanied by several

Chinese friends, each carrying some food: salt, butter, sugar, rice, tobacco and a small pig. It was his news, however, which interested them most, even though it was not at all encouraging.

"There is much fighting now in Singapore," he told them. "It looks very bad for the British and Australian forces. There are now only Japanese planes in the sky. No British planes left

"God, if Singapore falls, we're stuck here for good," Arthur moaned.

Kim Swee raised his eyebrows. "It is not good. The BBC news says that the Japanese have almost taken the Philippines and most of the East Indies. They are fighting in New Guinea and, according to the broadcast, Australia is threatened."

"Surely they can't invade Australia, too?" Arthur said.

"The BBC talked of America defending Australia," Kim Swee said. "American troops going to Australia. In time the Americans will be strong enough to push the Japanese back."

"But God knows how long that'll be," Arthur muttered. "Could be bloody years."

"Perhaps two or three years," Kim Swee said.

"Jesus!" Bomber whistled. "A bloke could go troppo stuck in here for that long."

"Troppo?" Kim Swee frowned. "What is troppo?"

Bomber smiled. "Looney, you know, out of his tree. Not a full quid." And when Kim Swee still showed no signs of understanding, Bomber twirled his finger around his head. "You know, crazy, bonkers, mad, offyer skull. That'll be us after two years."

Kim Swee laughed and then said goodbye for the day.

During that night Leo had a relapse. In the morning, he was unable to move and had once again lost the few words of speech he had regained.

Kim Swee returned the next morning, bearing more bad tidings.

"The Japanese seem to know that there are Allied soldiers in the jungle here. They have started searching the rubber plantations all around. I think there are some other groups of Australians, like yourselves, hiding in the jungle. It is very dangerous. We must be careful."

He told them that that evening, he and the woodcutter were leaving for Ayer Hitam, a town some thirty-five miles away, for news and supplies. He assured them that if the Japanese came near, they would be warned by his nephew. They should go further into the jungle to a small clearing. He took Arthur over a short, difficult path to show him the place and then bid him goodbye once again.

On two separate days after Kim Swee's warning, Japanese troops came into the area searching around and questioning the local Chinese plantation workers. Kim Swee's nephew managed to warn Arthur and Bomber and, on each occasion, they struggled to shift Leo to the safer hiding place. The make-shift stretcher they had made was impossible to manoeuvre, so they took it in turns trying to carry him 'piggyback'. Even though Leo had lost a great deal of weight since his injury, he still weighed around 120 pounds, sufficient to exhaust both Arthur and Bomber from the effort of carrying him.

On the second occasion, though, fear lent them strength when they actually heard the sounds of Japanese trucks coming through the rubber trees and then the voices of soldiers shouting and calling to each other as they searched the edges of the jungle.

That night, after they had returned to their shelter, Kim Swee arrived back from his trip to Ayer Hitam. He was extremely agitated.

"Singapore has fallen," he declared. "The British surrendered four days ago, on the 15th of February. There are thousands of British and Australian soldiers going to prison camps."

Arthur and Bomber were shocked. Although they had considered it a possibility, neither of them thought it could happen so quickly. Now, the ultimate fact of Singapore in Japanese hands had a fateful ring to it. It was as if the door, closing on all their chances of reaching freedom again, had finally shut.

"Where are they going?" Arthur asked Kim Swee. "Will they stay in Singapore?"

"They are going to Changi, the civil prison. It is on the eastern end of the island."

"Changi." Bomber repeated the word without emotion. It meant nothing to them at that time.

They sat in silence for a while and then Kim Swee, whose face had remained sombre and serious, said slowly, "We must also be very careful with the Malays. You must avoid them completely, if that is possible. There was a British soldier near here who was being cared for by three Chinese. He was injured, like you. Some Malays heard about him and informed the Japanese. The Japanese soldiers arrived while he was still in the yard of the Chinese house. They caught him and made him climb a coconut tree by jabbing him with bayonets as he climbed. Then, when they let him down, they tied him and the three Chinese to trees, tortured them--they cut out the muscles of their arms and other awful things-and then left them hanging there after they had died, as a warning to others." Arthur and Bomber listened to the story in silence. There was no indication that Leo had heard any of it. He lay, as if asleep, on his small, makeshift bed at one end of the shelter. Whether or not the frightening news that Kim Swee had brought them had impinged at all on his conscious or subconscious mind, they never knew. In the early hours of the following morning, Leo died.

9

SOON AFTER DAWN THEY BURIED Leo, as they had Claude, in a shallow grave they covered with leaves and brush. Again they said a few short words in the form of a tribute before they filled in the grave, but they had little time to contemplate Leo's death. The sound of trucks moving in the area beyond the jungle edge, accompanied, as before, by shouted Japanese commands, had them on the alert and moving quickly away from their shelter towards the more secure place further into the jungle. It was probably safe enough for them to remain in the area of their shelter, but they felt it best to be sure. The sounds of the Japanese trucks and soldiers were deceptively close. Actually, although they were separated from the jungle verge by only three or four hundred yards as the crow flies, it would have been impossible for anyone to have come at their position in such a direct manner. It had to be approached by a much longer, more tortuous route and that was possible only if one knew the way.

By the middle of the day, huge thunderclouds had built up and, as Arthur and Bomber waited, sitting under a large tree, the jungle became steadily darker. Soon the rain came and, as it grew heavier, they heard the distant sound of the Japanese vehicles leaving to return to wherever they were based. The two men slowly made their way back to their shelter. By the time they arrived, they were both completely drenched.

Just before dark, when the rain had finished and the clouds had passed over, Kim Swee turned up once more, sloshing through the mud of the rain-soaked path. When told of Leo's death, he expressed sorrow, but it was clear that, in one way, it was a relief to him. "Now," he said, "it will be possible for you to move."

"Again?" Bomber cried. "We've only just set up here."

"I am sorry," Kim Swee held his hand up apologetically. "The Japanese are convinced there are still soldiers here. Eventually they will start searching more deeply into the jungle and must find you. It is better that we move again."

"But where to next?" Arthur asked. "We seem to be making moves all the time."

"The old man, the woodcutter, has a brother in Sinkang, a kampong some miles from here. He is married to a Sakai woman. If you went there, she could take you to her people."

"Sakai? They're natives aren't they?" Arthur asked. "The tribes that live in the jungle all the time?"

"Yes. That is right. But they are good people, and they do not like the Japanese. I think you would be safest there."

Bomber and Arthur looked at each other. There was little they could say or do. They had placed themselves in Kim Swee's hands from the start and they had to admit that he seemed to have their best interests at heart.

"Okay, mate, whatever you say." Bomber stood up and grabbed one of the thick bamboo crosspieces of the ceiling. "We'll have a chain of these bloody huts built right across the flamin' country by the time we're through. How're we going to get there?"

"Ah Seng will take you, tomorrow."

By noon of the next day there had been no sign of the old man.

"I wonder what's keeping the old bugger?" Bomber said. "If we're going to go at all, we should be making a move soon."

Arthur volunteered to go to his hut to find out what was keeping him.

"We might as well go together," Bomber said. "If he decides to go from there, it'd be a waste of time if one of us was still back here."

They gathered what meagre supplies they had in a hessian sack and, picking up their only weapons-a small tomahawk axe and a parang, they set off for the trek to the woodcutter's hut.

They found the old man still in his bed. A Chinese youth of perhaps nineteen or twenty was standing beside the prostrate figure. He nodded a greeting to the two Australians. They recognised him as one of the group of Chinese who had brought them supplies at one of their previous jungle shelters.

The old man mumbled something in Chinese to the young man.

"Ah Seng says he is too sick to take you to Sinkang today. He has told me to take you there."

"Is he all right?" Arthur asked, moving a step closer to the wizened figure which lay motionless, as if on a deathbed. "Surely we can't leave him like this?"

The young man, who said his name was Ah Luk, motioned them to follow him outside. Once clear of the hut, he said, "It is all right. He says he is sick, but it is just the opium. He smokes too much opium." He picked up a small backpack by the door of the hut. "Come," he said, "we go now to Sinkang."

The journey to Sinkang took longer than expected. Ah Luk, although he seemed confident at the beginning, became more uncertain and somewhat nervous as they followed a path through the rubber plantations. After three or four miles, the path led them towards a house nestling back in some trees.

"Wait. Stop here." The youth held up his hand. "This is a Malay house. We must be careful."

As they stood waiting, sheltering in some shrubs from a light rain which had begun to fall, they saw two small children run inside the house.

"We must try another way," Ah Luk said, turning back. "There is another path." He led them back along the track for about a quarter of a mile and then off on a branch track through more dense foliage. He seemed to be searching for a track into the jungle, but without success. After they had tried two or three, Bomber whispered to Arthur, "This bloke's not a flamin' guide. He's got no more idea where he's going than I have."

It was also clear that he was frightened and wanted to return to the woodcutter's house, so after a brief discussion between Arthur and Bomber, they decided to let him go. It was a major decision to make. After weeks of being in the care of someone else, constantly under the watchful and protective eye of Lee

Kim Swee, they were now suddenly making a choice, of their own free will, to launch out on their own-with no idea where they were, how far they had to go to get to Sinkang, or where to go and who to see once they got there.

"This is crazy, really," Arthur said. "We're just as likely to run into a bunch of Malays or Japanese."

"No, we'll be right," Bomber said. "I'm sure we're not all that far from Sinkang."

So, after obtaining from Ah Luk an indication of what he thought was the best route to the kampong, they bid him good-bye.

"Thanks very much!" Bomber muttered as the man hurried off on his way back. "Thanks for nothing!"

Continuing on the route they'd been following, along the jungle verge, they came frequently upon small houses belonging to either Malay or Chinese plantation workers. Mostly they were able to get by without attracting attention, but finally they were spotted as they tried to pass an old wooden house in one corner of a plantation. A child they had not seen shouted and ran into the house, pointing back at the two Australians. Almost simultaneously, two men ran out of the house.

Bomber and Arthur stood transfixed for a moment, as did the other two men at the steps of the house, about fifty yards away.

"What'll we do?" Arthur looked at Bomber.

"Let's take a chance. Let's front 'em and ask the way to Sinkang."

The two Australians, clutching a parang and an axe, advanced towards the other two. At the same time, the men from the house began walking towards them with smiles on their faces and Arthur and Bomber saw, with relief, that they were Chinese.

The Chinese men greeted them by shaking their hands and patting them on the back. They could speak very little English, but they gestured to the house and, leading them there, made Arthur and Bomber welcome and introduced them to the rest of the family: the wife of one of the men, a couple of aged parents and six other children of various ages who stood around open-mouthed at the sight of the two bedraggled soldiers. Arthur and Bomber were given a large meal of pork, Chinese vegetables and rice, and put to bed on a mattress in an upstairs bedroom.

In the morning, after a large breakfast, the older son, one of the two men who had come out of the house the day before, led Arthur and Bomber to Sinkang. It was a devious route and a difficult track, and they both realised that without his aid they would never have found the way.

In Sinkang, a small kampong of about ten or twelve simple wooden houses with thatched or corrugated iron roofs, one of the first people they saw was Ah Seng. He had been looking for them and was as apologetic as he could be over the fact that his deputised guide had abandoned them. He introduced them to a local storekeeper, a bone-thin man of around forty who knew only one or two words of English. He gave them a friendly welcome, flashing, when he smiled, a big set of stainless steel teeth, and prepared coffee and biscuits followed by a large meal of rice and vegetables. Then he took the two men to a small shed at the back of his house which contained farm tools and fertilisers. There was also a quantity of sacking on which Arthur and Bomber rested for the remainder of the day and slept that night.

When they enquired about Ah Seng the following morning, no-one seemed to know where he was. He was supposed to take Arthur and Bomber to his brother, whose wife was then supposed to take them to meet the Sakai jungle people, but now the old man was missing.

"Probably chasing the bloody dragon again," Bomber said. "On the flamin' opium. What d'you reckon we should do?"

"Not much we can do," Arthur replied,' "but wait."

The two Australians were a great source of interest to the storekeeper and several of the other Chinese in the village, who were extremely kind and friendly, offering them cigarettes and food and all the while plying them with questions.

During a breakfast of rice and pancakes, the storekeeper, through another Chinese villager who spoke better English, told them of another group of Allied soldiers who were in the jungle nearby.

Both Arthur and Bomber were surprised and excited. "Can you take us to meet them?" Arthur asked.

"It is possible," the young man who spoke English replied. "Perhaps it can be arranged today."

There was a hurried conversation between the storekeeper and one or two other villagers who had been standing by, listening to the conversation and staring at the two foreigners. Then the group broke up and people went off in different directions.

"In a little while," the young interpreter said.

"D'you reckon we should just go off to see these blokes without waiting for the woodcutter?" Bomber asked Arthur.

"Well, it won't do us any harm. We can check up on what they're doing. They might have some other plans. But if they haven't, we've still got this meeting with the Sakais as an alternative."

Shortly afterwards, one of the Chinese people who had been in the storekeeper's house earlier came to them saying he was to be their guide and would take them in the afternoon to the other Allied soldiers. Arthur and Bomber spent a relaxed morning washing in a small stream nearby and enjoying a large lunch. Then, in the mid-afternoon, after saying goodbye to the storekeeper and his friends, the three men set off at a fast pace through the rubber.

A couple of hours walk brought them to a small Chinese house set up on thick poles in the manner of most of the houses in the area. Arthur and Bomber waited in the bushes nearby while their guide checked on the occupants of the house. They were four Chinese men who, once informed of the situation, welcomed the two soldiers warmly and, like the people of Sinkang, immediately offered them food and tea.

One of them spoke excellent English. "There are two British soldiers," he said. "They are not here now, but they will come tonight, late tonight."

In the early hours of the morning, Arthur was woken by the sounds of people arriving in the house and voices speaking softly in English. Shaking Bomber awake, Arthur got up quickly and walked into the front room where he was confronted with not two Allied soldiers, but six!

"G'day, mate," one of them said as Arthur stepped into the room. "Bloody good to see yer." He turned to his companions. "I knew they'd be 2/29th."

Arthur recognised the face immediately. It was covered in freckles, the nose had obviously been broken in some long-ago altercation either with a rugby goalpost or somebody's fist, and the curly mop of hair on top was carrot-red. Corporal H. R. Ryan had been in the same company as Arthur and Bomber, but in a different platoon. They knew him, of course, but not as well as the members of their own platoon.

"It's Ryan, isn't it?" Arthur said. "Corporal Ryan?"

"Bluey's the name." He reached out to shake Arthur's hand and that of Bomber who, still half-asleep, had emerged from the shadows behind Arthur.

"Hello, Sergeant Shephard," one of the others said as he stepped forward. "I see Brownie's not with you any more. He's gone, has he?"

Arthur recognised the young officer, Lieutenant Bill McCure, who had visited them in their tree house in the swamp.

"That's right, sir. Died not long after we saw you-4th of February."

McCure's face tightened. He looked at the floor for a moment, then shook his head. "Shame," he said. "Bloody shame. Good bloke, Brownie. And the other one?"

"The same, sir, about two weeks later. Not a chance, really. We couldn't do anything for their wounds. They were pretty bad."

McCure nodded, then turned towards his friends. "Now, let's see. Sergeant Shephard and, um--"

"Wainright, sir. Signaller Wainright," Bomber said.

"Yes, Signaller Wainright, this is Lieutenant Smylie."

"Jock's the name," a huge man with a large red beard said, smiling as he leaned over to shake Arthur and Bomber's hands in succession. At six feet six inches, Jock Smylie towered over everyone else in the room. Around forty years old, he was a former police chief in the British colonial administration of Malaya in Kedah, and one of two British officers in the little group of men.

The other was Lieutenant Peter Barlow, also sporting a beard, although it was rather more straggly than Smylie's. Somewhat younger, in his mid-twenties, Barlow was a blond, blue-eyed Englishman who'd been working on rubber estates in Malaya for some years prior to the outbreak of war. He was smoking a pipe as they were introduced. He took it from his mouth and smiled in a friendly way as they shook hands, but Arthur felt his reserve. If not snobbish, Pete Barlow clearly had ideas about the differences between 'officers' and 'men'.

Next came Lieutenant Scott-Skovso, a Danish officer who had been a member of a Dutch commando group, based in Java, which had moved to the Malayan peninsula. His double-barrelled name was the result of his English mother's insistence -on retaining her family name, Scott. Tall and slim, he, too, was in his forties. In typical European fashion, his beard was tidily clipped to a point, a 'Vandyke'. He had dark hair and dark eyes and spoke excellent English with a strong Dutch accent.

The last member of the group, Lieutenant Les Taylor, was a member of the Malayan Auxiliary Army, the hurriedly assembled force of civilian part-time soldiers who were called in too late to bolster Malaya's desperately inadequate defences. He had a wispy beard and moustache and although he spoke faultless English with what Arthur took to be an 'upper class' accent, the colour of his skin and his almond eyes showed that he was obviously Eurasian. He, too, gave a friendly smile and warm handshake to the two Australian soldiers.

"There's another group of troops knocking around here somewhere," Jock Smylie said after the introductions were over. "We're supposed to be meeting up with them tomorrow. We're going to try to get down to the coast and get a boat across to Sumatra. You chaps want to come along?"

Arthur and Bomber exchanged glances with each other and then nodded agreement.

"Sure, we'll come. But how're you going to get a boat? And where?" Bomber asked.

"We're not sure yet, but we've heard of others who've done it, so there's probably a good chance we can do it too."

The eight men talked among themselves for a few more minutes before one of the Chinese men who had been in the house when Arthur and Bomber arrived, spoke to Lieutenant Smylie in Malay. Smylie nodded and then turned to the others.

"He says we should try to get some sleep now because we have to leave at five in the morning."

Everybody nodded and, after a few more exchanges, found a clear space on the floor on which to curl up and try to sleep. Both Arthur and Bomber found it impossible to get any sleep during the three hours that remained. The sudden change in their fortunes, with what seemed to be an improvement in their prospects, filled their minds with thoughts of escape. Of course, they were no safer now, with six extra men, than they had been while hiding in the swamp, but somehow the fact that there were positive plans afoot made the situation seem more hopeful and their plight more bearable.

Shortly after 5 am, in pitch darkness, the little group set off with two Chinese guides on what was to be a five-hour trek. They were in rubber plantations the whole time, but by skirting the edges and sticking close to the jungle verge wherever possible, they were able to avoid any contact with plantation workers, even after it became light around 7 am.

Once again, they were led to a Chinese house where they were given coffee and some rice. Within a matter of half an hour, Lieutenant Kroon, a Dutch officer in charge of what he called 'a party of guerillas', arrived at the house. He had evidently been waiting nearby for Lieutenant Smylie's group to arrive.

He was a tall, thin man with sharp, angular features, approximately thirty years old. His English was excellent, but he spoke in a low, rather secretive manner, almost as if some unwanted person might be eavesdropping.

"I have thirty men under my command," he told them. "Two 'brigs'-that is, corporals-eighteen troops and ten convicts..." he paused. "To carry our barang." "Convicts?" Jock Smylie and Bomber both said at once, in surprise.

"Yes. They are from local prisons. They are all right... Malays and Chinese. They have been given their freedom now and promised a pardon when the war is over if they help us against the Japanese." He gave a sheepish grin.

"Where are they now?" Jock asked.

"We have a camp about two hours east of here. We have been there ever since we came up from Parit Sulong and..."

"Parit Sulong," Arthur interrupted. "When were you there?"

"After the Japanese took it." He shook his head slowly. "It is very bad there, awful. Many Australians are dead there. Their bodies are burnt and rotting. The smell is terrible."

" Jesus!" Bomber muttered. "But how do you know they're Aussies?"

"By the uniforms. We passed by several of them. There were many bloodstains on the trees too." He hesitated a moment, looking at Arthur and Bomber. "I am sorry, but it means that they were tortured by the Japanese."

"Bastards!" Bomber's face contorted grimly. "Fucking bastards!"

As they questioned Kroon further, Arthur felt mixed sensations of horror, fear and rage. They wanted to know more, but Kroon was unable to give any more details except what he had seen and surmised.

Lieutenant Kroon suggested that Jock Smylie's group, with Arthur and Bomber, should come to join his camp. "There is safety in numbers," he said.

Neither Arthur, Bomber, nor the others were convinced of this but when Kroon mentioned that his group had a wireless set, Jock and the others showed a keener interest in joining the Dutch party. It was agreed that Jock would go with Kroon to assess the situation and then report back. The two men left shortly before noon and by four in the afternoon a message from Jock, carried by a young Chinese man, had arrived back at the house telling the rest of the group to come to the Dutch camp.

Their trek took them through the rubber at first, then into the jungle, following a narrow and hardly discernible path up a steep mountainside. The going was hard, with vines and thorns tearing at their clothing but, by a little after 6 pm, they arrived at the campsite to find that a hearty meal of rice, with a large kerosene tin full of chicken broth, had been cooked up ready for their arrival.

The camp was set up in a small clearing on a gently sloping section of the hill. It was entirely surrounded by high jungle trees and dense foliage. Accommodation was nothing more than a few crude lean-to shelters, made of branches and leaves, strung around the edge of the clearing.

It was almost dark as the Dutch group gathered around to welcome them. Kroon was from a Dutch regiment which had been in Java. One hundred and fifty of them had come to Malaya to fight with the British forces as a commando unit, in the Labis area, at the time of the Japanese invasion. The two other officers in the Dutch group were a navy captain called Sauphert and Dr Van der Schroen. Sauphert, like Kroon, was in his thirties, while the doctor was older, in his mid-fifties, Arthur guessed. All spoke English, as did one or two of the Dutch corporals, but the other troops, who were actually Dutch Malays from Java, did not. The convicts, who were also Malays, were much less effusive and moved about quietly and, Arthur thought, somewhat sullenly, in the background.

A rough lean-to shelter had been constructed for the Dutch officers to sleep under. There was clearly not enough room for eight newcomers, so they slept on the ground under what cover they could find.

"We'll have to build more shelters for ourselves tomorrow," Jock said as they settled down for the night.

"Maybe not," Kroon's voice came out of the darkness. "Tomorrow we have a plan to escape from Malaya."

"What sort of plan?" McCure asked.

"Tomorrow we talk," Kroon replied. "We will have a meeting."

Arthur and Bomber, bedded down on the edge of the small clearing, without any cover, prayed that it would not rain. But the sky, what they could see of it through the overhanging jungle canopy, was clear and full of stars.

"What do you reckon their plan is?" Arthur said softly to Bomber.

"I don't know about their plan," Bomber whispered back, "but it's too big a group. These bloody convicts are a bit of a worry. Have you seen the look on some of their faces? And even his Malay troops don't seem really onside. I wouldn't like to trust any of 'em too far."

In the morning, a conference was held in the middle of the clearing to discuss a number of plans for the future. The Dutch scheme, as it happened, was basically the same as that outlined by Jock and McCure when Bomber and Arthur had first met them: to obtain a boat and sail it to Sumatra. According to Kroon, however, the Dutch group was well advanced in organising a boat to do the job.

"One of my sergeants, a Malay," he paused, "but a good man, has gone to a place near Parit Sulong to see about a boat, a fishing prow. But we also have news of another one at the village of Kangka, near here, which we must enquire about."

It was decided that two members of the British-Australian group, 'Mac' McCure and Les Taylor would accompany Kroon to Kangka the following day.

The three were away for more than twenty-four hours. On their return, they reported that the Japanese were very active in Kangka. Many of the Chinese residents of the village had been so intimidated and harassed that they had left. No progress had been made in obtaining a boat.

Later in the afternoon, however, the Malay sergeant, whose name was Ahmad, returned to the camp with the news that he had been able to arrange a boat for the group. There was a problem, though. A deposit of five hundred Malay dollars was required. After discussion, it was decided that they should all contribute what resources they had to a general pool or 'kitty' and that the money should be paid from that. It was also agreed that Ahmad should go immediately to pay the deposit and organise the boat to be ready for them.

Everyone then set about preparing themselves and planning the next moves. According to Ahmad, the boat would be made available to them somewhere on the Simpang Kiri River, below Parit Sulong. From there they must try to sneak the vessel about seven miles down the river to a point where it joined the larger Sungai Batu Pahat, the Batu Pahat River which, after another seven or eight miles, flowed out into the Straits of Malacca. The first part seemed relatively simple. The Simpang Kiri would be passing through jungle country, with no roads nearby, but the larger river would take them right through the town of Batu Pahat before reaching open water.

"We'll jump that hurdle when we get to it," Smylie said confidently as they neared the end of their discussions. "But first we've got to get ourselves organised and down to where the boat is."

The first group selected was to include all of the Europeans except Dr Van der Schroen and Captain Sauphert, and four of the Javanese troops. It was arranged that they should meet up with Ahmad at a rendezvous by the Muar-Parit Sulong road at midnight the following day, Sunday, 1 March.

Arthur began to worry about the journey. Over the past week or so, he had become afflicted with a severe case of tinea and was almost crippled in his right foot. The fungus had created a large hole between his second and third toes, and he found that it would often cause him agonising pain. Dr Van der Schroen had bathed it in some herbal mixture he made up, but Arthur was not very confident of its success.

"It needs powder," the doctor had said in his heavily-accented English. "And it needs dry, to dry up. But we cannot do these things." Although Arthur still had his boots, it was impossible, in the damp jungle conditions, to keep his feet dry, so the condition was difficult to prevent and, once established, almost impossible to clear up.

Arthur had also found that he was developing the condition in his crotch, a most uncomfortable circumstance, and also somewhat embarrassing because sometimes it became virtually impossible for him to walk properly without looking like some ridiculous, waddling duck. The prospect of a long march was not appealing.

They spent the next morning packing what gear they had and preparing food to take with them. By late afternoon all was ready, and they left the campsite with a Chinese guide, planning to travel through the night in the hope, that their passage through the rubber plantations would not be noticed.

Travelling as quickly and silently as possible, in single file, with no-one speaking a word, they passed the outskirts of Kangka. They heard the sounds of trucks and Japanese soldiers in the area, sounds which faded as they moved on, first into more rubber plantations and then a swamp. They held their course, a southerly one, as it took them deeper into the swamp and then through it.

Shortly before midnight, as they were nearing the Muar-Parit Sulong road, they heard shots-first a few single shots, then some brief bursts of automatic fire. They seemed to be only a short distance away, not more than a mile down the road to their left, in the direction of Parit Sulong.

"What the hell d'you reckon that was?" Bluey Ryan muttered as they all bunched up in the darkness, stopping to listen.

"Who knows," Bomber said, "but there's obviously a few Nips around. We'd better be careful crossing the road." He paused. "Anyway, what happens when we do cross it?"

"The rendezvous is close to the road, on the other side of it," Smylie said. "Ahmad should be waiting for us."

The group crossed the Muar-Parit Sulong road one by one, without incident. In the deep darkness of the moonless night, they were all but impossible to see from a distance of more than a few feet, and even then they appeared only as fleeting shadows. Once on the south side of the road, it took some time to find the rendezvous, but eventually, after they had located a particular tree with an unusual shape by a particular bend in the road, they decided they were there. There was a large bomb crater there, between the edge of the road and another swamp, but no Sergeant Ahmad.

Arthur and Bomber and Bluey Ryan sat down together on the edge of the crater. The Malays joined them, while the officers stood in a huddle beneath some rubber trees, whispering.

"I reckon it's time for some tucker," Bluey said.

"Too right. I'm starving," Bomber agreed.

They had each been carrying food which they had prepared at the camp the previous day-a packet of nasi goreng (fried rice) wrapped in banana leaves and half a small chicken each.

When the officers came across a few minutes later, they too sat down to eat from their food parcels.

"We have to wait for Ahmad," Jock Smylie said softly. "We'll post two sentries to keep watch for him, but I think the rest of us should try to get some shut-eye."

No-one needed coaxing. As it was extremely dark and there had been no more sounds of shooting, or any traffic on the road, they felt relatively secure. Stretching out where they were, in the mud on the edges of the crater, they all slept soundly.

By the first light of dawn there was still no sign of Ahmad. Smylie was clearly concerned at his absence and directed the group to move into some shrubs a little further away from the crater and the road.

He sat talking quietly with Kroon and the other officers for some time. A dispute developed over what to do about Dr Van der Schroen, Captain Sauphert and the others. Some considered that a party should be sent back to the old campsite to collect them and bring them to the rendezvous site. Others held the view that they should wait until the boat had been found and then brought to a safe place by the river. Finally, a decision was made that two of Kroon's men and the Chinese guide would return to the camp to collect the others and bring them back to the rendezvous, but by the time they reached agreement, it was 8.30 in the morning and already several trucks had passed by their position.

"It's a bloody dangerous time to be crossing the road," Bomber muttered to Arthur as the three men moved away from them in the undergrowth. "I don't know why the hell they didn't do it while it was still dark."

The little party followed the line of the road for a hundred yards or so to a point where they hoped to be able to run across with minimum exposure to any vehicle or person coming down the road from either direction. They waited for a short time, listening carefully and looking in both directions. A truck was heard in the distance. It came and passed and, as its sound gradually faded away, they made their run. At that precise moment, two Malays riding bicycles rounded the bend another two hundred yards to their right. The party hesitated a second and then continued quickly across the road to disappear into the rubber trees.

McCure, who had watched their crossing, also saw the cyclists and, from their reaction, realised that they had seen the three men running across the road.

"We'd better all take cover," he declared urgently, as he scrambled back from the roadside. "We'll be in trouble if those Malays tell the Japs."

They all lay still under the cover of the dense shrubbery as the two cyclists pedalled furiously past, looking nervously from side to side as they did so. Then, when the Malays were a safe distance away, the group moved further back from the road, each finding as secure and well-hidden a position as possible.

Within a short time, McCure's prediction was confirmed. A motorised Japanese patrol of three vehicles roared past. Moments later, another truckload of soldiers came along the road, more slowly. It passed their position and stopped further along the road to disgorge its passengers who, carrying their weapons at the ready, spread out on either side of the road.

As the group lay silently in the undergrowth, they could clearly hear the commands of the Japanese officers and the voices of the soldiers as they began their search. One of the patrol cars returned to join the truck and off-load some more soldiers. The voices came down the roadway towards their position. They could hear many footsteps on the road and the clanking of webbing, equipment and rifles.

"There they are," Arthur whispered to Bomber who was flattened beside him underneath a thick rhododendron bush. Through a tiny gap in the leaves he could see a portion of the roadway about forty yards away. "A couple of Malays and three or four Japs. Jesus! I hope they don't come in here."

But even as he spoke, the two Malays pointed from the road towards the crater area in which the group had been. They walked in through the long grass to the edge of the crater. Arthur could sense that others in the group were watching also, and holding their breath.

"If they come to this side of the crater, they'll see our bloody footprints," Bomber hissed.

"Sh!" Arthur jabbed Bomber in the side.

The two Malays stood for only a moment, then returned to the edge of the road. They spoke a few words to the Japanese soldiers and pointed up the road to the place where the others had crossed. They stood for a few more moments, looking around them on both sides of the road, and then moved away out of sight.

For a further twenty minutes there was activity on the road as the search continued, but eventually the Japanese soldiers rejoined their vehicles and drove off in the direction of Parit Sulong. The road was once again deserted and quiet, but word was passed among the group to remain lying in their hiding places without moving in case the Japanese had left someone to watch the area.

As the heat of the day and the humidity built up, the men were thankful for the shade provided by the dense cover in which they were lying. There was very little traffic on the road and the hum and buzzing of insects in the trees became soporific. Arthur dropped into a deep sleep, as did several of the others, waking some time later, soaked through with perspiration and feeling desperately thirsty.

About mid-afternoon, the missing Sergeant Ahmad turned up, seemingly from nowhere. He stood by the crater, looking around nervously, until Smylie called to him softly from the bushes. As the group gathered around, he gave them the disappointing news that he had been ill with malaria and had not been able to make contact with the boatman. He felt, however, that a second attempt could be made that night.

He also informed the group that the shots they had heard the previous evening had been Japanese troops rounding up three British soldiers who were being sheltered by Chinese. The news only heightened their feelings of uncertainty and fear of capture. After more discussion between the officers, it was decided that Ahmad should leave them again in the early hours of the morning to meet the boatman, pay him the agreed fee and arrange, if possible, for the boat to take the group the following night. It was a strange arrangement. They had no way of knowing what size the boat would be or how many men it could carry.

"We have to face the possibility," Jock told them, "that some will have to wait to be picked up later."

"Sometimes I feel we'd have been better off just staying in our little hut by the swamp," Bomber muttered to Arthur as they settled down again to lie and wait.

Just before midnight, Captain Sauphert, Dr Van der Schroen and the other members of the group arrived and settled into hiding places close to the rest. Ahmad left at 3.30 am, slipping off silently like a shadow. Arthur felt as if each of their lives were attached to this man by a thin and tenuous string. Everything depended on him, yet they had no control and they could do nothing to change the situation. As the new day broke and wore on and their food supplies were exhausted, the feeling of helplessness grew.

Again, the heat and humidity rose steadily. The men lay close to each other without speaking, as if in a torpor.

Then the rain came, torrents of rain, soaking them through. They lay uncomfortably in the mud, waiting. But Ahmad did not show up. The food situation now began to look more serious. There were discussions about what should be done. If the boat plan did not succeed, they would have to return to the old camp near Kangka.

The night passed and a new day began, the third since they had left the Dutch camp. Still no sign of Ahmad. Then, finally, as the group was becoming increasingly restive in the late afternoon, he turned up.

His news was bad. No boat. He had prowled up and down the river for many hours, but he had been unable to find the boatman.

CHAPTER TEN

9. Arthur , aged seventeen, in Salvation Army uniform with his E Flat tuba

10. Nancy and Betty Muller

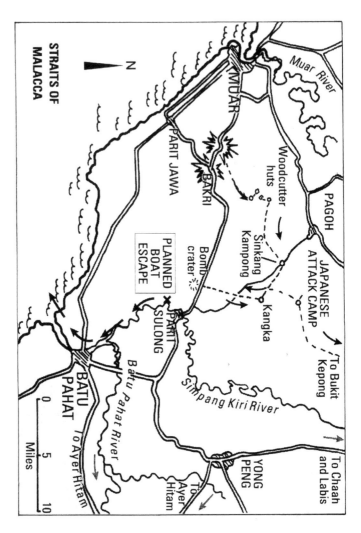

*Map 5. Approximate route followed in
attempts to find an escape boat*

10

"WHAT THE HELL DO WE do now?" Bomber mumbled disconsolately as they gathered around the Malay sergeant. "We're way out on a limb here. We've got to go somewhere."

The faces of all the men showed their disappointment and frustration. They began a long and urgent discussion to plan their next move. Some wanted to return to the jungle campsite to wait for a month or so in order to prepare another escape plan more thoroughly. It was also suggested that contact should perhaps be made with Chinese guerilla forces. There had been numerous reports of a growing Chinese resistance force that had begun forming in the jungles under the direction of the Malayan Communist Party. Some felt they may be of help in escaping from Malaya.

It was decided that Kroon and most of the Dutch group would stay at the rendezvous and make further attempts to contact the boatman while a ration party went back to collect more food from the old camp and the Chinese plantation workers who had helped them before. Bomber, Arthur and Jock Smylie's band volunteered to join the ration party.

The party slept until four-thirty the next morning then, following a different route through the rubber plantations, made directly for the old camp, reaching it in little more than two hours of fast travelling. Arthur, suffering badly from the tinea in both his feet and his groin, found the trek an agonising ordeal, except for several brief stops which were made at the houses of friendly Chinese who provided the ragged-looking troops with something to eat.

Food and supplies were taken back to Kroon and the rest of his men. They stayed at the rendezvous site for a further thirty-six hours before returning to the main camp, somewhat disillusioned.

In the days that followed, despite more disappointments, the boat project was kept alive with repeated attempts to contact the original boatman. The Chinese man who had made the original arrangements insisted that there had been no backing out of it. It was just that the boatman had been lying low because of the Japanese in the area. At the same time, the group began to work on improving facilities at the camp, perhaps subconsciously recognising and accepting the futility of their plans.

They built a shelter over the kitchen, as well as a number of lean-to sleeping shelters. Food was collected from 'outside' and a good supply was being built up in their makeshift pantry. They had fowl, duck, eggs, onions, cucumbers, cauliflower, limes, bananas, salt and plenty of ubi, a sort of jungle potato.

But the physical difficulties of living in the jungle were beginning to take their toll. Both Arthur and Jock were affected by fever, almost certainly malaria. Neither was completely immobilised, but they would be utterly drained and exhausted by only a few minutes of exertion. And there was the rain, coming almost as regularly as clockwork, in the mid-afternoon. In one way it was welcomed, for it cooled the stifling, windless air, but it turned the camp into a quagmire and left them all continually wet.

To make matters worse, there were endless arguments with the Dutchmen. Arthur found them aggressive and rude, mostly to their own Malay troops and to the Chinese who were helping them, but also to the Australian and British troops.

"I thought the flamin' poms were pretty rough, the way they talk to the locals," Bomber remarked of one incident in which Kroon shouted abuse at a couple of his Malay troops, "but this lot take the bloody cake! They're up themselves!"

The Dutchmen's overbearing behaviour was having an adverse affect on the attitudes of the Malay troops and the convicts. They began to show signs of resentment and rebelliousness, primarily towards Kroon, Sauphert and Van der Schroen, but also, by association, towards Jock's group, and

Bomber and Arthur. One of the Malays shouted and gesticulated angrily when McCure asked for some help with a new kitchen shelter that was being constructed. When McCure later suggested to Kroon that he should discipline the soldier, the Dutch officer admitted he had lost control of his men.

"Well, they'd better not try any funny business with us," Jock said, when he was told of the conversation. "We should keep alert and also keep an eye on our arms."

After two further arguments with the Dutch group--one about food, the other to do with sharing duties--a serious discussion was held between Jock's group, and Bomber and Arthur about separating from the Dutchmen to go and set up another camp elsewhere. There was no dissent.

Scott-Skovso, whom they had all taken to calling 'Scottie', spoke up. "I suggest that we should also try to contact the Chinese guerillas. From the reports we've been hearing, they seem to be getting well organised."

"They're bloody commos though, aren't they?" Bomber said.

"They're against the Japs," Pete Barlow put in. "Surely that's good enough."

"Absolutely," Jock agreed. "We should at least try to find out what sort of set-up they have."

Jock told Kroon and Sauphert of their intentions.

Kroon nodded slowly, "If that is the way you feel. It is your decision. It is of no consequence to me. You do as you wish. We will continue here with our own efforts."

The following day, Pete and Scottie left at ten in the morning to try to reach one of the Chinese guerilla camps. Their aim was not to seek to join them at this stage but simply to sound the Chinese out for future supplies of food and also for arms. The remainder set about preparing for the move which would separate them from the Dutch group.

Arthur's feverish condition deteriorated, however, so that by the following morning, when the time came to leave, he was unable to walk without aid. Kroon, in a rare act of charity, detailed two of his men to help Arthur. The trek to the new location was hard but not long, and as soon as they arrived, Arthur was able to rest in the shade of a large tree. The new site had been selected by local Chinese and was not far from a small Chinese kampong. Within less than an hour of their arrival there, Pete and Scottie arrived with a Chinese guide. They had made contact with the guerilla forces.

"The communists want us to come and join them," Scottie informed the group. "We didn't see their camp. Apparently it's over near Chaah. But they know about us and they say we should come to them for protection."

"Protection?" Mac smiled. "How's that?"

"Numbers, I suppose," Pete Barlow said. "But they've also got about two months' supply of food, so at least we wouldn't be hungry."

Opinion was divided as to whether they should join the communist guerillas. No-one knew a great deal about them. They were obviously a very new organisation and, as Jock suggested, "They're probably not very well trained, if at all, in guerilla warfare."

All agreed that the one big advantage the communists had to offer in any alliance was that they were locals. They knew the land and had contacts in every village and town. But even if they had decided to join the guerillas immediately, it was clearly something which could not be arranged overnight. The guide returned to his camp saying that, within a week, delegates would be sent by the guerillas to meet and discuss the situation and also to plan an alternative campsite for the Allied soldiers.

During this time, the little band began to build up their own supplies of food. Jock and Mac made several trips to the nearby village and came back with all sorts of food: fowls, coffee, sugar, ubi, ketchup, Craven-A cigarettes on one day; and margarine, kerosene and a nine-dollar pig the next.

They also began new attempts to find a boat to get out of Malaya. Pete and Scottie were put in charge of the project and, via their arrangements, two Chinese came to the camp on 17 March to tell them that, within a matter of days, a fishing vessel would be ready to pick them up at an agreed point on the river.

A new wave of excitement and enthusiasm swept through the group. There seemed good reason to believe, that, despite the previous disappointments, this time it might work. Jock's group went off to the Dutch camp, and to another nearby village, to collect more supplies for the boat trip, while Arthur and Bomber were left minding the camp.

About an hour after the others had gone, the two men were preparing some food-Bomber cleaning a fowl and Arthur making some coffee--when, less than a hundred yards away, a series of rifle shots rang out from the direction of the jungle track leading into the camp. With hardly a second's pause, Arthur and Bomber bolted for the creek, only a few yards from them. Running up the creek bed as fast as they could, they put as much distance between themselves and the camp as possible. They had had no chance to pick up any of their arms, food, or whatever meagre belongings they had before fleeing.

From where they paused, although they could see nothing, they could hear the sounds of voices, shouting at first, then laughing, as the raiders scoured and ransacked the little camp. As Arthur and Bomber hid in the bushes beside the stream, it began to rain. They waited and waited. Two hours later, when they carefully returned to the campsite, soaked and bedraggled, they found it almost a total wreck. All of their food, what arms there had been and anything else of value had gone.

A further two hours passed before the others got back. Scottie, who was exceptionally tidy, had lost everything he possessed whereas his friend Pete Barlow, who was generally very untidy and who left his belongings in a mess, found most of it intact. Jock Smylie's pack, containing most of the group's pooled money, was gone, but a slaughtered pig had not been taken with the rest of the food.

"Must have been Malays," Bomber said. "Muslims won't touch pig."

"But there were Japs there, too," Arthur added. "I heard them." '

"Yes, but it would have been the others who took the food and left the pig. The Japs wouldn't want any of it."

Everyone in the group was alternately angry, upset and depressed by the attack. They were also somewhat edgy in case the raiding party should suddenly return. The fact that they knew the location and had successfully attacked it once meant they could easily do it again.

"We can't stay around here," Jock said. "We'll have to move, and pretty smartly, too, I'd say."

"Tonight?" Bluey voiced everyone's fears.

"Probably not. But we should be ready to move first thing in the morning."

"Well, at least we bloody well won't have much to carry this time," Bomber joked, with no response. "But where do we go?"

They squatted in a circle on the ground for several minutes, discussing alternatives. The prospect of joining up with the Chinese guerillas was still there, but they had not yet sent the so-called delegates they had promised, so that option was not immediately available. The general consensus seemed to favour a move inland, away from the coast, at least until the boat situation improved. There was also the possibility of reaching either one of two secret arms and food caches which Jock and Scottie knew about. One was near the town of Labis, about forty miles by road from their present position, the other near Chaah, some ten miles closer.

The road distances, of course, meant nothing. If they were to travel to either one, it would have to be overland, through the jungle and rubber plantations. Another alternative was Sinkang, the area in which Bomber and Arthur had spent the first few weeks after Bakri. Finally, a decision was made to head for the area around the town of Chaah. They would leave late in the afternoon of the next day and travel only at night.

Jock felt it was safe enough to spend the night at the camp, but the following morning the group moved further up the creek to a safe place where they could spend the day without fear of another attack. Bluey Ryan and Les Taylor were sent off to advise the Dutchmen of what was happening, and also to see if they could spare some food supplies.

During their absence, Jock's fears of a second attack were confirmed. Voices and several shots, for no apparent reason, were heard from the original camp area. They could also see smoke rising into the air. It seemed that whoever had returned to the camp had set fire to the few rudimentary structures and shelters around the clearing. Fortunately, the intruders remained for less than an hour, so that when Les and Bluey returned shortly after 2 pm, with a few basic supplies of rice, ubi and a small chicken, the raiders had gone.

At about 4 pm, the eight men set off. They had no maps, only a general idea of the direction in which Chaah lay and the idea of following a line of hills which Scottie said ran in the direction they wanted to go. In the darkness, however, they soon lost their bearings. After about three hours, a halt was called and they decided to spend the night where they were and move on the next day.

They had a very sparse meal--a handful of dry rice and a tiny portion of the chicken, which was divided as best they could amongst eight. From where they stopped, on the side of a hill, they heard the unmistakable sounds of a small village in the valley below them. Not long after 8 pm several shots were heard from the direction of the village and they could see, in the distance, what looked like a large fire with heavy smoke rising into the dark night air.

They slept fitfully and uncomfortably on the ground, to be woken again at about two in the morning by more shooting.

"That's the bloody Nips down there, for sure," Arthur whispered to Bomber. "I hate to think what the bastards are doing."

They lay for a time listening to the sounds from the village, but soon there was only silence and, overcome by their own weariness, they drifted uneasily back to sleep, to be woken again, about 5.30 am, by heavy rain which drenched them within minutes.

"We might as well get a move on," Mac suggested, as they collected themselves together. "I think we should follow the crest of the hill until the sun comes up."

"Yeah, we might not see the bloody thing all day," Bluey sniffed. "What if we're headin' the wrong way?"

"Don't worry." Jock came up from behind and slapped him on the back. "We're on the right track. I'll bet on it."

No-one really wanted to take him up on the bet and they moved off on what was an ill-defined track. In the darkness of the night, they had not been aware of it but now, as the pre- dawn gloom gradually lightened, it became clear that they were on some sort of boundary trail or firebreak that had been cut in the forest. It was easy to follow along the crests of the low line of hills and, while they stuck to it, they made good time.

Arthur, who was still feeling the effects of his bout of fever and the tinea which had slightly improved, was able to keep pace with the rest but felt mightily fatigued by the effort. The rain had continued and the discomfort of slogging along, soaking wet, with their clothes hanging heavily on them, made the little group more gloomy than they might have been in better weather.

By noon of that second day, they were skirting the edge of a large plantation when Scottie, who was at the head of the column, held up his hand, calling for an instant halt and silence. The rain had eased and they had heard a noise ahead, an instantly recognisable noise...a baby crying!

Moving carefully forward to investigate, they found that it came from a small house on the edge of a rubber plantation. Watching the place for a while from the cover of the surrounding shrubbery, they saw a Chinese man, his wife and two young children, one of them the toddler who had been crying. After a brief discussion at the head of the column Jock Smylie left their concealed position and approached the man. He was initially surprised and frightened, then friendly. Jock spoke to him in Malay and explained the situation and where the group was heading.

The man, who was in his early thirties, called all of the others to come into his house from their hiding places in the bush. Although the family was obviously poor, he directed his wife to cook up a large meal of rice and fried bananas and cups of coffee.

The men stayed at the house, resting and partially drying their clothes, until about three in the afternoon when they moved on, following new directions given by their Chinese host. He had given instructions on how to contact another Chinese man further along the way who would guide them to the area near Chaah. Within little more than an hour, they had come to another small Chinese kampong where their contact was quickly located. Jock stood on the edge of the kampong in earnest conversation with the man for some minutes before returning to the group at the edge of the forest.

"He says he's a communist," Jock told the men. "He says he can take us to Chaah if we like, but he says there's a guerilla camp not far from here where we'd be better off. What do you think?"

Jock put the question to the group as a whole. There was some hesitation. The guide moved over to join them and spoke enthusiastically, in broken English, assuring them that it was a good camp and that they would be more secure there than making their own camp at Chaah.

The added prospect of a reasonable supply of food quickly convinced them. Without further hesitation, they set off to follow the guide along a series of tracks through rubber plantations, and then into the jungle, to eventually arrive at the guerilla camp at dusk.

The first thing that struck them was the size of the clearing and the number of people, although there were probably not more than two dozen, all of whom were Chinese. The first person they met, however, spoke very good English and was obviously proud of it.

"Good evening," he said as he shook their hands one by one. "My name is Chow See Ping. I am a schoolmaster. Or rather," he smiled, "I was a schoolmaster."

He was a short, rather stocky man who appeared to be in his late twenties or early thirties. His face was round, almost moon- shaped and he wore steel-rimmed glasses. His hair was parted in the middle and hung loosely on the sides of his forehead. Turning to the others beside him, he issued orders for food to be prepared for the eight men, and then proceeded to give them the latest news.

"Russia and America are both bombing Tokyo," he declared with authority. "Also Chiang Kai-shek's forces are already fighting in Kedah."

"Chiang Kai-shek?! In Malaya already?" Scottie and Jock exclaimed in surprise. "But they would have had to come all the way from China, through Burma and Thailand. How could they have come so far, here to Malaya, so quickly?"

Chow See Ping looked pained and slightly offended that they should doubt what he said. "It is true. It has been on the radio news. I have heard it." And then, as if to drop what might prove a difficult subject, he said, "I must tell you also that there are two British officers in Johore at the moment, making special arrangements for safe transportation of troops left behind the Japanese lines."

"British officers?" Jock asked. "Where are they now?"

"I cannot tell you," Chow See Ping replied, "because I myself do not know. I believe it is not too far. But I think you and your party should stay here with us until they are contacted."

Arthur and Bomber looked at each other and then at the other members of the group. "How long do you think that might be?" Arthur asked.

"I cannot say, but I am sure it will not be too long." The date was Thursday, 19 March 1942.

11

NONE OF THE EIGHT ALLIED soldiers present at that first meeting with the communist guerillas, particularly Arthur Shephard, could have guessed at the ultimate length of their association with them. They felt at the time that the possibility of organising a boat in which they could escape to Sumatra, or even India, was still quite real. Now, the news that there were two British officers nearby, charged with the specific task of getting stranded Allied soldiers out from behind enemy lines, raised their hopes even more.

From the moment of their first meeting, however, they realised that their stay with the Chinese would mean a much more prescribed way of life than they had been used to over the past few weeks. It would, in fact, be like being in the army again.

Their reintroduction into a life dictated by routine came with reveille at 6 am on the morning after their arrival at the camp. There was no trumpet played, of course, but Chinese men moved quietly around the large camp area shaking the prostrate forms, lying either in the open or under crude shelters, to wake them up.

There was a time for washing themselves and cleaning up, then a time for group exercise, then a period when breakfast was eaten, followed by some free time. Then, on the cleared area in the centre of the camp, there was a drill period. This was very rudimentary training in the basics of military discipline. In their first days in the camp, the Allied soldiers were not required to participate in these drill sessions, but they felt it would not be long before they were either persuaded or pressured into joining.

On the morning of their first day in the camp, a young, English-speaking Chinese woman introduced herself to the group as Ah Liong. She was extremely attractive. In her mid-twenties, Arthur guessed, but unlike many Chinese women, she was tall and slim. Her husband had been killed by the Japanese and she had joined the guerillas because she feared for her own life. After talking to the men for a short time about their past experiences, she brought them pancakes from the cookhouse and also some clothes: ordinary civilian shirts and trousers and some open sandals as well as some material from which to make sarongs. Many of their clothes, worn continuously through swamps and thorny jungles over the preceding weeks, were in tatters.

For Arthur Shephard, the chance to wear a sarong instead of trousers was a godsend. The painful tinea rash in his groin was only aggravated by trousers, whereas the sarong enabled air to circulate and begin to dry out the fungus infection. But his eager acceptance of the sarong, and the fact that he was the first in the group to wear it, gave the others an opportunity to poke a little fun at him.

"Jeeze, if only the blokes back in Melbourne could see you now, Shep," Bomber jibed. "They'd all be after you."

Everyone laughed. Arthur laughed. He didn't care. He just knew how much more comfortable he was. Within days, all of the others were wearing sarongs, if not all the time, at least when they were sleeping or relaxing around the camp area.

During their first few days with the communist guerillas, there was plenty to occupy them. Firstly, they had to build their own shelters. In this, Arthur and Bomber had a distinct advantage over the others because they had seen and participated in the construction of several shelters of varying degrees of sophistication. On this occasion, they had to seek out a reasonable spot and build whatever shelter they wanted for themselves.

The camp, although quite large in area, was smaller in numbers than they first thought. Groups of people seemed to come and go and while at any one time there might be as many as fifty in the camp, the average appeared to be closer to thirty. The site was basically just a section of jungle in which some trees had been felled to create a central clearing. On the outer edges, the clearing process involved only the shrubbery between the trees. Because of the damp, soft soil, the shrubbery was reasonably easy to pull out by the roots.

The procedure to build the simplest form of shelter was firstly to find two straight trees which stood about ten feet apart and tie a bamboo pole horizontally between them at a height of about six or seven feet. Then, after leaning a number of straight branches against the horizontal pole, layer upon layer of attap, or coconut or banana leaves, would be placed on top of the branches to form a sloping roof. With a rough drainage system built around the outside edges, the occupants could be protected from even the heaviest downpours which, in the generally windless conditions, came straight down instead of slanting in under the open sides of the shelter.

Arthur and Bomber's hut began to take shape quickly on the very edge of the jungle, a hundred yards or so from the main camp clearing. Having finished the shelter, they began to make beds for themselves.

As they were working, Ah Liong came across to talk to them. She was carrying a small baby in her arms.

"Is, er, is that yours?" Bomber asked.

She laughed. "Of course. This is my son."

"But...how? I mean, this is not really a very good place for babies."

"I have no choice," she said. "When my husband was killed I was alone. Do you want me to leave my baby outside?"

"No, of course not," Arthur said. "It was just that we were surprised to see him."

She looked down at the sleeping child and smiled. "He is all right. As long as we are together, he is all right. But this is not what I came to talk about. I came to tell you some news, bad news. Yesterday some Japanese troops came to a kampong only three miles from here seeking information about this camp."

The Japanese, they learnt later, had killed fifteen people there and set fire to the village. A young Chinese boy, wounded during the massacre, was brought to the camp and Jock, digging into the group's meagre medical supplies, found some disinfectant and dressings to help attend to wounds on his body and legs.

The soldiers christened him Lincoln, and tried to cheer him up, but it was a difficult task as he had lost his father, mother and his brother in the attack. The horrific picture the poor boy painted of the brutal Japanese killings kept most of the camp on edge during the next few days. It was felt that, under torture, one of the villagers may have revealed the camp's location. Two nights later, at around nine-thirty, the camp was jolted awake by a number of rifle shots in the jungle less than half a mile away. Within seconds, everyone was up and ready to bolt into the jungle along predetermined escape paths.

There was, however, no danger on this occasion. It had been two of the sentries firing at a party of their own men coming unexpectedly up the track with two Chinese prisoners. The whole camp, already aroused, gathered around to see the two men as they were shoved, hands tied behind their backs, into the centre of the camp parade ground.

It appeared, according to the patrol which brought them in, that the two men were suspected of being either spies or collaborators. They had been found carrying Japanese passes and pro-Japanese propaganda.

Chow See Ping wanted to set up a court of enquiry to try the prisoners immediately. He turned to Jock Smylie, "As leader of the British and Australian group, you will be one of the judges," he said.

Smylie was as stunned as the rest of the group, even though they were not being asked to participate. "I, er...I don't feel I have the right to judge. I mean, perhaps it's a little late at night to jump straight into a trial. Couldn't we leave it until daylight, tomorrow?"

"Perhaps," Chow See Ping nodded. "But we should interrogate them now, immediately."

The two men were subjected to harsh and threatening questioning, only parts of which Jock, Pete and Scottie could understand as it was all in rapid-fire Chinese. They were pushed back and forth between guerilla soldiers as questions were fired at them. Chow See Ping told them later that the men had steadfastly denied that they had been working for the Japanese, but could offer no adequate explanation for carrying Japanese passes. After about forty minutes of questioning, the guerilla leaders, including Chow See Ping, decided to postpone any fullscale trial until the following day. They ordered the two men to be tied tightly to a couple of trees and placed under guard until the morning.

Before they returned to their beds for the evening, there was some other encouraging news from the guerilla party that had brought in the prisoners. Apparently, another guerilla group had succeeded in destroying several Japanese Army staff cars and their occupants, in the Segamat area several days previously, by placing time bombs in the vehicles.

The prisoners were questioned again in the morning, but no new information was obtained. Clearly, Chow See Ping and the others were still unsure whether they were guilty or innocent, so they were left, as before, tied to two trees until their fate could be decided.

"I wonder what they'll do with the poor bastards?" Bomber had said to Arthur after watching the morning interrogation. Chow See Ping had been even more aggressive in his questioning than he had been the previous evening, shouting and pushing the two men towards three or four others who lashed into them with thick pieces of rotan--split bamboo.

"I don't know," Arthur replied, "but I wouldn't like to be in their shoes."

Arthur and Bomber were standing some distance away with Jock while the questioning proceeded.

"No," Bomber said quietly, "we wouldn't want to get on the wrong side of these buggers."

"It looks like we're stuck with them for a while, though," Jock muttered. '

"What about those two Brit officers in Johore?" Arthur said. "Isn't there anything we can do to contact them?"

The three men raised the subject later that day with CSP, as they were now calling Chow See Ping. They were given the same answer as before--there had been no news.

"It is very difficult at the moment," CSP explained. "There are now almost four thousand Japanese troops in Batu Pahat alone. Several hundred in Muar. They are building fortifications along the main roads and increasing their searching programmes."

"What about Chiang Kai-shek's forces?" Jock asked. "Any more news of them?"

"We have heard that Chinese paratroopers have landed in the Kuala Lumpur area and that this is one of the reasons for the Japanese build-up," CSP replied.

The three men nodded but made no comment. They all shared the same view, that the stories of Chinese troops in Malaya were no more than that--just stories. But where did they originate? And why were they told? Were they only for the benefit of Europeans like their little band, who found them difficult to believe anyway, or were they for the other Chinese members of the camp, to bolster their confidence? Whichever it was, it tended to undermine the confidence that the British and Australians had in any information that was given to them, including the story they had heard about the two British officers. Yet they did not want to appear disbelieving of CSP.

"Good! Good!" Jock smiled at the young Chinese man. "We hope they succeed in pushing the Japanese back."

CSP smiled too. "Yes," he said. "Yes." And then, as if an afterthought, "Oh, there will be two more Australians arriving soon, and one Indian."

"Australians?" they exclaimed together, and Arthur went on, "Where from? What unit?"

"I do not know, but I am told they are from--is it Victoria?"

"Must be 2/29th," Bomber grinned. "Bloody beauty. I wonder who they are?"

CSP moved to leave the three men and began to walk across the open clearing. He had gone only a few paces when he turned and said, "Tonight there will be an important meeting, at 2100. Please make sure all of your men are there."

The day passed uneventfully, with all the men working at improving their living quarters and beds. Their meals were considerably better than the diet that Arthur and Bomber had lived on during the preceding weeks. In the mornings, for breakfast, they had porridge. At other meals there was plenty of rice, with ample quantities of vegetables and pork. They could also cook up their own pancakes and have cocoa and sugar. They all made the most of it because they were well aware that there was no guarantee how long the situation would continue.

At the evening meeting, everyone was present except the perimeter guards, who were always watching the approaches to the camp. One other man had been detailed to guard the two prisoners. The two had been subjected to further questioning in the late afternoon but had not changed their stories or given any new information.

The meeting was held in the open clearing, with all the Chinese members sitting on the ground facing a group of four or five of the camp's leaders at the front. Two of these men, CSP and another, a slim man of about forty years of age, dressed in khaki trousers and a white, short-sleeved shirt, sat at a make- shift table with a lighted kerosene lamp in the centre. By the way CSP deferred to the newcomer, he was clearly senior in the guerilla hierarchy.

The eight Allied soldiers were all placed to one side of the Chinese group where they sat quietly and expectantly.

"Who's the joker in the white shirt?" Mac asked.

"Dunno," Bomber said. "I saw him around on the day after we arrived, but I haven't seen him since."

Shortly, the meeting got underway. CSP got up and spoke rapidly in Chinese. The gathering, with the exception of the Europeans and to their amazement, stood up and burst into song. They sang in Chinese but the song was easily recognisable by several of the British and Australian soldiers as the 'Internationale', the anthem of the International Socialist Movement and of Soviet Russia.

The Europeans stood up belatedly to join the Chinese and then sat with the others when the song finished.

The slim man in the white shirt remained standing and addressed the assembly for almost half an hour. He spoke in Chinese, although it seemed to Arthur that he spoke in two quite different languages. The change came abruptly after the first ten minutes or so.

"He's speaking Mandarin now," Jock Smylie explained when Arthur and Bomber looked puzzled.

"What was the first lot?" Bomber asked.

"Hokkien. A good portion of Malay-Chinese speak Hokkien."

At the end of his speech, which at times seemed like a harangue or at least an exhortation of some sort to the Chinese camp members, he turned to the eight Europeans.

"I am known here as Liong Quan," he said in excellent English. "I am Commander of the 13th Independent Company and on behalf of the Communist Party of Malaya, I welcome you soldiers of Australia and Britain to our Camp."

Although they could only see his face dimly by the light of the small kerosene lamp on the table, his appearance and manner seemed open and friendly towards them. His face was longer and thinner than most of his fellow Chinese. His voice was soft and confident, and it was clear from the silence accorded him by the Chinese that he was a man of some power within the Party structure. What the 13th Independent Company consisted of, none of the Allied soldiers knew. But, at that stage, the fact that LQ, as they dubbed him, was its commander, was good enough.

"We are all here in this camp for the same reason," he went on. "We have a common enemy, the Japanese, and a common cause--the destruction of that enemy. Whatever our beliefs or attitudes were before, or will be after the war, the important thing to remember is that now we are allies, friends. And, regardless of race, we must join together in our common cause."

He went on to speak for a period about the growth of the resistance against the Japanese throughout the peninsula. He spoke of numerous and mounting atrocities committed by the Japanese, not only against captured Allied soldiers, but against the local population. He then spoke about the Communist Party of Malaya and its socialist programme.

"The Party is now organising as an army," he said, "and for those of you staying to live and fight with us, it will be necessary for you to work as we do and to fit in with the ideals of the Party. You will have your fair share of food and shelter, but you will also have to contribute your work and your knowledge for the common good. For example, each night one of your members will share in the guarding of the prisoners for two and a half hours. Please draw up a roster to begin tomorrow.

"Also, we would like two qualified instructors, to begin tomorrow, with the aid of interpreters, to instruct our men in the use of rifles and Tommy guns. Please also nominate these men for tomorrow."

Then, switching abruptly back to Hokkien, LQ wound up the meeting and, with hardly a pause, moved off with CSP to a shelter at one end of the clearing, while the Chinese and Europeans also dispersed to their own shelters for the night.

"Smart little bastards," Pete Barlow whispered as they walked away. "You can see they're setting themselves up to take over, after the war's over."

"Not likely, old chap," Scottie put in softly. "Once we're back in, they'll have to toe the line."

"You think so? Like they're toeing it now?" Jock said sarcastically. "And this is in the face of torture and killings from the Japs. I don't think we'll have a hope after the war. Anyway, I agree with the bloke. The moment is now, and for the moment we're travelling the same path."

Several uneventful days passed. Arthur and Scottie successfully launched a basic rifle-training programme with Bluey and Les handling instruction on the Tommy and Bren guns. The camp had a substantial supply of arms and ammunition, with more coming in all the time. Local Malays and Chinese had collected large quantities of both Japanese and Allied weapons and ammunition, left after heavy fighting between the opposing forces, and they would either give or sell them to the guerillas.

But the guerilla army was so embryonic, and its members so inexperienced, that many of them had never before held a rifle or an automatic weapon in their hands, let alone fired one. The four Europeans began by getting them to strip the weapons, cleaning the parts and then oiling and reassembling them. Most of the guns were in poor condition, many having lain out in the weather for many days before being picked up. Once the guerilla students had stripped and assembled a weapon for the first time, they had to do the same thing over and over until they knew every part of it. Then they were taught the basic principles of firing, without actually firing any live rounds.

The camp leaders hoped soon to be able to organise a small shooting range, where, without wasting too much of their precious ammunition, the new trainees could carry out some live firing exercises. There was, of course, the problem of weapon-fire being heard from a long distance, something that worried LQ and CSP. It was certainly true that, over the past several nights in the camp, they had heard the sounds of heavy actions coming from many miles away. It was the rumble of large artillery or naval guns and not small arms, but they could not afford to take too many chances. These sounds of what seemed to be large-scale actions were puzzling to them because it was now almost six weeks since Singapore had fallen. Whatever they were, there was some small encouragement to be drawn from the fact that the Japanese were apparently not having a quiet time.

Other work on the camp was also proceeding well. A kitchen hut had been designed and built by Arthur, Bomber, Bluey Ryan and a few Chinese helpers. Around four-thirty in the afternoon of the day they finally finished the structure and were resting prior to the evening meal, Ah Liong came running up to them in a state of high agitation. Sweat was pouring from her, as if she had run a mile.

"The whole camp must be ready to leave in five minutes," she gasped.

"Why?" Arthur and Bluey asked in unison as they all jumped to their feet. All around the camp, people were now running, collecting gear together, throwing it into sacks, preparing to move.

"Japanese," Ah Liong shouted as she ran past and on towards another group of shelters in the trees further on. "Many Japanese coming from Chaah."

Arthur and the others tore back to their own shelters to collect what meagre belongings they had, along with as much food and ammunition as they could carry and were ready to move in little more than five minutes.

"Bloody bastards!" Bomber spat vehemently. "We've only just finished the flamin' cookhouse. They're not even going to give us a chance to use it!"

As they reported to the camp headquarters across the clearing, the panic seemed to have subsided somewhat, but, despite Bomber's momentary hopes that the new structure would be used at least once, it was clear that the whole camp would be moving anyway. Apparently its location had been given away and only the chance discovery of this fact by a guerilla spy in Chaah had made it possible for the warning to be passed quickly to the camp.

LQ issued orders that the two prisoners, who were still tied to trees, should be taken back under guard to 'Camp 7'. The rest, according to Ah Liong who translated for the Allied soldiers as they stood listening and trying to make sense out of the chaos, would move to 'Camp 8' about fifteen miles away.

The group that was to move numbered just over thirty and, shortly before dark, it set off led by two unexpected new-comers: tiny, half-naked natives.

"Sakai," Jock Smylie said, "Jungle people. They know every inch of this country like the back of their hand. I'm glad they're on our side and not with the bloody Nips."

The march proved to be tough going for everyone. At first they moved through lightly timbered country and then into deeper jungle where they could only follow narrow tracks, made either by Sakais or elephants. It was a slow and tortuous pro-cession as they trudged along in single file. The going was uneven and slippery, with the ground either a quagmire of mud or tan-gled with roots and vines. According to Ah Liong, who was walk-ing close to Bomber and Arthur, they were travelling through the jungle, instead of skirting it in the surrounding rubber planta-tions, because they wanted to avoid any of the Malay houses on the way.

"It is the Malays who are betraying us," she said. "It is happening like this more and more. We can no longer trust them."

Finally, after almost eight hours of scrambling through the darkened rainforest, when all felt close to exhaustion, they arrived, at around one-thirty in the morning, at a deserted Sakai village. In a small clearing, they saw a number of tumble-down shacks which had been built on high, wooden poles. Several of them were in the process of collapse, but three of the houses were sufficiently stable to provide shelter for the group until the morn-ing.

Sleeping until 6 am, the party ate a small meal of dry rice and some vegetables, and then set off again. They followed a more easily defined path for little more than two hours, eventually arriving at their destination--a new and totally undeveloped campsite which was to become 'Camp 8'.

With no more than a few terse commands in Chinese, the whole group was directed to set about building the new camp immediately. Cooking and latrine facilities were to be constructed first, according to Ah Liong's translation for the Allied soldiers, then they could pay attention to their own personal shelters.

"I reckon we could go into the building business when we get back home," Arthur said to Bomber, as he dumped a fresh pile of attap leaves on the ground beside the frame of a newly rising cookhouse.

"Yeah, we're getting pretty good at it. I wonder what the market for bamboo shelters is like in Melbourne right now?"

They were interrupted by the sounds of a new group of Chinese arriving in the camp area. They were led in by a young Chinese man called Ah Pen, whom Arthur and Bomber had been friendly with. They suddenly noticed that there were two Europeans amongst the party and also an Indian.

"Hey, look at that," Bluey called out to them. "They must be the Victorians they were talking about."

They all dropped what they were doing and strode quickly across to meet the newcomers. Of the Europeans, one was about twenty years old, dark-haired and well-built. The other was an older man, perhaps fifty or so, with grey hair. Arthur recognised them both 'as members of the 2/29th, although, as they had belonged to C Company, he hadn't known either of them well.

"G'day, I'm Roy Roach," the younger one said, shaking first Bomber's, then all of the other Europeans' hands in succession.

"This is my mate, Tom. Tom Percival. We've been trying to meet up with you blokes for a while now, but there was just too much happening for us to get to you." He turned to the dark young Indian soldier standing a pace or two behind. He grasped the man on the shoulder, bringing him forward. "And this is Gaje. Gaje Singh San... Sander...ah...you tell 'em Gaje."

"Sankrijal," the Indian flashed a brilliant set of white teeth in a big smile. "Gaje Singh Sankrijal."

"Gaje's from the Garhwals," Tom Percival put in. "The 5/l8th Garhwals. They were the blokes we took over when we first arrived at Bakri."

"He doesn't speak much English," said Roy, patting Gaje again on the shoulder, "But he's a good bloke, aren't you, Gaje?"

Gaje smiled.

The three men had been staying at Camp 7, the same one that the two Chinese prisoners had been taken to, about five miles further west than their present position.

"It's not a bad spot," Roy said, as he rolled a cigarette with some paper and tobacco that Bomber had given him. "But I think they're going to move most of the stuff here. They've got a wireless."

"A wireless?" several voices echoed.

"Have you heard any news?" Jock asked.

"Sure," Roy said with a smile. "What don't you know?" He was obviously enjoying being the centre of attention.

"We don't know anything," Bluey exclaimed. "Jesus, we haven't heard anything we could really believe for ages."

"Well," Roy said, taking a drag from his cigarette, "the Japs have got all of Java and Sumatra now. They're fighting in Burma and they've occupied Indo China. And, see if you can believe this one, they've bombed Darwin."

"Darwin?! When was that?"

"Over a month ago, according to the wireless. It was a BBC report, so it's probably right. Talked about 'the raid last month on Darwin'—apparently quite a bit of damage."

"Crikey, that doesn't sound too good," Arthur murmured. "I hope it doesn't mean they're going to invade Australia. Nobody seems to be able to stop the little bastards."

Over the next few days everyone, including the new arrivals, was busily employed establishing the new camp. A group of Sakais helped in the construction of huts, tables, seats, the kitchen, latrines and in clearing the bush between the trees. Food parties went out regularly to collect supplies from Chinese living nearby, and also fresh, wild vegetables from the jungle. These included 'brinjels', which were similar to eggplant; 'nebong', a sort of cabbage palm; 'reubon', young bamboo; 'ubi' and 'claddy', both of which were like potato.

A note was delivered to the camp from a British officer, Major Barry Couvin, who was apparently seeking news of other Allied soldiers in the area. Arthur wondered if he was one of the two British officers they'd been told of before but, once again, no-one would say exactly where this Major Couvin was. Nevertheless, LQ assured them that they could get a note through to him, so Jock sat down and wrote a letter giving details of the eleven Allied soldiers now in the camp.

Other news came in from different sources. Some of it, the men decided, should be taken with a grain of salt--for example, a report that all of the prisoners in Singapore were being killed off and only the officers spared. This, they thought, was not really believable, although an equally horrific story, brought in at about the same time by a Chinese messenger, they found quite credible. He told of six Indian soldiers captured near Batu Pahat. They had been tortured and killed by the Japanese who had cut them all over with knives and bayonets, poured oil all over them and then set them alight.

At the same time, there were conflicting reports of Allied engagements with the Japanese and of the war in Europe: Americans claiming a major victory in the Philippines, Chiang Kai-shek's troops fighting for Rangoon, Japanese ships sunk off Darwin, Singapore bombed by British and American planes, Russia fighting in Romania, Japanese warships shelling Bombay, British victory in North Africa, Russians in Finland.

"The whole thing seems so bloody remote," Arthur said to Bomber one morning, as they were eating some breakfast. "Here we are, stuck in the jungle, while all this is happening out there."

But whether they could believe the news or not, the extent of the war and Japan's tightening grip on all of South-East Asia seemed to have shrunk to virtually zero any chances they may have had of escape. With Java and Sumatra now in Japanese hands and their control of the entire Malayan peninsula so complete, shops throughout the country were now reopening and life in the cities and towns was beginning to return to a sort of normality, albeit a Japanese-run normality.

The Japanese began publishing new daily newspapers in Chinese, English and Malay. New Japanese-issued currency, with denominations from one cent to one hundred Malay dollars, was now in use. They had control of the telephone system, food distribution offices, schools (where the Japanese language was now a compulsory subject) and taxes. Chinese fishermen could start fishing again for a fee of twenty-five cents per week, landowners must pay twenty-five dollars per acre per year, while shop owners were subjected to an annual fee of four hundred dollars.

Other reports indicated that the Japanese had taken some four thousand Chinese from the Muar area and about five thousand from Malacca to train as soldiers. Apparently, the Japanese intention was to call up around forty thousand for training. Any misbehaviour by them would result in heavy punishment for their parents and relatives.

At the same time as these stories were being told in the camp, there were also reports of Chinese guerilla successes against the Japanese in other parts of Malaya: five hundred Japanese killed in the previous few days in Johore and four truckloads of dead Japanese brought into Muar from an undisclosed locality. The details of how these guerilla victories came about, if indeed they were the result of guerilla actions, was not revealed to the British and Australian soldiers. '

It was usually CSP who passed on these snippets of information to the Europeans and, on one occasion, he added with a smile, "We--that is, the Party--now have two 25-pounder artillery weapons in our possession."

"You're not bringing them here, surely?" Jock asked.

"Oh no. But we will have many more arms coming in here shortly. Today we will get thirty rifles, two Tommy guns, two Bren guns, and some binoculars. The next shipment will be even more."

"Where are they coming from?" Bomber asked. "From Bakri." "Bakri! Hah!" Arthur laughed grimly. "That's all our stuff."

The following day, at about mid-morning, a long procession of Chinese men and women of varying ages began arriving in the camp, carrying enormous quantities of arms and ammunition. They had been trekking for several nights through the jungle, trying to avoid any contact with the Japanese or local Malays. The huge pile of weapons, which they dumped in the middle of the camp clearing, totalled just over two hundred .303 rifles, three more Tommy guns, two hundred Mills hand grenades and thousands of rounds of .303 ammunition and .45 shells for the submachine-guns.

The large numbers of arms, although many of them were in a terrible state and, for the moment, quite unworkable, slightly increased the feeling of security in the camp. Arthur, Scottie, Bluey and Les, who had been in charge of weapons training, were now also charged with supervising the cleaning and re-habilitation of the newly arrived armoury. The main problem was rust, but, using a variety of available oils and plenty of manual labour, they managed, over a period of some weeks, to restore most of the weapons to working order.

It was during this period, in April 1942, that they began to experience their first problems with food. The numbers in the camp fluctuated between sixty and a hundred people, and the problems of feeding so many on a regular basis were consider-able. Previously, they had relied on being able to get supplies from local Chinese, but with the Japanese now keeping a closer watch on the Chinese civilian population, and food distribution generally, the whole situation became increasingly difficult. Con-sequently, the search for wild jungle vegetables became more and more important.

Every day, food-gathering parties would spend a large part of the day just searching for vegetables, not always with suc-cess. A vegetable patch was planted in the camp, but it took time for a decent crop to grow and although, on most days, they were still able to fill their stomachs and to satisfy their hunger, the food they were now eating was anything but a balanced diet.

Several in the camp, both European and Chinese, began to show the ill-effects. Arthur and Jock were both experiencing badly swollen and extremely painful feet. They were not aware of it at the time, but these were the early symptoms of beri-beri, a dreaded condition caused by lack of vitamins and proteins.

During April, there were many occasions when the camp ran short of food. During one such period, an old 'towkay', a Chi-nese businessman, who, with his family, had left his home to throw his lot in with the guerillas, was required to make a sacri-fice for the camp. He had brought his favourite dog with him, a beautiful Chow dog, that had been with the family for almost ten years. On instructions from LQ, the dog was killed and cooked for the evening meal.

Although Arthur and Bomber and several of the others in their group had befriended the animal and were shocked at the decision, once it had been made, and the dog had gone into the pot, they all ate it.

"A little strong," Arthur noted in his diary, "but not bad at all. The soup was excellent."

The old towkay and his family stayed only another week in the camp and then moved out. No-one knew how they would be able to re-establish themselves back in a Japanese-occupied town after an inexplicable absence, but the old man was determined to go. They never heard of him again.

On the same day the old towkay left, the two prisoners who had been with them at the previous camp and had been taken to Camp 7 arrived under close guard with instructions that they be held for further questioning. Bomber and Bluey decided to give them nicknames, christening one of them 'Lockheed', (which they shortened to 'Locky') and the other 'Lightning', after the new American fighter-plane which was just entering service in early 1942.

On one occasion, when Arthur was detailed to guard the two men, he was surprised to find that one of them, 'Locky', had a reasonable command of English. Arthur asked the man, who would have been about his own age, several questions. At first the man seemed to be rather guarded in his replies, but when he realised that Arthur was not another interrogator, he loosened up a bit and soon they were chatting quite animatedly. It was as if the young man was relieved to talk to someone normally about everyday things, instead of the constant, more serious line of questioning he had been subjected to for days.

He said he had been born in Kuala Lumpur, but his parents, who ran a hardware business, had moved to Labis and later to Segamat. He had originally studied to be a teacher, but his father had become ill and had asked him to work in the hardware store in order to help support the family.

He had, it seemed to Arthur, quite a reasonable knowledge of Australia, which was more than could be said for most of the other guerilla members of the camp.

"Do you come from Sydney?" he asked Arthur.

"No, from Melbourne."

"Ah, that is in the south, I think?"

"Yes," Arthur replied. "Much nicer than Sydney."

"So, you have lived in Sydney also?"

"Well, not actually lived there," Arthur said, "but I know it's not as nice as Melbourne."

Locky smiled. "Ah, I understand," he said. "It is that home is always best, yes?"

Arthur laughed. "Yes, that's right."

Two days after Locky and Lightning had arrived, a third prisoner was brought in and immediately subjected to harsh interrogation by several of the more militant Chinese guerillas. During the first questioning, the man admitted no wrongdoing or traitorous activities, but after two days tied to a tree, during which time he underwent a succession of brutal whippings, bashings and tortures from several of the guerillas, he finally broke down and confessed to having given information to the Japanese about arms being supplied to the guerillas by a Chinese supporter.

At a summary trial, which lasted only minutes, the man was sentenced to death and then forced to dig his own grave. The entire camp was called to witness the execution. Arthur and the others, having seen the beginning of the torture sessions on the first day, stayed away throughout the rest of the man's ordeal, leaving it to the three or four Chinese 'interrogators'. Arthur found he was sickened by the sight of the man being beaten and said so to his companions. '

"There's nothing we can do," Scottie told him. "This is their world here now. In their eyes, if we complain, it puts us on his side. And anyway, what he was doing was placing us all in danger. He has to go."

"Yes, but they don't have to do all this torture stuff," Arthur said.

Scottie had raised his eyebrows and shrugged his shoulders.

After the man had finished digging his grave, he stood in front of it with his head lowered and his eyes closed, quietly sobbing.

One of the guerillas stepped up behind him, placed a pistol at the back of his head and fired.

Arthur left the site, and walked back to his shelter, a confused jumble of thoughts racing through his mind, none of which would cohere into a satisfactory conclusion. Although he was not to know it, this was only the first of a long series of executions he was to witness during his time with the Chinese guerillas. In the villages and towns, Malayan society was becoming rapidly polarised. The Chinese segment of the population (roughly 45 per cent) was almost totally against the Japanese and supported the Allied cause, although on the surface they assumed an air of co-operation with the new masters of Malaya.

On the other hand, the Malays, who made up most of the rest of the population, seemed undecided--or at least divided. Large numbers of them openly supported the Japanese. Perhaps they saw the invasion as a means of breaking not only the colonial grip of Britain on their homeland, but also of undermining the commercial domination of Malaya that Chinese businesses had established over several generations. Some Malays supported the Chinese guerilla movement, but as the months stretched on, they were fewer and fewer. As a general rule, any Malay had to be treated with care, and some suspicion. There were very few who were privy to the location of the camps or to the guerillas' plans.

If any Malay or, less frequently, any Chinese townsman did anything to betray the location of a jungle camp, or the activity of the guerillas or their supporters in the town, a way would be found to assassinate him or her in their town or village, or alternatively, kidnap them and bring them to one of the camps for trial and execution. A pattern of brutal retribution was being established on both sides, with no lack of stories to fuel the mistrust and fear between the two.

On several occasions over the next few days, Arthur was again required to act as guard for Locky and Lightning and he found that, understandably, after the execution of the other prisoner, Locky was much more circumspect in his conversation. He was disturbed and upset. But over a period of time, as Arthur talked to him about things totally divorced from the jungle and their present situation, Locky relaxed somewhat and they enjoyed talking about his youth and life before the war. Locky was interested in comparing the life of a young person growing up in Australia to his own experience in Malaya. Arthur, too, found that their talks took him away from the harsher reality of their present existence.

Towards the end of April, CSP told the group about six Allied soldiers who had been cared for by Chinese near the town of Ayer Hitam. As the war passed them by and the Japanese overran Singapore, they decided to give themselves up. They were led, with a cord passed through their noses, by the Malay police in Ayer Hitam. They were joined by two European women who had their ears pierced and tied back with string behind their heads as a form of leash, and all of them, clad only in shorts, were led around by a Malay constable, PC4719. The man's number was reported and remembered by all for later retribution. The officer was reported to have made them sweep the streets and gutters, all the while being laughed at, abused and kicked by local crowds.

For Arthur and the rest of the group, the story only convinced them more that, despite the problems of food and illness, they were still better off in the camp with the Chinese guerillas than outside. Of course the story could well have been false and intended to instill just such feelings in the Europeans, but they had no way of knowing this and had to take it at face value.

Over the preceding days there had been considerable discussion amongst the Europeans about whether or not they should stay with the Chinese, or try to make it on their own. Pete and Scottie, who over the past few weeks had tended to be somewhat detached from the rest of the group, seemed determined to split off on their own. But, after a meeting, all the Australian troops, plus Jock Smylie, opted to remain with the guerillas. Pete and Scottie also reluctantly agreed to stay, emphasising, however, that it was only a temporary measure.

It was clear that Pete and Scottie thought of themselves as the 'old Malayan hands', with superior knowledge of the local scene, and better able to make it on their own than the rest. This minor example of 'class stratification', established quite early in the relationship between the members of the group, was exaggerated even more by the knowledge that Scottie, who had been working for the British colonial office in the State of Kedah prior to the war, had married the daughter of the Sultan of Kedah and was consequently a member of Malayan 'high society'. When this information became known, it resulted in a number of jokes about 'marrying into the business' and some good-natured ribbing from the Australians, particularly Bomber, none of which was taken in good humour by Scottie.

"It's all very well to joke about it, you crass bastards," he said on one occasion, "but I have no idea if my wife is alive or dead. All I know is that she was captured by the Japanese and taken to Singapore."

The food situation did not improve. For more than a week they had been living almost exclusively on small quantities of rice and claddy, the big, white jungle potatoes. Inspired, Jock and Mac sat down to produce a couple of makeshift fishing nets from mosquito netting and managed to catch more than thirty small fish, ranging from tiny baby fish to ones about four inches long, from a nearby jungle stream. On seeing their success, many of the others immediately set about making their own fishing nets. These efforts also met with success and there was new hope that they could tap a regular supply of protein. No-one knew, however, how long they could do it without fishing out the streams.

On 26 April, the question of splitting up was taken out of their hands. LQ came to them in the morning to inform them that the camp was disbanding. "We have information that the Japanese know about the camp and are preparing to attack us, so we must move again."

LQ waited for a reaction from the men. For a moment or two there was none. There was nothing to say. This, it seemed, was to be the pattern of their lives. Set up camp, move, set up camp, move, on and on and on.

"Where to this time?" Arthur asked LQ.

"I am afraid we are going to have to divide the numbers," he replied. "to go to two different places. Some will go to a new Camp 8, others to Camp 7." He looked at the men. "If you agree, we would like half of the Europeans to go to one camp and half to the other."

"Why?" Bomber asked.

"Because we need your help in training our recruits," LQ replied. "You have the knowledge of arms and explosives. If all of you are in one camp, the other will suffer. We will try to be flexible. If one or two of you would prefer to change after a while, that may be possible, but we must try it first. So please, amongst yourselves, decide how you will go. We move at ten tomorrow morning."

12

THE MOVE THIS TIME WAS accomplished with surprisingly little fuss. The new camp was not very far away, although the group with which Arthur travelled had to climb a very steep hill, negotiating all the while a narrow track through thick undergrowth. They arrived at the new site sweating and panting but relieved that the whole process had taken little more than two hours.

On their arrival they learnt with some satisfaction that, although they had divided themselves into two separate groups, the camps were only fifteen or twenty minutes away from each other. There had been some doubts expressed during the previous evening, when the split-up was arranged, but no-one seemed unduly upset by the arrangement now. Mac, Les, Roy and Bluey had opted to stick together and they were at the new version of Camp 8, some 500 feet almost directly below Arthur's camp, down the slope of the mountainside. Pete and Scottie had wanted to leave completely. They had plans for heading north, to follow some escape route that would presumably lead them out onto the north-western coast where they would renew their efforts to find a boat. But they were not ready yet. Pete was recovering from a bout of dysentery and it was felt that they would need a guide for some of the way. So, in the meantime, they decided to stay in the new camp, Camp 7, along with Arthur, Bomber, Tom, Jock and Gaje. A number of other Chinese members of the original camp, including the two prisoners 'Locky' and 'Lightning', went to Camp 9 which was near Batu Pahat.

Although the move had been made with relative ease, they had all felt the familiar reluctance to pulling up their roots and shifting from a place that was beginning to work. After putting so much effort into building a camp, it seemed a terrible waste of time to do it all over again.

The move was particularly annoying for Arthur. The tinea infection in his groin, which had been present for many weeks, had worsened. He could not sit down in any comfort and walking was extremely painful. For some time he had only been able to wear his sarong, as pants were unbearably irritating for him. He was able to obtain some relief by making a type of paste from crushed claddy leaves (a formulation recommended by one of the Chinese women in the camp) and then applying it to the affected area. But for several days, no claddy had been brought into the camp.

Arthur had found the treatment process most embarrassing. It required him to lie flat on his back, with his legs spread apart and held upwards, resting on the wall of the shelter, while he applied the thick green claddy paste to the fungus infection between his legs. But, as much as he disliked the process, it seemed to improve his condition, bringing considerable relief from the pain and irritation. He despaired when there were no claddy leaves available and asked that the leaves be brought back to camp whenever the claddy potatoes were collected from the jungle.

Shortly after their arrival at the new camp, CSP, who had stayed with Arthur's group, informed them that the camp would be reorganised along more military lines and that everybody would belong to a particular platoon. Arthur, Bomber and Tom Percival would be in 31 Platoon. Jock and Gaje were to be in 32 Platoon. Each of them was issued with a rifle and seventy rounds of ammunition. They had been carrying an assortment of weapons and ammunition whenever they transferred from one camp to another, but from now on, they were to be responsible for particular weapons. Pete and Scottie were issued weapons, but they were not allocated to a platoon. It was felt that, as they might soon be leaving, it would be better not to place them anywhere. f

CSP and some of the other Chinese leaders seemed undecided about Pete and Scottie. In theory, the Europeans and Allied soldiers were independent agents, but as the weeks went by, a subtle change in the relationship between them and the guerillas began to develop. For the guerillas, Malaya was their home country. They spoke the languages and had all of the contacts with the world outside the jungle, both in Malaya itself and, through a long, devious chain of spies and agents, to the Allied forces overseas. Because of this, they naturally assumed the role of commanders. They were more in control of the situation.

The Allied soldiers, like it or not, were being protected by the guerillas and the system that had developed and, almost without realising it, they began to accept the fact that they would have to do what the guerillas wanted them to do. At the same time, there was still something of a hangover of attitudes resulting from Britain's colonial domination of Singapore and the Straits Settlements for more than a century, and Malaya as a whole for half a century. In many ways, the Chinese guerillas could not shake off the feeling that whatever the white men said was correct. It was difficult for them to issue direct orders to the Europeans, particularly to people like Pete, Scottie and Jock, who had lived in colonial Malaya and had automatically adopted a superior attitude towards the Chinese.

The Europeans, it must be admitted, had considerable talent in terms of their knowledge and expertise in weapons, explosives, military tactics and organisation. The Chinese had begun to recognise this resource and to tap it. The Europeans, for their part, did everything the Chinese wanted them to do in this regard. They felt that the stronger and more resourceful the group became as a whole, the safer they would all be. Nevertheless, there was the feeling amongst them that they should not let the relationship slide too far down any road which might lead to complete subservience to the wishes of the guerillas.

One of the main frustrations they felt was that, while the guerillas had begun in recent weeks to take the initiative in launching surprise attacks on the Japanese, there was no indication that any of the Allied troops would be allowed to take part in future operations. Although their health seemed to fluctuate from one week to the next, they were all fully recovered from whatever wounds were received at Bakri and often felt well enough to join in any planned attack on Japanese installations.

CSP had brought news, on two or three occasions recently, of these actions. Guerillas had blown up the police station at Yong Peng. They had killed almost two hundred in a night raid on a Japanese billet in Kluang and had ambushed and killed a group of Japanese travelling by trucks between Segamat and Kluang. When details of another planned raid were discussed, before their recent change of camps, several of the Europeans had asked if they could be included.

"I am sorry," LQ told them, "but it will not be possible. This raid requires most of our men to be able to pass as locals, until the last few moments. This is obviously impossible for any of you." He smiled. "Perhaps on another occasion."

This was, of course, the major problem they all faced, not only in any clandestine activities, or attacks on the Japanese, but just in living and surviving in the jungle on their own. As Europeans, they were always obvious. Without friends, survival in Malaya for any extended period would have been virtually impossible. And being white was becoming even more dangerous as a result of new moves on the part of the Japanese to flush any Allied soldiers or other Europeans out of the jungle.

In all of the villages and towns, the Japanese had posted signs offering one thousand Malay dollars for each Australian or British soldier turned in by local Malays or Chinese. This was a considerable increase on the rewards offered immediately after the Japanese Army had swept down through Malaya. Now it was one thousand dollars, dead or alive!

None of the Allied soldiers needed reminding what sort of treatment they might expect if they were turned in alive. Although the tales of Japanese atrocities against captured soldiers had tapered off (naturally enough, as there were fewer and fewer Europeans left uncaptured), there were still stories of particularly barbarous acts in nearby towns which inevitably made them more determined never to be caught. The most recent involved five Indian soldiers who had been taken in the Segamat area. Like the six who had been captured at Batu Pahat, these unfortunate men had been tortured, then tied to trees and used for bayonet practice by the Japanese soldiers.

The Chinese guerillas, though, displayed hardly any greater humanity in their treatment of suspected traitors. The group had been in their new camp only a few days, fully occupied, as usual, setting up shelters, kitchens and latrines, when two new prisoners were brought in. Both of them were Malays.

The Chinese always referred to any prisoners brought into the camp as 'traitors', even though they had yet to be tried. The two men were clearly terrified. One of them was a man of about thirty, poorly dressed in khaki shorts and rubber sandals. He was probably a farmer, or a plantation hand. The other, a younger man, around twenty-five years old, was reasonably dressed in a white, short-sleeved shirt, fawn trousers and brown leather shoes. He was clean-shaven and his hair, although untidy at the moment, was neatly cut. A summary trial for the two men was ordered immediately.

Both men stood with their hands tied behind their backs in the centre of a large circle of onlookers formed by virtually everyone in the camp, including Arthur, Bomber, the other four Europeans and Gaje. LQ, CSP and two others sat at a makeshift table to begin the interrogation which was held in Malay.

During the past few weeks with the guerillas, Arthur and Bomber had begun to pick up and understand many words and phrases in Chinese, but because of the lack of opportunity, they had not learnt much Malay. Arthur had begun to keep a small language notebook, in addition to his diary, in which he wrote down commonly used Chinese and Malay words, but the pace at which the trial was conducted left him with little direct understanding of what was going on. Jock, Pete and Scottie all had a reasonable understanding of Malay and were able to give a fair translation of the proceedings, except for the moments when the interrogators became angry and shouted rapidly at the two prisoners.

According to Jock's understanding, it seemed that the older man, who worked on a plantation near the town of Paloh, had betrayed a Chinese family to the Japanese. The family, who lived in a nearby kampong, had apparently been supplying vegetables to the Communist guerillas. The Japanese had turned up and executed the whole family and then burnt their house down.

The younger man, who worked as a railway clerk in Paloh, was guilty of a different, but, in the eyes of the summary court, no less indictable act of betrayal. He had been approached by Communist Party agents in Paloh to help in arranging a clandestine shipment of heavy equipment and supplies between Paloh and Labis, about twenty miles up the railway track to the north-west. He had agreed, but on the day of the shipment, the Japanese were on hand in Labis to seize the packing cases and arrest the men who came to claim them. The guerillas immediately produced weapons and started shooting, but they were all killed.

The young railway clerk claimed tearfully that he didn't tell the Japanese about the scheme, that they must have been overheard, or that someone else had betrayed them. But the court did not believe him. The two men were sentenced to immediate execution by garotting.

This was the first time the Allied soldiers had witnessed this horrific and, as it turned out, terribly ineffective way of ending someone's life. They, along with the rest of the camp, were required to watch as a rope was passed around the necks of the two men. They were backed up to the trunk of a tree and the rope was tied around it. A large stick was then inserted through a loop in the rope and two guerillas began twisting it. Arthur's skin crawled and a cold chill ran through him as he watched the rope become tighter and tighter around the necks of the two unfortunate men.

They had previously been crying and begging for mercy. Now, they began to choke and gag for air and there was a look of desperate terror in their eyes. Their faces darkened to a red, then purple colour, then both men lost consciousness. They were left for a while, tied to the tree, then untied and dragged a few yards to a shallow double grave that had been dug before the trial began. They were unceremoniously dumped in.

"Look," Bomber cried to LQ, who was standing at the end of the grave, "the poor bugger's still breathing."

"So's the other one," Jock said. "Look."

One of the Chinese guerillas who had been standing by with a shovel, ready to fill in the grave, realised what was happening, stepped over to the unconscious figure of the plantation worker and delivered a heavy blow to his head with the shovel.

LQ shouted an angry command at the man in Chinese and the man stepped back. Then he issued another directive to the same man and another who was also holding a shovel. Together the two set about filling the grave with the soil piled up around the edges.

"But they're still breathing," Arthur said.

"Never mind," LQ turned to Jock, a tight smile breaking across his face. "They will suffocate now."

As the two workers piled the remaining sods of soil into the grave, the crowd of Chinese onlookers, who had mostly been silent until this point, began clapping. When their applause had died down, the little group of Europeans separated themselves and walked slowly back towards the main camp area.

Halfway across the clearing, Arthur broke off from the group and walked on his own to the trees at the camp perimeter. He felt sick and disturbed. The previous execution they had witnessed had happened much more quickly and was, in some ways, he thought, more humane, somehow more acceptable. He found he was deeply shocked at the way these two men had been treated. And yet, as they were clearly enemies and a threat to his survival and that of his comrades, he found himself accepting the fact that they should be executed for their 'crimes'. But inwardly, he could not avoid feeling sorry for the two men, along with a sense of unease about his own part as a witness in the process. He found it difficult to comprehend how the Chinese could laugh and applaud such brutal treatment.

Several days passed with no major developments. The food carriers began to bring in a supply of claddy leaves which Arthur eagerly seized in order to produce a paste to apply to his inflamed groin and feet. The food supply generally seemed to improve for a while. Rice was plentiful and there were reasonable quantities of nebong, bamboo shoots, flour, from which they made pancakes, and, quite frequently, fish.

Despite the improved food situation, there was still a good deal of sickness in the camp, mainly fevers caused either by malaria or dengue. Dengue, although rarely fatal, was an extraordinarily debilitating disease to deal with in the jungle. Once the virus was passed on by a mosquito, the onset of illness was quite sudden and acute. High fever, excruciating joint pains, and intense pain behind the eyes were the symptoms that accompanied dengue, as well as almost total incapacitation. Both Jock and Gaje came down with what was thought to be dengue fever, and in Camp 8, further down the mountainside, Mac and Bluey had also both fallen ill, as had several Chinese in both camps, including Ah Liong's baby.

Over the past few weeks several families with children had come to join the camp. The reasons were varied but the most common was Japanese persecution, or fear of reprisal by the Japanese for some action--more often than not, aiding the guerillas. The families were generally billeted on the opposite side of the camp area to the Allied soldiers and normally there was not a great deal of contact between the two groups.

Ah Liong, however, had always been an exception. Since the very first day of their association with the communist guerillas, she had acted as an interpreter for the Europeans, and they often spent time talking with her. Her boy was now six months old. She was still breastfeeding him and he had seemed relatively healthy. Now he had a fever. There was little that Arthur or the others could do but offer Ah Liong encouraging words. Their meagre medical supplies, which had not included any cure-all for fevers anyway, had long since been exhausted.

Arthur, who felt some relief at not having come down with fever himself, also found that the continued applications of claddy paste to his groin and feet were beginning to show results. In both areas there was a marked improvement to the condition of his skin. Also, on the earlier advice of Jock, he had begun exercising by walking around the parade ground which, at this new site, was relatively small--about twelve yards long by eight yards wide. Arthur estimated that forty-four times around the edge of the field would be roughly a mile. On his first day he walked around exactly forty-four times and found the process reasonably easy and quite enjoyable, as both his feet and groin were not troubling him. The next day he increased the distance to eighty-eight circuits, which left him with some aches but feeling much the better for it, so he resolved to walk every day, increasing the distance each time.

Arthur's circumnavigation of the parade ground began to attract attention and some friendly jibes from the Chinese, as well as crude ribbing from Bomber and Tom, but as Arthur felt considerably better as a result of the exercise, he ignored them all and continued with his rounds.

On rising from his bed one morning, Arthur felt uncomfortable--a strange sensation in his right side. There was no pain but, as he attempted to walk, his body moved awkwardly. Bomber noticed it immediately.

"What's the matter, Shep?" he asked. "Are you all right?"

"I don't know. It's my shoulder. It seems to have dropped."

"Yeah," Bomber said, as he looked more closely. "It's drooping all right. Does it hurt?"

"No, but I seem to have lost any strength in it." He made an effort to raise his arm in front of him. "If I try to lift it, I can't get it any further than my waist."

" Jesus," Bomber muttered. "What's happened? When did it go wrong?"

"Must have been during the night. It felt all right yesterday."

Arthur knew that it must have something to do with the shrapnel wound to his neck but he could think of no reason why it should collapse so suddenly. Although a feeling of tightness had remained in the muscles of his shoulder after the wound had healed, his arm was almost as strong and useful as it had always been. Now it was virtually useless.

Once the first shock of the discovery had passed, during his conversation with Bomber, Arthur found that by bending over to his left, he could raise his right arm a little higher. He resolved to include this movement in his training on the parade ground. And so he began, each day, sometimes standing still in the middle of the clearing, sometimes while walking around it, to try to lift his right arm. At first he had to lean awkwardly to the left to do it at all, but gradually he was able to raise it a little more each day and, over a period of several weeks, the muscles began to strengthen and he was able to raise it once more to shoulder height. It remained, nevertheless, a difficult movement for him, and although he was not the cripple he thought he might be, his right arm was never again as strong as his left.

During this period, one of the food parties that went out daily to collect vegetables and whatever supplies they could from the surrounding villages and farms, shot a bullock. It was a domestic animal which was found roaming in the jungle. When word was brought back to the camp late that evening, groups of carriers were sent out immediately to cut the beast up and to bring back as much meat as it was possible to carry. They would have to sleep near the carcass in the jungle that night, but hopefully they could butcher it and get a good supply of meat back to the camp the following day.

There was a feeling of excitement in the camp as they waited for the meat. For weeks at a time they lived on vegetables alone, with the occasional addition of fish. Although they were surviving, the vegetables they were able to collect were not sufficient to provide them with a balanced diet. Many in the camp were suffering from dietary deficiencies, lack of protein and vitamins. The thought of beef for dinner gave everyone a lift.

When the carriers began arriving, late in the afternoon, covered in blood from the great hunks of red meat they were carrying on their shoulders, a cheer went up from the little camp and groups of people ran to relieve the men of their burdens.

Every person in both Camp 7 and 8 had steak with their rice that evening and the next. But by the third day, the meat, having been left hanging from the trees, had begun to go off, so the two chief cooks at Camp 7, whom Arthur and Bomber had christened 'Slim' and 'Shorty' put all of the meat into huge bowls of soup that lasted the camps a further two days.

Food had now become a constant preoccupation. Because of the increased difficulty in getting supplies from villages and kampongs, the camps had to be more self-reliant. For the first time, Arthur was able to join the food parties on their foraging missions in the jungle. His self-administered tinea treatment had been largely successful, making it possible for him once again to wear pants which were far better than a sarong for scrambling through the jungle to look for wild vegetables.

Most of the time they brought back the staple nebong cabbage palm, the ubi and claddy potatoes and bamboo shoots, and, on some occasions, papaya and coconuts, although these fruits were hard to find and generally regarded as a rare treat. Durians, they were told, would be in season soon and this was something which the Chinese in the camp seemed to anticipate with great relish. None of the Europeans in Camp 7 had ever tasted durian before--apart from Jock, who, when asked what they tasted like, would only smile knowingly--but on the basis of what the Chinese said, Arthur and the rest looked forward to trying the fruit.

The opportunity to go out on the vegetable-gathering forays pleased Arthur considerably. Sitting around in camp, unable to move because of a sore and inflamed crotch, had been extremely irritating and boring for him. Even without the enforced inactivity experienced by Arthur, the others often found they had time on their hands and little to do to fill it. Tom Percival had produced a pack of cards many weeks earlier when he first joined the camp and it had proved a godsend in terms of something to keep the group occupied during the frequent long periods when nothing seemed to be happening. In time, however, the cards became dog-eared and worn out, so a new pack was made up from pieces of cardboard collected from various food packages that came into the camp.

Jock, Tom and Arthur also managed to produce quite a workable game of Monopoly, which also provided them with many happy hours. When they first began to play the game, many of the Chinese guerillas would stand around and watch, fascinated.

"D'you want to have a go?" Bomber asked one.

Within days, several of the Chinese were playing. They lived up to their reputation as born traders, quickly becoming adept at the game with a natural talent for acquiring properties and arranging deals to their own advantage. But Arthur and the others held their own and no-one seemed to be able to win consistently or to dominate the game. This enabled it to remain one of the most popular games in the camp for as long as they stayed together.

As the weeks passed by with no further moves, they experienced a sense of relative calm and security. The food situation fluctuated. Sometimes certain items were short for a while, but on occasion they would receive small luxuries like cocoa and sugar and even corn kernels, which they made into popcorn. Simple though they were, these unexpected treats would lift everyone's morale considerably.

One night, a guard on the perimeter of the camp shot a bear. The shot naturally sent the entire camp into a mild panic.

Everyone was on instant alert for an imminent attack. But when the reason for the shot was discovered, there was much relief and laughter all round. The bear was quite a large, black animal, about four feet tall. A party went to the guard post to carry it back into the camp where it was cut up immediately. 'Slim' and 'Shorty' prepared bear for breakfast and curried bear for dinner. Arthur noted in his diary that both meals were 'delicious'.

Arthur and the others were well aware that the Malayan jungle was home to quite a large assortment of wild animals, although in the six months or so that they had spent there, none of them had met anything that was particularly dangerous. The shooting of the bear so close to the camp served as something of a reminder that they were, at times, a little over-confident when wandering about on their food-gathering expeditions.

The guerillas had informed them in some detail about the types of animals they might meet. These included the Malayan Sun Bear which they had just eaten. Although it is mainly a herbivorous animal, the Sun Bear, according to the Chinese, is a very aggressive beast, tending to attack humans in any meeting rather than run away. It has, as they saw on the carcass, powerful teeth and claws which could inflict terrible wounds. They could also reasonably expect to meet, their guerilla informants told them, leopards, panthers and tigers, as well as a large variety of deadly snakes.

The incidence of tigers in the area was expected to increase, the Chinese said, because of the durians. Tigers, it seems, although they are carnivorous, have a passion for durians and when they ripen, they will climb the trees to knock the big fruit down, or take ones that have already fallen to the jungle floor, tearing off the rough outer skin with their claws to get at the inside.

There were a great many durian trees in a nearby area of the jungle. Many years ago, a tribe of Sakai natives had planted a number of durian seeds and, although the tribe had long since moved on, the durians had flourished and bore fruit regularly. CSP and others in the camp had told the Europeans about the grove of trees, warning them at the same time of the danger of tigers.

Whether or not the warnings had been as specific in Camp 8 as they had been in Camp 7, Pete and Scottie, apparently deciding there was no real danger, set off on their own from Camp 8, a day or so later, to collect durians, without letting anyone know.

As they approached the area where the durian trees grew, they realised, from the sounds they could hear, that a tiger was already there. Fortunately it was so engrossed in its durian feast, it did not hear their approach, or, if it did, was more interested in what it was doing than anything else. As Pete and Scottie gingerly peered at it from behind some bushes about thirty yards away, it just continued to munch and tear at the large fruit, which it held on the ground between its paws. The two men, having picked up a couple of durians from the ground, backed cautiously and quietly away from their position and then, when they felt they were out of earshot, broke into a run- and-scramble all the way back to the camp.

Their story, which they told on their return, met with an unexpectedly hostile reaction from LQ.

"You have endangered your lives by doing this," he said. "You must not do this again."

"But what about the durians?" Pete protested. "Are we just going to let them lie there on the ground and rot? They're in season now and we'll miss them unless someone goes and gets them."

"We can send a party," LQ said, "but it must be armed for protection. You were in great danger, and this is not permitted. You will keep to your huts for the next three days."

Pete and Scottie both smiled at this but did not create a scene or continue the argument. They left to walk back to their shelters.

"Bloody ridiculous," Pete said. "He's behaving like a damn schoolmaster, telling his students to behave."

"Right," said Scottie. "The only bloody lives we endangered were our own. Why should they worry? We don't have to take that from him."

In general, the others were also surprised at the strength of LQ's reaction. It was, after all, only their own lives that had been endangered. The incident left them with the impression that perhaps the Chinese guerillas placed a higher value on the lives of the foreigners, or regarded them as more important to their cause, than the foreigners themselves had realised.

Despite the problem with Pete and Scottie, relations with the guerillas seemed to be good. One night, after finishing their evening meal, Arthur, Bomber and Tom, as well as Jock, who had recovered from his fever, sang a few songs around the campfire. The Chinese listened fascinated, but without any understanding, as the Europeans went through some of their old favourites. On the second occasion, the Chinese decided to join in with great gusto, singing together in Chinese and Malay and then listened entranced to the foreigners as they sang their own English and Australian ballads. Several of them were bawdy, bar-room songs which, when translated and explained to the guerillas, brought loud laughter. They then contributed their own bawdy Chinese songs.

At first the singing was done in groups, but as feelings of shyness and embarrassment receded, individuals stood up to give solo performances and the whole thing began to take on more the air of a concert than an after-dinner singsong.

After the success of the first night, singing became quite a regular feature of camp life. There were some who were concerned that the noise of singing might be heard some distance away and could be a threat to their security. But, as with the fires, the density of the jungle foliage all about protected them. It deadened the sounds so effectively that virtually nothing could be heard as little as two or three hundred yards away. Scouts were sent out in various directions to check on the distance the sound carried. They found that, in most cases, even the sentries on watch at the approaches to the camp could not hear the singing so, barring exceptional circumstances, the sing-along nights were given general approval. They proved to be a popular event which brought a degree of happiness and laughter to the little camp.

On more than one occasion, as he lay on his back, gazing up at the clear patch of sky above the clearing and listening to the Chinese singing, Arthur was struck by the strangeness of the situation. Above, countless millions of brilliant stars, and sometimes a moon, shone down on this tiny group of people, sitting in the middle of a dense, absolutely dark jungle, their faces illuminated only by the flickering light of the campfire. As they sang, Arthur found it difficult to believe that there was a war going on and that the world outside, beyond the trees, was peopled by enemies.

During most of this time, although Camp 7 was their home, Arthur and Bomber were often able to make their way down the mountainside to Camp 8 to visit Mac, Les, Bluey and Roy, who seemed to enjoy a little more living space. It was a bigger camp, but it also contained considerably more people and there seemed to be a greater involvement in anti-Japanese actions. Arthur and Bomber noticed guerilla soldiers there undergoing more rigorous training than was given at their own camp. They also saw quite a few wounded in a hospital shelter.

On most of their trips down the mountain, they would go to play cards, or perhaps a game of volleyball, with their comrades. Sometimes Jock, Tom and Gaje would join them, but relations between Jock and Mac McCure had soured some weeks earlier after a simple argument. Now they would not speak to each other. Pete and Scottie also did not participate. They had begun to keep very much to themselves and were not particularly friendly to any of the others whether they were from Camp 7 or Camp 8.

Scottie appeared to have an inexhaustible supply of tobacco but, apart from one or two occasions when he gave a few ounces to Arthur and Bomber, he never shared any of it with the rest of the Europeans. Even when they begged him for a smoke, he would just refuse. Where he obtained it, no-one knew. He was also never without money, even though all of the others had long since exhausted whatever supplies of cash they had. If a Chinese courier or agent was going into Paloh, Chaah, Yong Peng or Labis to carry out some clandestine mission, Scottie would often slip a few notes into his hand with a request for items like soap or razor blades or some other small luxury.

Most of the other Europeans had long since given up trying to shave and, unlike the Chinese, who generally had little facial hair, now sported large, bushy beards and long hair. Arthur's beard had long been an object of considerable interest to the Chinese and, on occasions, even amazement, especially to new arrivals in the camp, who acted as if they could hardly believe their eyes. This was because, although the hair on Arthur's head was blond, his beard, for some reason, was as red as a carrot.

When a barber arrived at Camp 8 about this time and began cutting hair, several of the men decided to take advantage of the young man's expert services. Scottie and Pete were the first to do so, but when the others saw the results, they began to have second thoughts. Both Pete and Scottie were completely shaved-- not only faces, but heads also. They looked like a couple of billiard balls.

After a little thought, Arthur decided to do the same. A plague of ticks had struck the camp and, a few days previously, Arthur had pulled thirteen of them from his beard, head and, more painfully, from his scrotum and amongst his pubic hair. All of the men had also been troubled from time to time by lice. By shaving his head and beard, Arthur felt he would be able to avoid both. Once he was in the barber's chair, however, he compromised by keeping his moustache.

13

DURING JULY OF 1942, THERE was a shake-up of some sort in Camp 9, which was near Batu Pahat. The reasons for the action were never revealed to the Europeans, but Camp 9 was suddenly disbanded and, after a difficult trek, seventy of its members arrived at Camp 7 carrying an assortment of weapons, including six Bren guns, four Tommy guns, two Lewis machine-guns as well as a great deal of ammunition and grenades.

They also brought a wireless that wouldn't work and two batteries. They all appeared to be in good spirits when they arrived, as a result of having openly marched along a stretch of road with the Communist Party flag flying and all of them wearing khaki caps embossed with a red star emblem. Two Malays who saw the group marching along, four abreast, panicked and fled for their lives.

In addition to the first group, there were seventeen others still to come, according to their leader. These included about half a dozen sick and wounded and the heavily armed party that had stayed behind to escort them more slowly through the jungle. The main group also brought news of recent bold attacks by Chinese guerillas on the Japanese near the town of Jasin. Apparently, Japanese soldiers regularly used a certain mess hut near the town, but when they ate they left weapons stacked neatly in another hut next to it. Biding their time until nearly all of the Japanese were in the mess hut and seated at their meal, the guerillas attacked, quickly killing the guards outside the building, then bursting inside to spray the unarmed soldiers with automatic-weapon fire, killing most of them. They then made good their escape with a large number of weapons collected from the adjoining hut.

They brought news, too, of another group of four Australian and three English soldiers living in another guerilla camp beyond Batu Pahat. They had no information as to their names, or what units they had belonged to, but said that there had apparently been six Australians in the group which had been wandering and living in the jungle alone. Two Malays had evidently reported the group to the Japanese and two of the Australians had been captured and killed. The others had managed to escape and had later met up with the guerillas and decided to join them. The guerilla leader telling the story, who called himself Cheung Ho, took some delight in adding that the two Malay informers had ultimately been picked up by the guerillas and brought in for trial.

"They were, of course, found guilty," he said. "And it was the Australian soldiers who carried out the execution. They insisted. They were very angry over the death of their comrades."

"I wonder who they are," Arthur said, after Cheung Ho had finished his story. "We should try to get a message to them somehow."

News of any kind was always important to them. He and all his comrades hungered for any snippets of information about the world outside, no matter how small. Almost every day they would hear planes, sometimes large numbers of them, passing overhead, flying either north or south. But, unless they could see them, they had no idea whether they were Japanese or Allied aircraft. The guess, though, was nearly always Japanese.

The jungle canopy around the camp was so high that there was only one clear patch of sky, about eighty feet directly above the camp. By climbing high into one of the trees, a good view could be had to the south-west over what looked like an endless sea of jungle and rubber trees, but any planes that came over, had generally disappeared from view by the time someone had climbed the tree. Sometimes details of planes that had flown over came in to the camp later, reported by other people who had observed them, but they were often conflicting and therefore unreliable. One person would report sixty unknown planes over Muar and twenty over Pagoh. Another person would describe the same flight as being fifteen over Muar and two over Pagoh, and say that the planes had three green stripes on the wings and white markings on the rudder--none of which meant anything to Arthur and his friends.

On several nights, about this time, a single aircraft would fly in circles, either very high or very low over the mountainside, passing, on a number of occasions, close to where the two camps were situated.

"They are trying to see our fire," LQ had said the first time after they had doused the campfire with water. He laughed. "I think it will be very difficult for them to find us this way."

Because of the possibility of being located by their smoke, they adhered rigidly to the practice of not lighting fires until after nightfall, always under cover of the jungle canopy and not in the open part of the clearing where they might be visible from above. They also made a practice of burning only dried timber that gave off little smoke, and never burning damp or green leaves.

The night flights continued for about a week during July, apparently without any success for the Japanese--they stopped as abruptly as they had started.

It was during this period that a new leader, Sou Lim, arrived in the camp. Sou Lim, they soon learnt, was equivalent in rank and authority to LQ, but lived a double life as an agent in the world outside, under the Japanese. He was a stockily built man of about thirty-five with a small, wispy black moustache. He wore glasses, which gave him a somewhat studious air, but his large mouth and toothy grin were probably more indicative of his jovial and gregarious character. In the months that followed, the Allied soldiers were to see a great deal of Sou Lim, whom they naturally dubbed SL. They grew to know him well and to look forward to his visits and the news he would bring, whether it was good news or bad, believable or not.

On his first visit, Sou Lim brought news of the war in Europe: "Russia has taken Finland in the north," he told them in almost perfect English, "and they have gone through Bessarabia, Romania and Jugoslavia in the south. And," he paused for maximum effect, "the British are bombing Berlin."

Although Arthur and the others greeted this information with approving nods, it was difficult for them to become excited by it. Even the news that, a month or so earlier, there had been

British landings in France and Italy was greeted with private scepticism. They never allowed Sou Lim to think that they did not accept his news as gospel truth, though, for fear he might stop bringing it to them. They preferred to have doubtful news, or even news they didn't believe, rather than no news at all.

The stories Sou Lim said he had heard about the Far East, were that Chinese troops were fighting in Thailand and were close to Bangkok. He also said that over five hundred American bombers, including twenty Flying Fortresses, had bombed Japan. He reported that three attempted Japanese landings had been made in Australia and that Australia was still being bombed by the Japanese.

SL became a regular visitor to the camp. He never stayed more than a few hours, sometimes overnight, but he was nearly always able to pass on some news of the war in other parts of the world. When it was contradicted, or shown by his own later news to be patently wrong, he displayed no pangs of conscience at having misinformed them. "I will just tell you what I hear," he said one day. "You can make of it what you will. Some of it may be wrong, but some of it will also be correct."

Whatever the news, Arthur began to record it in his diary during July:

Germans using gas. Japs using gas in north. Two-thirds Burma retaken by Chinese and Indians. Japs cut off in Rangoon. Siam occupied by Chinese. Japs lost 120 ships in Coral Sea battle. Reports of Chinese guerilla warfare in Singapore; blowing up cars and lorries as they drive along. Unconfirmed news that Stalin will enter Germany next month and finish the war.

Only a small percentage of these news snippets came from Sou Lim, but if they had accepted even half of them at face value, they could have been forgiven for believing that it wouldn't be too long before Malaya was retaken by the Allies and their stay in the jungle would end. With a bit of luck, they thought, on one or two occasions when the news had been heavily in favour of the Allies, they could be free by the end of 1942.

On 17 July they celebrated half a year since the battle at Bakri, and on 30 July, the first anniversary of their departure from Australia on board the SS Marnix. So much had happened in that year. Arthur and Bomber sat around that evening, after supper, gazing into the small campfire, reminiscing about the times they'd had on board the boat on the trip to Singapore.

"It was as if we were going on a bloody holiday," Arthur said. "If I'd known this was going to happen, I'd have booked through a different travel agent."

Bomber laughed, "Me too. One that sent us to Tahiti or South America." He was silent for several moments. "I wonder how Jim and Jack got on. And where they are now. Remember, on the boat, how Jim was always winning at 'Crown and Anchor'?"

"Yeah. He wasn't so good at '500' though, or 'Pontoon'. Borrie Wiles used to always clean up at '500'."

Most of the two weeks they'd had on board the Marnix, a converted passenger ship, had been spent reading, writing letters, playing cards or just lying around in the sun. When the battalion had joined the vessel in Melbourne, virtually all of the 35 officers and 943 men were in high spirits, treating the voyage as an adventure. It was a great opportunity to get away from the bitterly cold climate of their camp at Bathurst on the high plains to the west of Sydney. They'd had eight months of intensive weapons training and platoon, company and battalion exercises, most of which had been in the Bathurst area. But although this period of training had brought the 2/29th to a level of skill and proficiency they all felt proud of, they were nevertheless glad to be on their way, even though they were leaving home, family and friends behind.

Although it was supposed to be classified information, virtually the whole battalion knew they were off on a sea voyage, as part of the 27th Brigade, to either the Middle East or Malaya. For most of them, all that mattered was the fact that at last they were going somewhere and that it was going to be warm wherever they went.

The embarkation was a complicated procedure. The Brigade, consisting of the 2/26th Battalion from Queensland, the 2/29th from Victoria and the 2/30th from New South Wales, as well as the 2/15th Field Regiment, the 27th Anti-tank Company, the 2/12th Field Company of Engineers and a number of other support groups, was to board three different transport ships in three widely separated parts of Australia. One part of the Brigade would join the Johann Van Olden Barneveldt in Sydney, another group, including Arthur and the 2/29th, would board the Marnix in Melbourne, while the third would travel almost 3000 miles across the country by train to join the SS Sibajak in Fremantle.

Although there would be no time for home leave before their departure, the train trip to Melbourne offered one last fleeting opportunity to see family and friends. The military authorities would not permit anyone to be at the dockside at Port Melbourne while the ship was being boarded or when it sailed, but they did make arrangements for the troop train carrying the 2/29th to stop for a brief period at Flinders Street Station in Melbourne and for relatives and friends to be able to be on the platform while the train was there.

Arthur had said goodbye to his mother and his brothers and sisters on his last home leave only ten days previously, not expecting to be coming back through Melbourne again. However, he was able to let Nancy know by phone and, as she worked only a few blocks from the railway station, she was able to take time off from work to try and meet Arthur. She struggled through huge crowds on the platform to find an advantageous position and stood there, waiting for the train to come in. Then, as it pulled slowly into the station and glided to a halt, she searched, for Arthur amongst the faces of hundreds of soldiers hanging out of the carriage windows. It seemed a miracle to her that she found him, with all those men in identical uniforms, but she did. The time was all too brief. Their goodbyes were said, and amidst shouts of encouragement and flowing tears, the train pulled out on its way to Port Melbourne.

"I'll write to you," Nancy called. "Write to me."

"I will," Arthur shouted back as the train gathered momentum.

"I'll be waiting for you," Nancy yelled, but she couldn't tell if Arthur heard her as his face was lost behind the crowds of other people that crammed the platform.

When the SS Marnix steamed out of Port Phillip Bay into Bass Strait on the evening of 30 July, instead of turning due west for Western Australia, which was to be its next stop, it kept heading almost due south, some 300 miles south of the normal shipping lanes across the Great Australian Bight, before turning west.

So, as the morning of 31 July dawned, Arthur and the rest of the troops on board awoke to find that their first day of ocean voyaging was hardly a pleasure cruise. The Marnix was ploughing through rolling grey seas in the Roaring Forties.

After a layover of two days in Western Australia, during which time virtually all of the troops went ashore into Fremantle and Perth for their final leave, the Marnix sailed, in convoy now with the Johann Van Olden Barneveldt and the Sibajak, for its unknown destination. Although they sailed off into windy and rough conditions, less than a day out of Fremantle the sea became calm and the weather balmy. The men crowded the decks, sunbaking, chatting, playing cards and betting on where they were going.

On 11 August, three days out of Fremantle, they got confirmation that cold weather was not going to be a part of their future when all heavy and warm clothing on issue to them was withdrawn and they were reissued with new items of tropical clothing. Amongst them were the British-designed 'long shorts' which, in hot conditions, could be turned and buttoned-up like shorts. Then in the evening, when the mosquitoes came out, they could be unbuttoned and let down around the ankles, like long pants. The fact that none of them seemed to fit caused some initial problems.

"Our ship has all the pants to fit blokes six foot three and over," Bomber complained, "And the bloody Barneveldt has all the pants that fit us."

"You can change them when we get there," the quartermaster told Bomber and Arthur, who both had pants that hung over their feet in folds on the floor.

"Not much good to us now, though, is it?" Arthur said. "And anyway, where are we going and when do we get there?"

"You'll see, in a couple of days."

"So, it must be Singapore," Bomber smiled.

That Singapore was their destination was now an open secret, but it was confirmed to all on board the following day, when they sighted land and sailed through the Sunda Straits, past the remnant of the great volcano Krakatoa, and began heading up the east coast of Sumatra.

As they entered Singapore's bustling harbour early on the morning of 15 August, more than twelve hundred men lined the rails of the Marnix. For many, particularly the Victorians, it was the first time they had ever been in the tropics, and for most, it was their first visit to a foreign port. All were fascinated by the sights, sounds and smells of Singapore.

Disembarkation began shortly after their arrival and went smoothly despite a sudden, extremely heavy tropical downpour which drenched large numbers of the men. Once ashore, the battalion was taken in trucks, driven at breakneck speed by Indian drivers, out along the east coast road to Katong, where they were quartered in the spacious school buildings of St Patrick's College.

Most of the men from the 2/29th, including Arthur, immediately felt the effects of Singapore's hot, humid climate. After a cold Australian winter, which in retrospect had been invigorating, they now found themselves living in a bath of continual perspiration and feeling enervated and lethargic. The brigade commander, Brigadier Maxwell, decided to meet the problem head-on so, within forty-eight hours of their arrival, they were launched into an acclimatisation programme that consisted mainly of marching. Marching every day. They marched all over Singapore, from east to west and north to south and, although they complained, after a very short while they seemed to be adapting to the high humidity and becoming used to life in the tropics. They even looked forward to the regular drenching that invariably came around three in the afternoon, in the middle of their return journey to camp.

"Another three minutes, no more," Bomber said once, looking at his watch as they marched along, sweat dripping from their faces, their shirts soaking wet.

"Five bob says its five," Jim Kennedy whispered from the side.

Other faces around them looked up at the towering clouds darkening above them, and then at their watches, "Six minutes," said Jack Roxburgh, "I'll put five bob on it, too."

"Eight," said Borrie Wiles.

"Four," Arthur whispered from the front rank of the platoon.

And by the time rain came, nine minutes later, Frankie Fox had won himself thirty shillings and all of them were laughing and revelling in the cooling effect of the downpour.

On the first few marches, they were carrying no equipment or arms, just wearing shorts, boots, long socks with gaiters, khaki shirts and their slouch hats. And when the rain started, they just kept marching, being instantly drenched to the skin. The rain would usually last about half an hour, so that by the time they returned to their quarters at Katong, around 4 pm, they were almost dry again, but much cooler and in good humour.

On several occasions during the month they spent in Singapore, the unit was given local leave and town leave, usually only for the two days of a weekend. Local leave enabled them to go only into Katong, the local village and virtually a suburb of Singapore, but no further, while a 'town leave' pass allowed them to go into the centre of Singapore. Leave in Katong was relatively tame, usually involving a visit to one of the local restaurants or the Roxy theatre to see a movie. Town leave, on the other hand, was an opportunity to 'live it up'.

Shortly after their arrival at Katong, Colonel Robertson, the CO of the 2/29th, had addressed the troops on their 'responsibilities in a foreign country' and on the 'standards of discipline and behaviour expected of Australian soldiers living amongst Asiatics'. As an additional precaution, whenever a soldier left the camp on any sort of leave, he was given what was known as a 'blue-light kit', consisting of three condoms and a small tube of antiseptic ointment.

When the troops of the 2/29th and the other Australian battalions were first given leave to go into downtown Singapore, they found, to their surprise, a range of restrictions on them that had nothing to do with their own commanders. Whereas in Sydney or Melbourne they could walk into the best hotels in town and order a drink, in Singapore, the best hotels were reserved for officers.

Arthur, Bomber, Frankie Fox, Jim Kennedy and Jack Roxburgh had once strolled into Raffles Hotel, only to be confronted at the door by a British military policeman.

"Do you have passes?" he asked, barring their way.

They each produced their town leave passes, which carried their name, rank and serial number, what battalion they belonged to and how long the pass was valid for.

"Sorry, boys," the MP said. "Can't let you in."

"Why not?" Arthur said. "We're only going in for a drink."

"Officers only in here."

"Officers only?" Bomber spluttered. "Is their money better than ours?"

"Sorry, but that's the way it is."

In addition, they learnt that there were many places where liquor was sold, but where they could not get served. In general they found that they could only buy the local beers, Anchor or Tiger, at places which also served food, and it would only be sold to them if they sat down and ate at the same time, and left the empty bottles when they finished.

It was not long before someone discovered a place called Taylors Brothel in the 'Old World' entertainment area of Singapore. In the upstairs lounge room of Taylors, whether you wanted a woman or not, you could be served with whatever liquor you required, whenever you wanted it, with or without food.

When the word got around, Taylors, and several other establishments like it, became the most popular venues for the Australian troops. Arthur and his friends from 1 Platoon would gravitate there on their leave days, and spend the afternoon and evening playing cards and drinking, in most cases without any involvement with the girls. The madam would hover around, looking after their drinks and joining in good-natured banter with the men. Usually, several of the girls would sit and watch the card games and talk to the Australians, excusing themselves from time to time, for twenty minutes or so, if a customer wanted them in the rooms downstairs.

Later, Arthur and Bomber would sometimes recall, with much laughter, an incident that took place there. It had been on a rainy afternoon when Arthur and several of the men from his platoon were at Taylors, playing poker. One of the young Chinese prostitutes had taken a fancy to an even younger soldier, still in his teens, that they'd nick-named 'Foo'. She sat next to him as he played and, during the afternoon, made it clear that he could have the benefit of her services without any payment.

"Go on, Foo, be a sport," Bomber kept urging him. "Do the right thing by her."

"But I'm in the middle of a game," the young man kept insisting.

"She likes you," Bomber said. "She wants to do you a favour and you keep knocking her back."

The girl smiled and kept cuddling up to Foo. She began to fondle him in front of the others. Foo became increasingly aroused and agitated.

"Just a minute, fellas," he said, putting down his cards and beginning to undo his fly. Then, without leaving his chair, he lifted the girl's dress and pulled her onto his lap. Spreading her legs, she straddled him and, with a laugh to the rest of the men sitting around the table, began to ride up and down on the young man. The card game stopped as all the players around the table laughed and joked and called encouragement to both Foo and the girl.

Within minutes, with the girl pounding away and laughing happily, Foo's face grimaced as he came to a thrusting climax, to the accompaniment of shouts and cheers from all at the table.

"Drinks for everyone, all round," Bomber cried. "What a performance!"

Foo eased the girl off his lap, adjusted his fly and then reached for his cards from the table. "Now, where were we?" he said to a chorus of hoots and laughter.

Unfortunately for Arthur and his comrades, their period of 'living it up' in Singapore was short-lived. Exactly one month after their arrival, the 2/29th was on its way north, across the causeway at Johore Bharu and into Malaya by train, through very different country than they had seen except in small doses, during their marches around Singapore island. The train passed through long stretches of thick jungle, then miles and miles of rubber, coconut and oil palm plantations, then more miles of jungle, more rubber plantations and more jungle--jungle deeper, thicker, greener, more tangled than any of them had imagined.

"Just as well we had plenty of experience in this sort of country back home," Arthur joked as the train rumbled along.

Jim Kennedy, sitting next to Arthur, was staring out the window. "Not exactly like Bathurst or Bonegilla, is it? It's not going to be much fun charging around through that stuff."

"Let's hope we don't have to," Bomber said.

Their new camp, in the town of Segamat, came as something of a shock to the 2/29th. It was in a school, or rather next to it, in a large open field. But it was by no means ready to accommodate some eight hundred men. The crowded conditions they found in the collection of large wooden huts was made worse by the fact that two of the huts had only recently burnt down and had not yet been replaced. More new huts were being built, but it would take time. The drainage in the camp was so bad that the regular daily deluges of rain invariably flooded the whole area. It was also discovered that many of the huts were home to a number of large cobras which had to be cleared out before anyone felt really safe about sleeping in them.

But despite these initial problems, the general feeling about Segamat was good. Most of the men liked it. It was a pleasant country town in the centre of which there were wide streets lined with colonnaded shop fronts. The area around the town itself was very picturesque with a number of big, old colonial houses surrounded by spacious lawns and trees and many open, grassy public places and parks. The surrounding countryside was dotted with large rubber plantations, run mainly by English or Scottish managers and worked by Tamil Indians who lived in settlements on or near the plantations. Throughout the district there were also many small kampongs whose Chinese and Malay inhabitants were usually occupied in small farming operations. Beyond, there was the jungle, which in some areas, despite plantation development, came within only a few miles of Segamat township.

After a few days spent settling in and improving the conditions in the camp, the battalion quickly began to adapt to life in Malaya. A march through the streets of Segamat was given an enthusiastic reception by the local people of all races, Malay, Chinese and Indian--and, of course, the small European community. The Australian troops, generally occupied during the week on various exercises and manoeuvres as well as weapons and equipment training, were given local leave in Segamat on the weekends. As Arthur and his friends soon discovered, by comparison to Singapore, there was very little excitement to be found in Segamat. However, the town did provide them with a wealth of gastronomic adventures.

On Arthur's first visit into the township with Jim Kennedy and Jack Roxburgh, he was overwhelmed with the variety of wonderful aromas issuing from the little restaurants and sidewalk stalls that lined the main street of Segamat. Walking amongst the tables of one Indian restaurant which had spread itself out onto the tiles of the footpath, Arthur stopped to look at the exotic dishes spread before one Indian customer.

"Doesn't that smell great?" he said to Jim Kennedy and then, to the customer, "What is it?" But the Indian at the table speaking no English, simply shook his head and shrugged his shoulders.

The manager of the restaurant was quickly on the scene along with a small group of onlookers who had begun to gather, probably to see why the foreigners were pointing at the food on the table. Arthur asked the manager the same question: "What is that?" and pointed again at the man's food.

Again no comprehension, so Arthur turned to Jim and Jack, "Let's just sit down and order. Maybe they'll understand that." The three men then sat at a nearby table and pointed again at the man's food and then at their own table, saying: "The same as that here, please."

A babble of excited conversation ran through the crowd of onlookers, which had now grown to more than a dozen locals. The manager shook his head and went away looking perplexed. Within moments, a young boy emerged from the kitchen area and approached Arthur's table.

"Excuse me, do you speak English?" he asked them.

"Well, I hope so," Arthur laughed and then said, "Yes, we do. Do you?"

"Yes, I am a student at Segamat High School. What do you want?"

Arthur pointed again at the man's food. "We want that. Those things he is eating, whatever they are, we want that. It smells beautiful."

The boy looked as perplexed as the manager, who was presumably his father or uncle, now standing in the background watching the proceedings. "But there is a white man's café just down the road." He pointed to the other side of the street.

"White people do not come here."

The three Australians were amazed.

"I couldn't care less about the white man's cafe," Arthur spluttered, "Whether it's just down the road or two miles away. We want to eat here. Aren't we allowed to eat here?"

"Yes, yes," the young boy said excitedly. "Yes, yes, you are allowed to eat here. Don't go away." He turned and spoke quickly to the manager, whose face lit up in a smile as he approached the table again.

"Now," Arthur said again to the boy and the manager, "we want all that stuff that that bloke is eating and we want enough for the three of us. Okay?"

"Okay, sir. Yes. Yes. Everything okay. Coming straight-away, sir."

Early on in their stay in Segamat, Arthur and several of his comrades in 1 Platoon befriended a young Indian boy who came around the campsite almost every afternoon to talk to the soldiers.

"What's your name?" Arthur asked him one day as he sat down to watch several of the men playing cards.

"Peter."

"Peter what?"

"Peter Koran."

"How old are you, Peter?" Arthur asked.

"Eleven."

"And how is that you have time to come here every day? Don't you go to school?"

"Of course." The boy looked at Arthur as if it was a stupid question. "Every day I go. But school is only until three o'clock. Then it is finished."

Peter became a regular visitor to the camp and seemed to have made 1 Platoon, and particularly Arthur, whom he called 'Mr Shep', his special friends. Arthur taught him to play 'Snakes and Ladders' and, if Peter was visiting and Arthur had the time to spare, they would always play. More often than not, much to his delight, Peter would be the winner.

During October and November of 1941, despite the fact that Japan and the Allies were not yet at war, there was a general feeling of rising tension in the Far East and South-East Asia. News of increasingly strong concentrations of Japanese sea, land and air forces in southern Indo-China and the South China Sea was taken seriously in Singapore and London, where the British War Office warned that Japan might be expected to attack Thailand, the Philippines, the Dutch East Indies and Malaya.

As the degree of readiness of the Allied forces in Malaya was stepped up, Arthur's battalion and the other elements of the 27th Australian Brigade were ordered, in the last days of November, to prearranged war stations. For the 2/29th, this meant a move to Kluang airfield, about seventy miles by road back towards Singapore. One company was sent to Kahang airfield, about twenty miles north-east of Kluang on the road to the east coast.

On the day of their departure from Segamat, young Peter Koran came to the camp to say goodbye. He was clearly upset.

"Have you got something for me to remember you by, Mr Shep?" he asked.

Arthur thought for a moment and then went to his pack. On their winter uniforms, which were now no longer with them, they wore brass insignia--two shoulder badges saying AUSTRA-LIA and two collar badges depicting the AIF rising sun. Arthur dug them from the bottom of his pack and brought one of each to give to Peter.

"Oh, thank you, Mr Shep," the boy said. "I will keep them forever."

Arthur laughed. "Forever is a long time, Peter. You don't have to keep them that long."

"Until I see you next time, then," Peter said.

"Okay, mate." Arthur patted his back and shook his hand. "Good luck. . .until next time."

On 6 December, about midday, a Hudson bomber of No. 1 Squadron RAAF, operating from Kota Bharu on patrol over the South China Sea, reported sighting three Japanese troop transport ships, escorted by a cruiser, sailing about eighty miles south of Cape Cambodia. Two later sightings from Hudson reconnaissance aircraft reported one group of twenty-two troop ships, heavily escorted by cruisers and destroyers, and another group of about twenty transports, all heading west towards the coast of southern Thailand and northern Malaya. The invasion of Malaya, timed to coincide with the Japanese attack on Pearl Harbour, began shortly before 1 am local time on 8 December 1941.

While British and Indian forces in the northern parts of the Malayan peninsula struggled to contain the Japanese there, the Australian forces, charged with the defence of Johore State to the south, geared themselves for the expected onslaught. The 2/29th battalion remained in its position around Kluang airfield for almost a month until the major Japanese breakthrough at Slim river signalled the failure of the northern Malayan defences. The Japanese forces then struck southward with astonishing speed, prompting General Gordon Bennett, the Australian Commander, to move the 27th Brigade back to the Segamat area on 7 January 1942 to meet an expected Japanese thrust down the main trunk road from Kuala Lumpur to the south. The 2/30th Battalion was positioned on the main road west of Gemas, with the 2/26th behind it and to the north, between Gemas and Batu Anam, while the 2/29th was stationed at Buloh Kasap, between Batu Anam and Segamat. It was here, on 17 January, that Arthur and his comrades boarded the transport vehicles that carried them to the small section of rubber plantation on the road between Bakri and Muar and the engagement which was to begin Arthur's long sojourn in the jungle.

14

IN THE LATTER HALF OF July, Arthur, Bomber and Gaje began to spend more of their time down the mountainside at Camp 8 than at their own camp. They found they enjoyed the company of the four men there more than that of Jock, Tom, Pete and Scottie at Camp 7. Jock and Tom, they found, were rather dry and humourless, while Pete and Scottie, as always, had been aloof, preferring to keep largely to themselves than to mix and be friendly with the two Australians and the young Indian soldier. Arthur, Bomber and Gaje all got on reasonably well with the four in Camp 8 and so, before long, it was decided, without any objections from LQ or the other camp leaders, that they should make the move permanent.

At this stage, the food at both camps was once again reasonable in both amount and variety. They had rice, bamboo shoots, ubi potatoes, durians and, occasionally, fish. After they had settled into Camp 8, Bluey, Bomber, Les and Arthur began a routine of going out from the camp each day to collect bamboo shoots and nebongs. Collecting nebong involved cutting down the big palms with an axe and then trimming the hard outer leaves away to get at the inner part of the tree where the cabbage-like 'heart' was situated.

The trees were often large and sometimes, when they had cut more than they could carry back to camp, they would hang the remaining ones in a tree and return for them the next day. They had to take care to hide the palms well because if a Malay or any enemy came across them, they could assume that someone was coming back for them and might lay an ambush.

Arthur, Bluey and Les returned one day from one of these expeditions, each carrying a big nebong they had cut on the previous day. It had rained heavily as they made their way back to the camp and they were all thoroughly drenched by the time they handed their nebongs over to Slim and Shorty in the kitchen shelter. As they stood talking to the two cooks, LQ began to make his way urgently across the clearing towards them.

"Here's trouble," Bluey said. "He looks like he's got something on his mind."

"We will be moving in two days time to a new camp," LQ said, even before he arrived at the cookhouse shelter.

"Oh no," Arthur moaned.

"Why?" Bluey asked. "What's wrong with this one? The Japs aren't coming are they?"

"No," LQ said, a little apologetically, "fortunately, it's not that."

Not counting the move that Arthur, Bomber and Gaje had made to Camp 8, they had spent almost three months without moving and most of them were reasonably happy with their situation.

"The new place will be better for us," LQ went on. "More space, more secure."

"Where is it?"Arthur asked.

"Not far, only a few hours away. It is an old Sakai camp."

Two days later, all members of both Camp 7 and 8 moved. Although they didn't expect it, it was a relatively simple transition. Each person carried his or her own possessions, which were fairly meagre, plus two rifles or other weapons and some ammunition. There were several Chinese families living in the camp, one of which included among its members a small, elderly woman, who, although not normally frail or weak, had been ill for several days. Her family carried as much as they could, but there was one bag left over. Arthur volunteered to carry it.

Shortly after breakfast and well before the main groups left from either camp, a group of 'agitators' moved out from Camp 8. This was a new practice, which, according to LQ, would be adopted each time they made a major move.

"They will go to a certain place, well away from our route," he explained, "and create a disturbance, perhaps start some shooting, that will attract any Japanese in the area. And then, when the enemy arrives, our men will disappear in the jungle. In the meantime, we will have made our move without being noticed."

The new camp was hardly more than a few miles from the ones they had left, but it was definitely better than either of them. It had a much larger clearing--room for a good volley-ball court, Arthur thought, as they marched into the camp--and there were two Sakai huts still standing.

Everyone seemed happy with the new site and began to settle in quickly. As Pete and Scottie were still determined to separate themselves from the rest, even if only marginally, they were given permission to build a place for themselves a little way off in the jungle.

Within the first few days, another bear was killed, once again providing bear steak first and then, as the passing days had their effect on the meat, bear stew, soup and finally bear curry. There were large numbers of monkeys in the area, too, but no-one in the camp seemed able to shoot them.

Arthur and Scottie, the two rifle-trainers, despaired over the level of marksmanship of the Chinese they tried to teach. However much they attempted to explain the basic principles of holding the rifle firmly, aligning the sights with one eye closed, holding the breath and then squeezing the trigger-not pulling on it-they could not master it. They would keep both eyes open, hold the rifle too loosely, so it kicked hard into their shoulder on firing, and they'd pull the trigger too quickly, jerking the rifle off the target as they fired.

"They can't hit a bloody barn door," Scottie would often moan.

But when both Jock and Scottie tried to shoot a big monkey that had been sitting in the branch of a tree, at a distance of about fifty yards, and missed, nobody complained too much about Chinese marksmanship any more.

They continued, in the new camp, the programme of restoring and repairing various types of arms that had been collected. Many of the weapons that had been brought from the camp near Batu Pahat had still to be brought up to working order while several were so damaged as to be good only for spare parts. But it was usually relatively easy to make up a workable weapon from broken ones.

They also began, at this time, to travel further afield on hunting expeditions. They were seeking seladang, the big, black, hump-backed wild Malayan cattle which roam the jungle fringes. Seladang, they were told, do not frequent the deeper parts of the jungle as they are a grazing animal preferring the grass that grows in more open spaces. Yet they, like the guerillas, had an interest in staying away from civilisation, so the animal had developed considerable cunning in avoiding contact with humans, while at the same time not confining its activity to the deeper jungle. On several occasions while out with hunting parties, Arthur was shown the cloven-hoof tracks of a large seladang, as well as that of wild pig and elephant, but they saw no sign of the animals themselves.

Once established in the new camp, they began, for the first time, a vegetable planting programme. In previous camps there had always been an excuse not to start--either the soil wasn't right, or there wasn't enough room, but mostly it was because they were forever anticipating another sudden move. The new camp, by contrast, seemed to inspire them. There was, of course, no guarantee that they would be there any longer than at previous camps, but for some reason they felt that this one would be home sufficiently long enough for them to raise a crop of vegetables.

Arthur, Bomber, Bluey, and Les began the process by digging up a large patch of earth in one corner of the clearing and then planting whatever vegetables they could find. Several amongst the Chinese followed suit, helping them on the patch they had begun and starting smaller gardens in other parts of the camp. Seeds were brought in from outside for panjan (cabbages) and kacan (beans) and they planted spinach, bamboo shoots, ordinary potatoes, as well as the ubi and claddy wild potatoes. In addition, they put in marrows, a type of squash, melons and even tomatoes. The exercise was a great morale booster for the camp. Everyone was very positive about the new gardens and felt sure that they would be there to harvest the crops.

Parties still went out into the jungle to collect wild vegetables, but one of the forays, on which Arthur, Les and Gaje were together, almost ended in disaster. The three were clambering through a section of dense, virgin jungle in which, from a distance, they had seen some cabbage palms a few days earlier. It had been raining heavily and the ground was thoroughly sodden. As they moved up a slight slope through some thick patches of rotan bushes, the prickles and thorns on the bushes tore at their clothes and skin. Gaje slipped on the muddy slope and fell awkwardly. As he put his hand out to grasp for support, he yelled in pain as a large thorn on the bush he grabbed, went right through his finger. Fortunately it was in one piece and they were able to pull it out cleanly, although it left Gaje with a sore and bleeding finger.

The trio continued looking for nebong, collecting about ten small ones, of which Arthur had five slung over his shoulder. Deciding to head back to the camp, they began to negotiate a steep slope when Arthur also slipped, sliding on his feet first, then tumbling down the slope with the nebongs rolling beside him. At the instant of his arrival, in a great heap, amongst some bushes at the bottom, Arthur felt a stabbing, burning sensation in his left arm and, as he turned, glimpsed a large brown snake vanishing into the bushes. On his arm there were two neat puncture holes in the skin, both bleeding.

"Shit!" Arthur shouted. "A bloody snake got me."

"Oh, my God," Les said, as he slid down beside Arthur. "What kind of snake was it?"

"Wouldn't have a clue," Arthur said, holding his arm, already breaking out in a sweat, mainly from fear. "It was just brown, that's all. I didn't see much of it."

"We'd better get back to the camp fast," Les said, helping Arthur to his feet and down a smaller slope towards a rough track.

"What about my nebongs?" Arthur complained.

"Leave the bloody things," Les said, hustling him along. "We can get them later." But Gaje picked up two of the fallen cabbage palms and carried them back to camp, which was fortunately only about twenty minutes away.

By the time they arrived at the camp, Arthur was sweating profusely. When LQ was informed what had happened, it was clear that he regarded it as serious. He ran to where Arthur was sitting on a log. Others had begun to gather around, questioning Arthur urgently about the snake. Arthur's reply, 'a brown snake' did nothing to satisfy LQ and he produced a rusty old razor blade with which he slashed Arthur's arm in the area of the bite.

Bomber, who had just arrived at the group as LQ made the cut, stepped forward. "Here, give us a go. I'll do this. I'll be the bloody vampire."

He took Arthur's arm and sucked at it, spitting the blood onto the ground and then sucking again, repeating the process three or four times.

"Coffee," he said, in between sucking and spitting. "Put some coffee on, plenty of it." Then, hoisting Arthur up from the bench, he said, "Okay, Shep, now walk!"

With Bomber supporting him on one arm, and a Chinese on the other, Arthur was made to walk continually around the parade ground for the next two hours. He was not permitted to stop, not even while he drank the continuous cups of coffee that were brought to him.

"You gotta keep moving," Bomber insisted, as they circled the clearing, "so you don't get drowsy."

Gaje's injury to his finger, although very nasty, had paled into insignificance beside Arthur's. He was treated with a poultice of sugar and soap, an unconventional, but no less successful treatment than Arthur's. Whether the snake that bit Arthur was deadly or harmless, Bomber's prescription seemed to work. By the following morning, Arthur reported that he felt none the worse for the experience, except for the fact that the coffee had kept him awake all night.

The rains came now, every day. Torrential rains which confined everybody in the camp to their shelters. Arthur and Bomber would join Les and Bluey to play cards for hours at a time as the rain pelted down on the roof of their hut. Fortunately, the thick mat of grass and leaves remained perfectly waterproof and they were able to look out through the sheets of rain falling across the parade ground as it was turned into one large lake.

It was during one of these regular downpours in late August that a Chinese messenger and another young man, dressed in a khaki uniform and seeming to be a Malay, came into the camp, soaking wet after a long hike from Batu Pahat. They were carrying some medical supplies from the camp at which the

Dutchmen had been staying. After a few moments Arthur recognised the man in uniform as one of the Javanese soldiers attached to Kroon's group. As the British and Australian soldiers had not received any news of the Dutchmen for some months, they were glad to hear that they were still alive and apparently reasonably well, although they had made no more progress with their plans to escape Malaya by boat.

What really interested them, though, was the Chinese messenger's news of two British soldiers who had arrived in Johore State, after an extraordinary three hundred mile trek through the jungle from the Slim River in Perak State in the north. There had apparently been six of them when they originally headed south. The Chinese man relating the story couldn't tell them what had happened to the other four--whether they had died in the jungle, been captured, or what. He simply didn't know. He knew only that the two survivors, whose names were Bennett and Stewart, were both members of the Argyle & Southern Highlanders Regiment. The two had been split up when they were attacked by Tamil plantation workers near Segamat, but had independently met up with Chinese guerillas who had taken Bennett first to a camp near Jementah, then to one close to Bukit Kepong. Stewart had been taken to a camp near Tangkar, where they were raided by Japs, but he escaped to meet up with Stewart again at Bukit Kepong.

The messenger also had information about an Australian soldier called Ronald George Moorfoot of Sydney who had died of fever and been buried by the guerillas at Mount Ophir.

"He was 2/29th," Bluey said. "I didn't know him, but I remember hearing his name. I think he was in D Company."

They could find out nothing more about the man other than the simple facts passed on by the Chinese runner. He had not been connected with the other two British soldiers.

The news created great interest amongst the little group, and that evening, after they had eaten, Arthur sat down to write a letter to the two men. He did not have much hope that it would ever reach them, having failed in previous attempts, over a period of some months, to make contact with the British officer called Couvin in Johore. They were never sure if it was because their letters hadn't arrived, or if they had, because the replies had not been delivered. The end result was the same--they had no confidence in the mail system. They also considered the possibility that their Chinese 'hosts' did not want them to make contact with other Allied soldiers, although no-one could come up with an adequate reason for this, if it was true. Couvin, it seemed to them, had just 'disappeared'. They did not want the same thing to happen to Bennett and Stewart.

After they had heard all the news from the messenger, the Javanese soldier who had accompanied him and helped carry the medical supplies, announced that he did not want to return. He spoke almost no English, but made it clear in Malay that he would prefer to stay with this group than return to the Dutch. There was some discussion amongst the Chinese about whether or not he should be allowed to stay. They had no objections. Then Les asked if it might upset Kroon.

"Who cares if he's upset?" Scottie said. "This bloke obviously doesn't get on too well with Kroon, and no-one can blame him for that. In my opinion he's making the right decision. Let him stay."

He had introduced himself as Private Smit Tonsea Matoengkas. No-one seemed to know whether the 'Smit' was a surname or perhaps a Dutch nickname he had picked up. He seemed reluctant to talk about it. There was speculation that he might have a Dutch father, but as Scottie said, "he doesn't look at all Eurasian". In his green Dutch uniform, topped off with a Junglegreen cap, he looked pure Javanese: small, dark and wiry. But he smiled a lot and insisted that he would be very happy to stay with them. Everybody, including Arthur, seemed equally happy to have him. They nicknamed him Smit.

One of the early surprises at the new camp, which they christened 'The Cabbage Patch', was the arrival of 'Locky' and 'Lightning', the prisoners they had met months previously in the first guerilla camp.

"Jesus," Bomber exclaimed when he saw them being led into the camp, under guard, with one other prisoner, "I'd forgotten about these buggers. I'd have bet quids that they'd copped it ages ago."

"Yeah," Bluey said. "I wonder why they've been kept alive."

Since the two men they had seen garotted in May, there had been three more executions during June. Two had been Chinese and one Malay, all bayoneted for 'crimes against the people': armed robbery in the Parit Sulong area. In July a prisoner had been taken on suspicion of being a traitor, but he'd been freed after an investigation. Now, to see Locky and Lightning again was a surprise to them. They had come to accept the fact that 'justice' in the jungle was summary and swift. There must be some unusual circumstance, they thought, for these two men to have survived so long. The three men were put into one of the Sakai huts and an armed guard was placed outside it.

The following day, the third prisoner was to be brought to trial. He had evidently been a senior Chinese employee on a rubber estate. He was in his mid-forties, portly, conservative and relatively affluent in his appearance. It was alleged that he had a number of spies working for him, finding the location of various Chinese guerilla camps in the area. When he got the information, he would relay it, for substantial sums of money, to the Japanese authorities.

The trial was delayed because LQ had to leave the camp for three or four days, but as soon as he returned, the court was assembled and Locky and Lightning were brought out to witness it. It was a short, sharp affair. The man denied every charge, but there were other Chinese witnesses, including two women whose husbands had been killed, according to their testimony, because of the prisoner's treachery. Their evidence against him was damning.

He was convicted and sentenced to death. The 'disposal squad', as the executioners were called, would be Bomber, Roy and four of the Chinese guerillas. The selection was made by LQ and two other guerilla leaders. Both Bomber and Roy protested but, as LQ put it to them, "It is an honour to execute our enemies. It will be regarded as cowardly if you refuse." Whether they liked it or not, the Allied soldiers were told that they would have to take turns in participating in the execution of convicted traitors.

There was some discussion about the execution method. Some were in favour of garotting, but bayoneting was selected again as it was clearly quicker and easier, though no less horrifying or painful for the victim. Both Bomber and Roy did their job, but they were badly shaken by the experience. They left the scene of the execution quickly and Roy would not speak to anyone for almost two days.

Two nights later, almost certainly as a direct result of having witnessed the trial and execution of the Chinese traitor, Locky and Lightning made a bid for freedom and escaped. Gaje was on guard when, around midnight, the two prisoners burst out of the door of the hut, knocking him to the ground, and ran into the jungle. A terrific commotion followed as people ran up and down the jungle tracks trying to find the two escapees. But because of the inky blackness of the moonless night, they had no success.

At first light in the morning, their tracks were discovered leading across a creek and heading north. Arthur and Les and two Chinese followed the tracks, which began to circle around the camp and then began heading south, but the country became more difficult and they lost the tracks. Search parties continued the hunt all day, many of them going very far afield, and the word was spread amongst friendly Chinese living in the rubber estates beyond the jungle.

At about four-thirty in the afternoon, four rifle shots were heard from the south and, not long after, a runner arrived in the camp, not with news of Locky and Lightning, but of a huge seladang that had been shot. During the next twenty-four hours, attention was divided between searching for the two escapees and getting the enormous quantities of meat from the seladang back to camp. Without refrigeration, there was far too much for them to eat before it went off, so three large loads were given to Chinese employees living on the nearest rubber estate. It was dangerous for them to take it, but all of them were eager to accept.

Two days after the escape, Locky was recaptured and brought back to camp by two Chinese rubber estate employees armed with shotguns. The two prisoners had been sleeping in a drain. Awoken by three Chinese, they tried again to escape. Locky was held, but Lightning succeeded in getting away. Later, he had gone to a house and asked for food and, while drinking a second cup of rice broth, saw his pursuers through the window as they came towards the house. He bolted through the back door and began climbing a hill at the rear of the house. He was chased by the men and, about a mile from the town of Pagoh, although shot several times, managed to elude them. The following morning he was found wandering around by the boundary of the estate, in a daze because of his wounds. He was killed on the spot by several rifle shots.

In the camp, Gaje was reprimanded for allowing the two prisoners to escape. A meeting was held to decide his punishment. For a while, the Allied soldiers all feared that Gaje might be singled out for exemplary treatment and that his punishment would be severe. But LQ and CSP decided that all that was necessary was for him to have his rifle confiscated for a few days.

Five days after his initial escape, Locky was put on trial. Whatever reasons the guerillas had for keeping him and Lightning alive all those weeks and months were no longer valid. By attempting to escape, they had settled their own case. Guilty or not of whatever previous crime, Locky was now guilty of escape. He was sentenced to death.

LQ requested that the Allied soldiers send some of their members to accompany the execution party. Arthur, Les and Bluey were nominated. They followed as Locky was taken, stumbling and tripping, a hundred yards or so along a track to a point where, in a small clearing, a grave had been dug. Until this point he appeared resigned to his death, saying nothing, showing no signs of emotion. But now, as he stood in front of the grave with his hands tied behind his back, tears began to run down his face.

LQ held out a rifle to Arthur. "It is your honour this time."

Arthur looked at his two companions despairingly, contemplating for an instant the possibility of refusing the offer.

"Oh, Jesus," he said under his breath as he took the weapon and spent a minute or so checking it over. The thought kept running through his mind that he didn't really want to kill Locky. True, the man had put the entire camp in danger by escaping. Even if he didn't intend to disclose the camp's whereabouts to the Japanese, if they ever got him, they had ways of extracting details like that. But Arthur and the others had quite liked Locky. He thought back to their early meetings in the first camp, before they had all been separated, and remembered that he had enjoyed his discussions with the young man.

Arthur stepped up behind the man as he stood in front of the grave. Although he still said nothing, Locky was shaking violently. Arthur raised his rifle, pointing it at the back of Locky's head. The small crowd of Chinese stood around, watching and waiting silently. Suddenly Locky dropped to his knees with a soft moan and Arthur was momentarily distracted. He lowered the rifle to the back of the man's head again and fired.

15

ON THE MORNING OF 2 September, Arthur and Bomber had their first success with their new ratcatcher. A storekeeper from a nearby kampong had brought two or three into the camp and Arthur, Bomber and Bluey had set it up the night before using a small piece of fish as bait. It was simply an oversized mouse-trap with a very powerful spring that would have easily re-moved the finger of anyone handling it carelessly.

Their first catch was a big, fat, brown rat which lay in the trap with its neck broken. They immediately skinned it and took it to Slim and Shorty to cook up with the evening meal. Because they had been the ones that provided it, Arthur, Bluey and Bomber were given most of the flesh of the animal, while the rest of it--the bones and innards--went into a soup, with those of one other rat that had been caught, to be fed to some of the camp's sick. They set the traps regularly and, although they did not always succeed, they seemed able to average a rat for dinner at least once or twice a week until the local rat population diminished to zero.

With the vegetable patch beginning to produce, the meals in the new camp were, for a while, of very reasonable standard. At times they were able to supplement their vegetarian diet with some roast monkey and, on one occasion, a goat and even a large tortoise which the Chinese found wandering around in the jungle. They roasted it in its shell and what remained, after the evening meal, was curried for breakfast the next day.

It was, however, mainly rice and vegetables that sustained them. There seemed to be ample supplies of dried peas, flour and coconuts which were brought in from outside, but as the vegetable garden, 'the cabbage patch' as they called it, began producing, the range of vegetables increased considerably.

The long beans were growing well and they would crop some of the potato leaves, to eat with their rice and in soups, long before the potatoes themselves were ready to pick. The first cucumbers were picked only thirty days after the seeds had gone in. Slim and Shorty began to develop real kitchen expertise and every now and then would produce hot curry puffs for the camp as a 'late supper' which they would have with coffee.

They also revived the practice of regular concerts, the pattern of which was invariably adhered to. They would begin with speeches and exhortations from LQ and other Communist Party leaders. These would be followed by some songs from the Chinese, which were nearly always about patriotism and revolution, and then songs from the Allied soldiers which were more light-hearted. Then they would often have a small play. The plots generally contained fairly strong propaganda, such as Japanese soldiers raping and killing Chinese civilians, followed by Chinese guerillas attacking and wiping out a Japanese installation. Alternatively, it might revolve around a complex piece of treachery on the part of a civilian who is caught, tried and executed by the party. To Arthur and the others, there never seemed to be much humour in the plays, although very occasionally a comment or action by one of the participants would bring a sudden burst of laughter from the audience.

It was during these periods at the 'cabbage patch' camp, when food was reasonably plentiful and the concerts provided some regular entertainment, that Arthur often felt life in the jungle could be endured for quite a long time. The only trouble, he thought, was that nothing ever lasts for long. Something always turns up to change it.

And, as if to fufill his fears, life in the latter stages of 1942 became increasingly difficult for them all. It was not the Japanese that caused it, or the food, but illness. They had all had minor health problems during the preceding months, which was understandable considering the conditions under which they were living, but the 'cabbage patch' camp was amongst the best they'd been in. And yet, within little more than a month of settling in there, they seemed to be hit with all sorts of ailments.

Old Tom Percival was laid up with severe tonsillitis. For several days he couldn't eat, couldn't talk and was running a high temperature. Then Bluey began complaining of bad pains in his back. He came back from his turn on guard duty one day to get a greatcoat because he was shivering, and then was laid low with fever for days. Scottie was next, as well as a few of the Chinese-all with fever. They supposed it was malaria, although nobody seemed to be sure. Arthur had been reasonably surprised that malaria hadn't hit them more severely much earlier. From the time of their first arrival in Malaya, right up until the battle at Bakri, there had been quinine tablets to take, but in the jungle they became a thing of the past. A few came into the camp from time to time, but never enough for everyone. Yet, despite the lack of quinine, there had been very few outbreaks of malaria.

Arthur was convinced that if they stayed at the 'cabbage patch' camp, things would have improved, but by late September they had to move once more. Again, it was not a great distance, only five or six miles, but the move was complicated and arduous, involving several trips back and forth between the two camps in order to transfer all of the food and equipment.

LQ, when pressed to explain the reason for this particular move, assured them that it was not because of any new threat from the Japanese but because there was a possibility that their food supplies would be cut if they remained. He never explained how this might happen, or why it had not been considered before they went to 'cabbage patch' in the first place.

Heavy rains during the night before the first transfer of supplies had made the track wet and the going very difficult. All of them, except for Bluey and Tom, who were still sick, shifted a large amount of stores to a deserted house deep in a rubber plantation, about two-thirds of the way to the new camp. They then returned to 'cabbage patch' for the night, with instructions to be ready to set off with the next load of supplies at six-thirty in the morning. But heavy rain delayed the first group's departure until about 10 am. In the early afternoon, Arthur and the rest of the Europeans followed in the second group, arriving at the house footsore and weary, after making a long detour because of flooded creeks, at about 4 pm. Guards were posted as they bedded down for the night in and around the old house. All were up again at five in the morning for a less arduous trek, of about an hour, through the jungle to the new camp.

"Not as good as 'cabbage patch'," Bomber remarked as they made their first survey of the site.

"No," Arthur agreed, "but still a hell of a lot better than some of the places we've been."

They had all been reluctant to leave 'cabbage patch' which had been relatively comfortable and easy to live in. It was sad for them, too, to leave such a successful garden which had begun to provide them with substantial quantities of vegetables, although LQ seemed to think that they could still use the old plot as well as planting vegetables at their new camp.

"We will send food-carrying parties back there from time to time to crop the vegetables and bring them here," he told them.

"We'd have to be careful in case the Nips find the place and start to keep a watch on it," Jock put in.

"Of course," LQ smiled, "but I think it is possible."

LQ's plan was eventually put into practice, but because of the distance between the two camps, no-one went regularly and there was an unavoidable change in the food they ate. Although it was often difficult to pinpoint which variations in their diet had any effect, Arthur began to realise that, once some sort of balance was achieved and a reasonable level of health maintained for a short period, sometimes only a few weeks, then even the most subtle change could bring about a marked deterioration in their health. For several, including Arthur, it was beri-beri that seemed to sit 'waiting in the wings' for their vitamin levels to become un-balanced. When that happened, first their feet and then their legs would become badly swollen.

It had affected Arthur once before, when they had first joined the guerillas, and now it came back with a vengeance. It began with his left foot which, within three days of the first symptoms, had swollen so badly and was so painful he found walking difficult. Bomber suggested he should see a Chinese doc-tor who had just joined the camp.

"But what is he a doctor of?" Arthur asked. "Is he a regu-lar doctor, or a herbalist, or what? I mean, he could be a bloody doctor of music as far as we know."

"Well, you won't know unless you go and see him, will you?" Bomber answered.

The Chinese doctor was a herbalist. He recommended the leaves of a jungle plant which Arthur was to make up into a paste and apply to his foot. Arthur told him that he was highly qualified at making pastes and, on leaving the doctor, collected a bundle of the leaves to begin the process once more, with not much hope that it would achieve the required results.

The paste had practically no effect and his condition gradually worsened so that he could not walk at all. Bluey made him a pair of crutches which helped for a while, but when both feet were affected, he was unable to use the crutches. He felt as if his feet were bags filled with water, which is almost exactly what they were. If left unchecked, beri-beri has the effect of 'filling up' the body with fluid, starting at the feet, gradually bloating the whole body until the lungs fill and the victim drowns.

As Arthur's legs became more swollen, he found he was able to press his finger into the flesh of his foot to a depth of almost an inch. When he removed his finger, the indentation would remain for up to forty minutes. At the same time, he began to develop what he thought was a boil on his left leg. He soon realised, though, that it was a tropical ulcer. His left leg, which was the most badly affected, had now turned an ugly, deep purple colour and was causing such pain that Arthur found it almost impossible to sleep. He returned to the doctor in desperation.

This time the doctor decided on a different approach. He took off his herbalist's cap and, producing a box of needles, became an acupuncturist. He put five of them in the offending leg. Apart from almost sending Arthur crazy with pain, it seemed to have no effect. It was not like lancing a boil, where the evil stuff beneath the skin is released. Arthur's leg remained unchanged.

It was a depressing time for him, not helped by the fact that there seemed to be continual rain, not only during the day but all night as well and, during the early hours of the morning, it often became very cold. The only things that helped to raise his morale during this period were monopoly and cards. The players would sit in Arthur and Bomber's shelter as the rain poured down in sheets all around, and play for hours on end, using a dog-eared, homemade pack of cards. Monopoly was the most popular, mainly because it was possible for more people to play and the games often lasted for the whole day or even longer. The Chinese were also always keen to play.

They were fortunate that this was a period in which not a great deal happened to disturb the routine. There appeared to be no imminent danger of Japanese attacks, although there were persistent rumours coming in from informers and agents that the Japanese were planning a series of major campaigns to completely flush out and destroy the Communist guerillas. For the time being, however, all was quiet. Five elephants generated the only excitement by tramping along a narrow track near the camp one night, startling everyone with the fear that the Japanese were coming through the jungle with a couple of bulldozers.

Within a few weeks, for no apparent reason, Arthur's beri-beri began to ease and he found he could walk again, with pain and difficulty at first and then, gradually, with more ease. The tropical ulcer remained, though. Several other members of the camp were also suffering from similar infections. Arthur's was about one inch in diameter and a quarter-inch deep, just above his ankle. He kept treating it with herbal pastes, hoping to keep it in check. Although he had never yet seen such a case, there were stories of ulcers which had become so bad that the sufferer's leg had had to be amputated. He didn't want that to happen.

Many in the camp were also down with fever. Ah Liong's baby was once again sick. He had never fully recovered from his previous illness and, to Arthur and the others, did not seem to be a very strong baby. Not long after their arrival at the new camp, he began to run a very high fever. He ate practically nothing and looked very pale. Everyone feared that he would not last unless the fever could be broken and the child could start eating again. The doctor examined him and administered what herbal remedies he had at his disposal, but to no avail. For almost a month the child lingered in a pitiable state. He made a couple of rallies which, for brief periods, gave Arthur and the others hope that he might pull through. And then he died.

Ah Liong was distraught. She was only a very young woman and, since the murder of her husband, the child had been everything to her. When the baby had been well, she had often spent many hours sitting with him in her arms, talking to the Europeans as she tried to improve her English.

While the baby was ill, she had become quiet and reclusive and neither Arthur nor any of the other Allied soldiers had seen her for many days prior to the baby's death.

After the child's burial, Ah Liong began to leave the camp in the morning to spend the day alone in the jungle, returning at night only to sleep. She followed this routine for almost a week until LQ, sensing that something should be done, gradually began to place some demands on her time, requiring her to perform a number of tasks. Slowly, as she became more occupied with the jobs, she began to return to normal, although for a long time she remained quiet and subdued, avoiding, if possible, contact with people.

During the first few weeks after leaving 'cabbage patch', they heard, along with the rumours of possible Japanese campaigns against the jungle camps, many new stories of Japanese atrocities. They included terrible acts against captured guerillas and Allied servicemen, but also against Chinese and Malay civilians.

One story told to Arthur and his comrades involved a group of Malay forestry workers and their families. Their kampong, of about two hundred inhabitants, elected a spokesman to go to the Japanese to explain to them that, under the Japanese food distribution regulations, they were not getting enough to eat and that something would have to be done to help them. The Japanese officials told the spokesman to return to his kampong and then bring everyone in the village back with him. He did so and the Japanese questioned them one by one. Some said they had no food, others said they had very little. Those who said they had no food-about half of them-were moved to one side. The Japanese then shot and bayoneted them all to death. They then told the rest to return to their village and to get by with what they had or face the same fate as the others.

On at least one other occasion, however, large-scale killings were precipitated by a guerilla action. In Johore Bharu, the Communist Party used to buy potatoes secretly from Malay and Chinese growers to supply several camps in Johore State. At one stage the growers refused to sell to the Party buyers because they could get a better price for their produce across the causeway in Singapore. In retaliation, the guerillas raided the growers, as well as a couple of Japanese installations, for food supplies. After the Japanese learnt the full story, they killed six hundred Chinese in Johore Bharu.

Another story told of the fate of an Allied soldier caught in the Yong Peng area. The Japanese had beheaded him with a samurai sword and stuck his head on a pole in the town as a warning of what awaited those who remained in the jungle and those who helped them. A similar story related to them during this period involved six Allied soldiers caught in the Batu Pahat region. Not only had they been killed by the Japanese, but they had had their noses cut off. The messenger who told the story did not know whether it had been done before or after they had died. Either way, the story was sufficiently disgusting to make it somehow all the more believable.

They took some satisfaction, however, in news of Japanese misfortunes. There was a report of a shipload of wounded Japanese that had arrived at Batu Pahat, possibly from Borneo, where Japanese newspapers admitted there was heavy fighting. Another report in from Malacca told of several trainloads of dead Japanese soldiers, all packed in ice, arriving from either the north or the south, it wasn't known, to be loaded into a large ship which left, presumably for Japan.

On one occasion during this time, LQ arrived back in the camp after a brief sortie into the town of Chaah. While he was talking to Arthur, Bomber and Bluey, Arthur noticed that his watch was two hours fast.

"Your watch is wrong," Arthur told him.

"No," he laughed. "There is nothing wrong with it. This is Tokyo time. The Japanese insist that Malaya also works on Tokyo time, so everybody has to set their watches to it. If you are found wearing a watch with a different time, it will be confiscated and you could be sent to prison."

"But that means sunrise in Malaya is not until 9 am," Arthur said incredulously.

LQ shrugged, "That is how they want it."

His other news that day, however, was more important and more relevant to their lives. He had learnt that over three

242

thousand Japanese soldiers had arrived in the Batu Pahat area with the specific task of combing the jungles for the guerilla camps and eradicating them. This was in mid-October. Over the next few days, several more reports came in that tended to confirm the theory that the Japanese were indeed planning major operations, although it seemed they would not be confined to this area. Information from Batu Pahat indicated that only five hundred had arrived and that the figure of three thousand was the total for the state of Johore.

For two days after receiving this information, they heard heavy explosions coming from the west, many miles away. They could not be absolutely sure, but the regularity of the explosions made them reasonably certain they were hearing some kind of sustained artillery barrage. A day later, they learnt from LQ, who had left camp to find out what was going on, that the bombardment was taking place about twenty miles away near the town of Gresik. The Japanese were shelling a small piece of jungle territory between Gresik and Tangkar and anyone coming out of the jungle was stopped and searched. If they had proper passes, they were put to one side for further questioning. Those who had no cards were taken off somewhere else, where, according to LQ, they would be submitted to interrogation under torture and then put to death.

As each day passed, and more and more reports came in of Japanese troops arriving in several of the small towns in the immediate area, a noticeable degree of tension began building in the camp. Three truckloads arrived at Pagoh and there were others at Yong Peng and Kluang.

Everybody in the camp was told on several occasions that they must all be ready to move at a moment's notice. Arthur was thankful that his legs had improved enough that, in the case of any emergency, at least he'd be able to walk. Both Scottie and Bluey's fevers had passed also, so most of them were in a reasonable state to travel if it suddenly became necessary.

And on 20 October it did. Arthur, Bomber, Gaje and Bluey were sitting down to an evening meal, cross-legged on the floor of their shelter, with bowls of fairly colourless reubon, ubi and rice in their laps, when a messenger came rushing into the camp with word that a force of Japanese soldiers was on its way towards the camp. It was at that moment, he said, less than two miles away.

"Hurry! Hurry!" he kept shouting to everyone in both Chinese and Malay.

No-one needed any urging. Within seconds the camp was like an anthill that had been disturbed by someone poking it with a stick. People ran in every direction, collecting whatever could be carried. Several escape routes from the camp had long since been planned. The one Arthur and his friends took was almost invisible from the camp itself. It led up a track to the rear of the camp and then turned sharply up a very steep hill. It would have been a difficult path to follow without anything to carry, but it was particularly hard-going with a heavy load. Everyone was carrying something, but many of the Chinese whose specific camp function was to act as porters for food and equipment were carrying enormous loads and they were close to exhaustion by the time the group arrived, over two hours later, at a position where they stopped and bedded down for the night.

The weather was cold and windy and Arthur, Bomber, Bluey and Gaje all huddled together by a tree trunk to keep warm. Arthur had a vivid dream that he was at home, telling his mother about the whole situation as if it were in the past and the war was over. He had returned to Melbourne, safe and sound and was sitting down in the family's lounge room in Coburg and talking about the jungle and the camps, and this particular escape from the Japanese. It seemed a good sign, he thought, when he woke. Maybe it would come true and, one day, he really would sit down in that old, comfortable chair in the corner and tell it all, just as he'd dreamt it.

In the morning they were all packed and ready to move again, although no-one was quite sure where. Three men were sent back down to check the camp, while another was sent to Pagoh to find out what was happening there. He returned from the town eventually to say that there were at least four truck- loads of Japanese plus a huge contingent of bicycle troops there.

By the middle of the day, everyone was hungry and thirsty, as well as tired. A food party that had gone out earlier returned with some potatoes which were eaten later in the afternoon-- one or two each, with no water. They would have to be rationed, LQ informed them, to only half a cup of water each per day from now on.

"There's no bloody way we can stay here," Bomber said as they settled in for a second night. "No water, no food, no space. We'll have to move somewhere."

The night was even colder than the previous one. Gaje lent one of his blankets to Arthur, who had none. It made some difference, but everyone was still cold and miserable. The rude shelters of their last camp seemed, in retrospect, like luxury. During the night they heard more explosions in the distance but had no idea where they were coming from or what they were.

In the morning, they learnt from LQ that their camp had not been attacked or searched by the Japanese. Apparently they had not found it, but it was still considered too dangerous for them to return. There were at least eight truckloads of Japanese in Pagoh-over three hundred soldiers. They could be there for some time, according to the information coming in, because food trucks had also been seen arriving there to supply the troops. Their own evening meal on that third night was one cup of rice each.

Another night waiting, not knowing what might happen. LQ had disappeared again, late in the afternoon, and was still not back by the following morning. Arthur asked one of the carriers where he had gone and was told that he and some others were looking for a new campsite.

During the morning, a runner came up to their encampment with the news that there were still more truckloads of Japanese soldiers arriving in Pagoh. He told them that the explosions heard on the second night had been caused by Chinese guerillas who had thrown some grenades into a group of Japanese soldiers and then run for it, disappearing in the jungle. In retaliation the Japanese burnt down seven houses, having forced twenty-one people into two of the houses before setting them alight. The messenger also said that they had taken several people suspected of collaboration with the guerillas, buried them up to their necks in the ground and them mounted guards over them to let them die slowly.

The following morning, after heavy rain had thoroughly soaked them during the night, it was decided that they should

return temporarily to a site near the camp they had left, to prepare for a bigger move shortly. Not long after 9 am, they began
sliding and stumbling down the muddy trail, for about half an
hour, until they finally reached the old camp, which was a surprisingly welcome sight for them all. They bathed in the stream
and felt much revived by it, even though they knew they would
not be staying long. To plan the next move they shifted a few
hundred yards up the course of the stream to a small clearing
which was thought to be more secure.

In the midst of constructing temporary lean-to shelters
in this new spot, there was brief panic. A runner came in saying
that seven truckloads of Japanese were ready to leave Pagoh and
they were believed to be heading for the jungle verge near the
guerilla camp. But after everyone was told to be ready to fight
and run, news came that the trucks had driven off in another direction.

They relaxed again and, over the next few days, continued to work on the new shelters. Even though it was difficult to
be enthusiastic about it, as they all knew they would be moving
again at any moment, the rain provided considerable incentive
for them. It was falling heavily almost every night, and often during the day. Fortunately, during this time, they were able to eat
reasonably well again as a carrying-party had been sent off to the
'cabbage patch' camp to bring back several large loads of vegetables which had been growing and producing beautifully in their
absence.

There were sufficient vegetables growing now to warrant
sending a gathering-party back there every couple of days and
this LQ decided to do. The only drawbacks were the distance (it
took at least two hours in each direction) and the weather. The
rain seemed to be almost continuous, night and day.

On the evening of 1 November, after a day of continuous
rain, Arthur and Bomber were just settling down for the night in
their shelter, which was not very successful in keeping out the
rain, when the whole thing started to move.

"Christ!" shouted Bomber, "Did you see the wall move?"

"No," Arthur said, sitting up, "but I felt it."

Within minutes, there were no doubts left in either of
their minds. One side of the shelter was beginning to move.

"Come on. We better get out before the flamin' thing falls on top of us," Arthur shouted, throwing his blanket to one side.

Before they could do anything else, though, the whole shelter collapsed around them, covering them in dripping wet banana and attap leaves, bamboo poles and mud.

"God Almighty!" Bomber cried as they struggled out from under the mess. "What a bastard! Now what are we going to do?"

The rain continued to bucket down, drenching them both to the skin. Suddenly, there was a terrible crashing noise off to their left, in the jungle. "just a bloody tree falling," Bomber muttered. "But let's get away from here. Maybe Bluey and Gaje can fit us in."

Picking up their rifles and whatever other belongings they could find in the darkness, they moved off to Bluey and Gaje's shelter, about fifty yards away, to spend the rest of the night cold, wet and miserably uncomfortable, but at least under cover. Before daybreak they heard another six large trees falling in the jungle nearby. The heavy rains had weakened their roots, allowing them to topple over.

In the morning, the rain stopped and by 9 am the sun broke through the clouds. It was enough to prompt Arthur and Bomber, bedraggled and wet, to stagger out into the small clearing in an attempt to dry the clothes they were wearing. As they stood in the sunlight, steam rose from them as if they were on fire, and for a while they thought they might be able to complete the drying process. Soon, though, more heavy clouds darkened the sky and it was once again raining. The two men shook their heads in disgust and were setting about the task of rebuilding their wrecked shelter when LQ walked up to them to advise them not to bother.

"It will be a waste of energy," he said, "I think we will be leaving tomorrow."

For a moment, Bomber and Arthur said nothing. What was there to say? Moving had become part of their life. They had no choice.

"Where to?" Arthur asked.

"Another camp. But this time, a long way."

"How far?"

"At least two days, maybe more. We must go soon. We have new information from Pagoh. The Japanese are back there. There are many more in Muar and we believe they will continue looking for us. They know we are in here, so it is only a matter of time before they get to us."

16

THERE WAS VERY LITTLE THAT Arthur and Bomber had to do to prepare themselves. They had their rifles, ammunition and a few personal things to carry. But the main loads consisted of food which was divided, as equally as possible, amongst everyone. They were also given prepared meals which the cooks had been working on since the previous evening. This ration, of a plate of cooked potatoes and six mugs full of uncooked rice for each person, was intended to last for the whole trek to the new camp.

At 10.45 am a runner came puffing into the camp with news that a force of Malay police had arrived at the nearby rubber estate and that Japanese soldiers were also on the way.

The advance guides were sent off immediately and the camp began to follow them, moving slowly in a long column.

At first, passing through a plantation of young rubber trees, they found that the going was easy. Then they moved into a rubber estate of more mature trees which had obviously just been tapped and they had to exercise more care. In most cases the plantations were badly neglected, which was generally better because it meant there was little likelihood of meeting people. Sometimes they would leave the plantations to cut through sections of jungle, although most of the time their guides managed to find and follow an ill-defined path. According to a rather battered compass, which Jock Smylie had managed to acquire and which he consulted regularly, they were heading in a north-easterly direction.

The trail they followed led past a great many wild jelutung trees, similar to chicle trees from which the sticky sap is collected to make chewing gum. Many of the trees showed signs of having been tapped. Arthur and Bomber thought that perhaps their guide may have been an illegal tree-tapper, because he knew the route so well.

By mid-afternoon they had been going for four hours without a break, most of the time in a northerly direction. Arthur's pack felt like a leaden weight on his back and both he and others in the group were showing signs of weariness. But there was no indication that they might be stopping. Fortunately, there were no large hills for them to climb and they plodded on until around 4.30 pm when they came to a clearing in the jungle not far from the edge of the plantation. They ate a meal--one or two potatoes, washed down with water-then, after guards were posted out some distance from the rest of the group, they bedded down for the night, finding what shelter they could under bushes and trees.

Fortunately there was no rain so they were able to stay dry during the night, rising at six to breakfast on bowls of bubor, a rice porridge which the cooks had been preparing since 4 am. They were on their way at 7 am, once more following the curved and twisted tracks that seemed to be designed to go wherever the jelutung trees grew.

Soon they came to an old timber track which had been used by elephants. There were huge footprints and quite recent droppings along the trail and at one stage they heard an elephant trumpeting in the jungle not far away. Although the going was no easier than the previous day, somehow they didn't seem to be as tired as they had been then. Even by the middle of the day, after five hours of walking, Arthur felt no qualms at the prospect of covering the same distance in the afternoon.

Shortly after midday, they came to a small river which provided a temporary barrier to their path and they decided to stop for a meal-break. A fire was lit and some more bubor was prepared. For some reason the Chinese, or at least a small group of them, broke into a brawl over the food and how it was being shared out. Bomber, Arthur and Smit, the young Javanese, stood by in amazement, watching.

"What the hell are they going on about?" Bomber said. "Bloody disgusting. There's plenty of bubor there for everyone."

And there was. They waited until everyone had been given their ration, and there was still plenty left over. Arthur and the others left them all, still muttering and scowling, and went down to the river for a swim and a brief sleep in the sun. Arthur often found that, even when lying on a rock or on bare ground, he could drop into the deepest of sleeps. He found he enjoyed these instant dozes as a sort of release, an escape to a different world in which none of the troubles and hardships of their real existence were present. They must all have needed rest because none of them moved until after 3 pm, by which time heavy clouds had begun to gather.

Moving off again, the group crossed the river a little further up at a point where large boulders provided an easy crossing. They were led off into the jungle by their guides, again following a rough track which all but a trained eye would easily have missed. In less than an hour, the clouds had built up into massive thunderheads. The sky had become dark and was intermittently lit by flashes of lightning, followed by distant rumblings of thunder.

The order was given to stop and make camp before the rain came, so everyone, or nearly everyone, set about constructing shelters. Bomber and Bluey started building a shelter for two, while Arthur and Smit hurriedly worked on a separate lean-to, completing it just as the rain began to fall in torrents. As soon as Arthur and Smit had settled in away from the rain, two Chinese splashed up to the shelter and dived in with them, squeezing four into a space just big enough for two, and immediately began to complain because there was not enough room.

Arthur and Smit were both stunned. The two men were 'soldiers' they had not seen before. They had arrived in the old camp from the Batu Pahat district only a couple of days before the camp moved off on their current trek. Neither of them said anything at first, despite the fact that the manner of the two Chinese men was quite aggressive. But when one of them tried to take over Arthur's 'tikka', the woven mat he used to lie on the ground, he could not restrain himself.

"Listen, who do you blokes think you are? Coming in here, pushing your weight around. Why the hell don't you build your own bloody shelter?"

There was no way of knowing how much they understood, but they clearly knew he wasn't happy. One of them, who had an ugly scar running down his face, snarled, "You English can no longer speak. When this war finish, this is our country, not yours."

"Listen, mate," Arthur snapped back. "First off, I'm not English! I'm bloody Australian. Understand that? Australian. There's a big difference. And secondly, as far as I'm concerned, when this war's over, you can have your country. But just don't come around here blaming me for what the flamin' poms have done to you--or come in here pushing your bloody weight around. Now piss off!"

Arthur pushed him out into the rain while Smit, who had so far remained silent, tapped the other one on the back and motioned for him to go too. Arthur felt that the situation could have become nasty. The two men were obviously a couple of rough customers and, if it came to an all-in brawl, they could more than likely have handled themselves well. As it was, they moved off into the rain, swearing back at Arthur and Smit in Chinese, while Arthur called after them, "And just remember that, mate," he tapped himself on the chest, "Australian, not British!"

After they had gone, Arthur and Smit rearranged themselves and, when the rain eased, managed to light a small fire in front of their shelter to dry out their clothes. There were a few more showers during the night, but fortunately they were able to stay reasonably dry under the shelter and to sleep quite soundly until they were woken at 6 am.

They packed immediately and took to the trail without breakfast. It was still dark, but the trail was not difficult to follow, apart from roots and other obstacles, including a number of fallen trees, which barred their way. They were travelling, as usual, in single file and after a couple of hours word was passed back from the front of the column that they were entering what was known as the Hutan Simpan, or the Forest of Chaah. It seemed to Arthur no different from the type of jungle they had been passing through for days, but they were told that at some stage in the past, this whole area, a large tract of territory around the town of Chaah, had been declared a reserve by the Sultan of Johore and in this forest no rubber planting, timber felling or cultivation of any kind was allowed.

Eventually, a little after eleven, they arrived at a clearing in the jungle which had quite obviously been a camp like theirs. LQ came around to talk to them and told them that, for the time being, this would be the end of their journey.

Over the next few days there were several more incidents to strain the relationship between the Europeans and the Chinese in the camp. A supply of potatoes, cauliflower and other vegetables came in, but also some tobacco, which they had all been waiting for. Again, the Chinese were issued first and there was none left for the Europeans. Les Taylor talked about it with LQ, who, of all of the Chinese, seemed the most sympathetic towards the Allied soldiers. The following evening LQ called the whole camp together for a lecture in an effort to try to heal the rift that was fast developing between the two groups.

"Whatever the differences there may have been in the past, or at present, between the Chinese people in Malaya and the British, or European people, we must push them aside and forget them," he told the assembled group. He had spoken first in Chinese and then in English, but in both versions he was stern and without humour. Waving his hands and gesticulating sharply, it was as if he were a teacher admonishing his students. "We must be friends, allies, to fight against the Japanese who have not only occupied our homelands in Malaya and raped and killed our families, but for years have been destroying our Motherland. They are our enemies and we cannot fight them if we fight amongst ourselves. All are equal here. Anyone who disobeys this law will be severely dealt with."

LQ's comments seemed to cool things down considerably and Arthur and the others were able to settle into the new site with less aggravation than had been apparent before. They had developed a system by which they could quite quickly and easily make themselves comfortable and keep dry, even in the heaviest of rain, so that moving on to another camp was no longer a great worry to them. Arthur felt that this must be the way that gypsies or Aborigines approached life--one place was as good as the next, and if they had to keep moving, then so be it. As it happened, they only stayed three weeks at this camp.

In the beginning there seemed to be a good supply of food available and Scottie, in one of his rare periods of generosity, gave Arthur and Bomber a few small issues of tobacco. There was another camp nearby which LQ told them was the headquarters of the 3rd Independent Guerilla Company. The camp had a radio, so they began to receive regular news reports once more. It was a combination of both Allied and Japanese news, so they had to take the often quite different reports of the same event and make up their own minds which to accept. In any event, they took the attitude that whether it was true or false, it was just good to hear something from the outside world.

The news they received included stories of fierce fighting in Russia, slight Allied gains in North Africa, French workers sabotaging munitions and aircraft factories and heavy British bombing of Germany. Closer to home, they heard of fighting in northern Australia, Japanese reinforcements being sent from Malaya to India and China, and local forces of Tamils and Malays being formed throughout Malaya to guard the roads at night.

They also learnt of some of the increased difficulties under which people outside in the villages and towns were now living. Anyone wishing to visit another place must first report to the local police station and advise them where he or she wanted to go, who would be seen there, why they wanted to go and how long they would be there. When they arrived at their destination, they must report to the local police station there and advise them of the same details. Then, upon their return, they must report back to the first police station within the time originally allocated for their journey. There were also more horror stories of Japanese attacks on houses close to the edge of the jungle in the Muar area, which they had begun to burn down. Several people found wandering around without correct passes or satisfactory excuses had had their legs cut off, according to one story.

A week after their arrival at the temporary camp, their numbers were swelled by another group of eighteen men and one woman, all Chinese, who had arrived after a long trek from Bukit Kepong where they had been in a battle in which three Japanese had been killed. They came into the camp carrying a variety of arms: British .303 rifles, Japanese carbines, a Belgian rifle, a German Mauser and an assortment of sporting rifles. They were fed and told to settle in and to make shelters.

Sou Lim and two others arrived in the camp around this time. It had been many weeks since they had seen Sou Lim, who, as head of the 3rd Independent Guerilla Company, had a number of other camps under his charge as well. He told them that, for the time being, the headquarters of the company would stay at the other camp nearby, but that he would soon be needing six of the Europeans to help him with some projects. He would not elaborate, but said he would tell them all more 'shortly'. He also explained that the Party had increased the number of its local headquarters from five to ten in Johore and was forming two more.

During their brief stay at the temporary camp, there were a couple of bad scares which had them all packing up and scuttling up the mountainside at the back of the camp. The first was the result of a message which came in saying that Japanese troops were arriving at the kampong at Senahkung. Everybody in the camp, except the sick ones and Mac, who was acting as guard, moved up the hill. Jock was amongst the sick who stayed behind. He was down with a severe bout of fever and there was little that could be done except to hide him in the bushes off to one side of the camp and hope that he would not be discovered. Bomber, too, was ill with beri-beri. His legs and arms were swollen and sore and he had great trouble in climbing the steep sides of the mountain to the ridge which they followed some distance to an open space where they eventually spent the night.

The ridge was very steep on both sides of the track and they had long, open views to the south-west. It was a beautiful sight. The sun was setting and the whole of the western sky was aglow. Arthur felt like a bird in a cage, looking out at a world he could see, but not live in. The beauty of the scenery was soon forgotten, though, as darkness fell and they were beset by swarms of vicious mosquitoes which harassed them all to such an extent throughout the night that they got little sleep. In the morning, a runner came up to their position with the news that the scare had been a false alarm, so they all trudged back down the mountain.

A day or so later, Sou Lim again raised the issue of the six Europeans he needed for his as yet unnamed 'special projects'. They would join the headquarters camp, he said, and, although the camp was close by at the moment, it seemed, from the way he spoke, that they would move somewhere else before long. This meant that the Europeans would be separated on a more permanent basis.

In a meeting held on 14 November, Sou Lim explained that the balance of the Europeans not joining the headquarters camp would travel to a special 'weapons' camp which was being established closer to the coast. They were needed to help repair and refurbish weapons and to train the Chinese guerillas in their use. It was decided that Mac, Bluey, Les, Tom, Gaje and Smit would eventually go to the weapons camp, while Arthur, Bomber, Roy, Pete, Scottie and Jock, if he was well enough, would join the headquarters group at a new site to be decided. There was some dissension about the make-up of the groups and about the general concept of splitting up. Although there had been disagreements amongst them, generally they all got on with each other reasonably well and some felt they should stay together. Mac said that if there was going to be a split, he wanted to be with the headquarters group, but Sou Lim convinced him he was needed as the senior training officer in the weapons camp.

It was not until the last week in November that LQ advised Arthur's group to be ready for their move. Sou Lim had left some days previously, heading for the new camp. The site, according to LQ, "has the best water supply we have seen. But most importantly, we will be free from the constant danger of betrayal by Malay villagers."

Ever since their arrival at the camp near Senahkung village, there had been a continual feeling of insecurity. The Chinese were constantly concerned about traitors in the area. There were, LQ said, several untrustworthy people in the kampong, who, if they became aware of the camp's existence or occupation, might alert the Japanese.

The move to their new base would be a long and difficult one, through dangerous territory and lasting several days. LQ would not be coming with them, however, as he was going to take command of another camp. One of the other guerilla leaders, Ah Yen, would take them to the new campsite. Ah Yen had been, as far as Arthur could gauge, about number three in the camp hierarchy. He was about twenty-five years old, taller than most of the other guerillas, very ambitious and a stickler on Marxist ideology and dogma.

On the morning of 26 November, they were told that they should get ready to leave later in the afternoon and that for several nights they would travel only during darkness. Everyone was issued with one mug of rice each, three potatoes, a spoonful of ikan bilis (very small dried fish) and one and a half pancakes. They would be able to set off with full stomachs, though, as they would be given an evening meal before leaving.

Jock, however, was too sick to move. He was still down with fever and would have to stay with Mac and the others, due to move to a temporary camp near Bukit Kepong, some miles to the west, in a few days time. LQ told them that the two British soldiers, Bennett and Stewart, of whom they had heard many weeks earlier and to whom Arthur had written, were now at the Bukit Kepong camp. When Jock was better, the three of them would all be brought to the camp where Arthur's group was now heading.

Just as they were beginning to leave, at about 6.30 pm, a runner came in with some news from the Pagoh area. Evidently the Japanese had finally attacked the old 'cabbage patch' camp, subjecting it to heavy trench-mortar bombardment before sending in their forces...only to find no-one there. Everyone laughed and discussed the fact that it was encouraging to think that the Japanese intelligence was apparently so far out that they could still think the camp was occupied weeks after it had been vacated.

As Arthur and his companions collected their gear and started to move out, Mac, Bluey, Tom, Les, Gaje and Smit stood by to shake hands, say goodbye and wish them good luck. They all felt they would see each other again before long. Their experience over the past months, of being constantly on the move and changing camps, had given them all a flexibility and acceptance of the impermanence of almost everything they did, so the idea of separation was looked on as just a temporary situation. Although Arthur could not know it, all but two of the men with whom he was exchanging friendly goodbyes, he would never see again.

When they left the camp, the sky was overcast and the night soon became so dark that Arthur could hardly see his hand in front of his face. For a while, where the track was reasonably clear and familiar to some of the group at the head of the column, there were no problems. Sometimes, when they were crossing a small rubber plantation in which there was open ground between the trees, the going was relatively easy, but when they entered the jungle again, it became so dark that they had to tie themselves together with short pieces of rope.

The main guide had no light, but he was able to find the way to another rubber plantation through which they travelled quietly and quickly for some time until around 9 pm a large, dark shape loomed suddenly out of the blackness. It was an old wooden house. There were no lights showing, but it was apparently occupied by friendly Chinese as, after whispered conversations which Arthur and the others could just hear, a man emerged from the house with jugs of water, from which they drank eagerly, and which were passed down the line and then returned.

Moving on, they came shortly to Senahkung village and there everyone became doubly cautious, almost creeping on tiptoe, with hardly a sound being made. But even their best efforts were not sufficient. While passing close by two houses, a man came out into his yard with a flashlight which he waved towards the path. It fell on the faces of three or four of the group who were slinking along next to some shrubs. He gave an involuntary gasp and turned to move back to his house. Before he could reach it, two guerillas ran up to intercept him in order to make sure he made no further noise. They whispered urgently to him. He replied equally quickly and earnestly, also in a whisper. He was Chinese and he assured the men that he would say nothing. Apparently satisfied, the two guerillas melted back into the shadowy file that had continued passing by, while the man scurried back into his house, shutting the door behind him. He had had a narrow escape.

Not long after passing Senahkung, they entered another stretch of jungle and soon came to a small river. They found a point where a tree had been laid across the stream and the group began to cross it. Unfortunately it must have been rotten, because it broke in two while the second man was crossing it, catapulting him into the water. He struggled out on the far side and a search was begun for another crossing point. A place was eventually found further downstream, but they had been delayed considerably. The camp leaders were worried by the delay because they had a tight schedule to keep to. It was important for the group to be at a certain place by dawn.

As they pressed on, they came out of the jungle and onto a good track, partly overgrown by grass but showing signs of having been used by cars or trucks in recent times. This track, which they believed to be some sort of plantation access road, enabled them to travel fast and to make up time.

At about 10.45 pm they approached a house on the right side of the track and began to pass by it, silently. Just as the last members of the group were almost past it, however, a voice came from the darkened verandah. Evidently a Malay man had been sitting there, probably unable to see them clearly, but listening to the soft sounds of the column as it went by.

"Mana pergi? (Where are you going?)" he called. "Siapa sana? (Who is there?)."

The group stopped and stood silently in the darkness for almost a minute while the call was repeated. Arthur expected shots to ring out from either side at any moment, but nothing happened and they moved on carefully and quietly for another two hundred yards or so. They were told to be still and to wait while Ah Yen, along with a tough young guerilla soldier Arthur knew only as LN, crept back to the house from one side with their knives drawn. Ten minutes later they returned, nodding with satisfaction.

Arthur heard no details at the time but he later learnt that the man had been killed. Approaching the house from the side, Ah Yen and LN had seen the man leave the verandah and move quietly across the garden, peering into the darkness and listening in the direction which the main guerilla group had taken. They took him from behind, without him knowing what had happened, and he was dead within seconds.

As the group moved on again, they came, at about 1 1.30 pm, to the main road linking Labis to Yong Peng. After waiting and checking in both directions, they crossed the road quickly and slipped into the jungle on the opposite side. It was always considered risky to cross roads, because they had been told that the Japanese now kept permanent watches on certain stretches of road. Of course they knew it was impossible for them to watch every road for twenty-four hours a day, but on a trip like this their senses were heightened and, in the darkness, it was easy to believe that there were dozens of eyes watching.

In the denser jungle on the far side of the road, the going slowed down to a crawl. They were without any lights and the guide was having trouble finding the way. On several occasions they had to stop and wait while he searched around at the head of the column for the correct track. At two-thirty in the morning, they came out of the jungle again and into a large rubber plantation which they were told was the Socfin Estate. There, in the open spaces between the rubber trees, they were able to make good time--and they needed to. Word was passed back that they would have to cover eight miles in the next three hours. They had to reach a particular place where they could re-enter The jungle by 5.30 am, because the Tamil rubber-tappers would be starting work at 5.45 am and the group must not be seen by the tappers.

They moved on at a fast pace. There was no moon, but at least the sky was cloudless and there was dim starlight filtering down through the trees. Even so, Arthur found it difficult to see beyond the second or third figure in front of him. All were following the leader blindly and wordlessly, a single file of dark shadows snaking silently through the trees. '

Just on 5.30 am, they finally came to the spot where they were supposed to leave the plantation and re-enter the jungle. They moved in through some high shrubs to a rough track which they followed for some time before finding a place where they could lie down to rest. Their concern about timing had been justified because, within minutes of stopping to rest, they heard groups of Tamil rubber-tappers passing nearby on the plantation road, singing and talking loudly amongst themselves.

After resting for almost an hour, they picked up their gear and moved off quietly to find a place, a couple of miles further on and deeper into the jungle, where they could sleep safely for the day. All in the group were tired. They had covered some twenty miles since they had left the camp and parts of the going had been tough. They had a meal of potatoes and flour cakes and some people ate their rice. Arthur decided to keep his until later. He had managed to sleep for a few hours, but he was experiencing considerable pain in his right shoulder. The old wound was troubling him again. The weight of his rifle and the pack he was carrying had aggravated it to such an extent that he wondered if he would be able to continue in the same manner for another night.

Shortly after four in the afternoon they set off again, making initially for a place where they were told they could expect an evening meal. After about half an hour, they moved out of the jungle and into the rubber plantation again. Arthur felt suddenly nervous. They had gone to such lengths to avoid the rubber workers in the early morning and yet now, while it was still full daylight, they were walking through the open rubber trees. Ah Yen assured them, however, that it was perfectly safe. The plantation workers had all finished work earlier in the afternoon and gone home by this time.

They crossed the main tributary of the Muar River, again by using a fallen tree trunk. As one end of it was partly submerged in a swift-flowing current, crossing was a difficult process and 'Whiskers', one of the Chinese kitchen helpers, fell in. There was some merriment as he was fished out, but the line quickly moved on, covering the next couple of miles in little more than half an hour. They arrived, shortly after 5 pm, at a small wooden house owned by an elderly Chinese man who seemed genuinely pleased to see them, particularly the Europeans. He made quite a fuss of Arthur and the others and set about preparing a meal of nasi goreng and hot tea.

Ah Yen had wanted them to move off again by 5.30 pm because there was a patch of jungle he wanted to pass through before darkness overtook them completely. But as the meal had to be prepared in two batches, the schedule was upset and they were not able to leave until well after 6 pm which found them, shortly afterwards, floundering around in the jungle in the dark and making only about half a mile an hour.

Eventually they came out into the rubber once again and continued on until about 10 pm when they stopped for a brief rest. Ah Yen told them then that they still had sixteen miles to go and that it must be done before 5 am for them to be out of danger. After only fifteen minutes rest they were on their way again and, within only a few more minutes, the guide at the head of the column came upon a house to one side of the track. A signal went back along the line for everyone to stop and be quiet. They listened and heard voices, speaking Malay, coming from the house. Leaving the path, they skirted widely around the house, making sure that they could not be seen or heard.

Around midnight they passed a collection of tin sheds, coolie lines housing the Tamil workers who tapped the rubber each day. A dog barked, a voice from inside called out to the dog and then a man appeared with a light. Fortunately it was only a kerosene lantern, but once again there were anxious moments as they all stood in the shadows, waiting for the man to go back inside the shed. The route they followed now took them almost exclusively through the rubber. On several more occasions they heard dogs barking, but they were far enough away to keep going without fear. Just before 3 am they reached a railway line, the main line running south to Johore Bharu and Singapore. Taking care, they crossed the line and plunged on through the rubber trees, going hard and racing against time. They reached the main road heading south to Ayer Hitam at about 4.30 am and, having crossed it, travelled only a further fifteen minutes through rubber trees to another old house where they were welcomed by a group of Chinese who, along with Ah Yen, assured them that they were now safe and amongst friends.

They rested for a few hours in the grass on the edge of the jungle not far from the house, which was part of a small kampong. The people in the kampong prepared a delicious breakfast of rice and pancakes with hot tea and brought it to the members of the group as they lay in the long grass. It had an extraordinary effect on their spirits. To suddenly feel that they were in friendly territory immediately lifted their morale.

One of the tough little soldiers, a rather humourless type, a staunch Marxist whom Jock had christened 'Stalin', suddenly burst into song. Everybody laughed and cheered as they listened to him. He was singing in Chinese, so neither Arthur nor any of his comrades knew what he was singing, but they assumed the songs to be either patriotic or Marxist.

After resting quietly near the house until 9 am, they moved through the jungle for about one and a half hours until they came to what was clearly an old guerilla camp. Arthur thought that perhaps this was where they might stay, but Ah Yen was already informing everyone that they would be moving again within only half an hour. This was, however, a good place to bathe, he said.

There was a clear, fresh stream running by, with a deep pool in one part of it where they were all able to wash properly for the first time in several weeks. After everyone had freshened up and washed, the group moved on once more, but only a further two miles into the jungle to yet another camp, which, although it was deserted, had the appearance of having been occupied until very recently.

"This is where we stay," Ah Yen informed them with a large grin spreading across his face. "Our journey is now finished. Last night we travel thirty-five miles over. Now everybody rest."

Neither Arthur nor any of the others needed encouraging. They were all footsore and weary. Building shelters could wait. They just lay down and slept where they were.

This camp, in which it appeared they were going to settle for some time, was on the edge of the great, jungled spine that runs virtually the entire length of Malaya. This particular piece of jungle ran almost unbroken all the way to Pahang, Kelantan and Siam. If it had been physically possible, one could have travelled the entire distance, some three hundred miles in a direct line through the jungle to the north, and only cross one major road and one railroad track.

Although the realisation of this, when Arthur first saw their position on one of the maps, was a little daunting, it was also, in a way, reassuring to know that they had such a vast hinterland of jungle behind them as a perpetual escape route from the Japanese. On the other hand, they were now considerably further from the coast than they had been at any stage since the Japanese overran Malaya, so the chances of an escape by boat, as they had originally planned, were now virtually zero.

Arthur felt that most of the others had also put those plans to the back of their minds to concentrate on staying out of Japanese hands and staying alive.

Over the next few days they began settling in. It was the same process as usual: building shelters first, making sure the latrines were right, getting the kitchen and messing facilities under cover and operational. A fair amount of construction had already been done on the place, but they still had plenty to do to get things working properly. They started work on another garden, planting large numbers of seeds and cuttings which the people from the kampong some miles back had given them.

The same kampong also now began to supply them with all sorts of food, the best they had seen in months. They had pig and fish and pumpkin, rice, potatoes, marrow, all sorts of green vegetables, curry, tobacco and tea--everything they needed.

Perhaps it was the food, or the attitude of the kampong people, or a change in the members of the camp, but now everyone seemed to be able to get on well with each other. The Chinese began to treat the Europeans as if they were one of their own. The whole feeling in the camp was a tremendous improvement over what it had been during the earlier part of the year.

During the first week in December, which was also their first week in the camp, a daily routine was set which everyone was advised to follow. Unless on food-gathering or guard duties, the day would run like this:

0600-0610: Reveille and pack--up (they had to be ready to leave every day with whatever clothes, arms, or portable goods they owned, at a moment's notice)
    0610-0730: Exercise
    0730-0800: Washing
    0800-0820: Rest
    0820-0900: Study
    0900-1000: Makan (breakfast)
    1000-1020: Rest

1020-1100: Study
1100- 1400: Drill
1400-1420: Rest
1420-1500: Reading
1500-1630: Washing
1630-1800: Makan (dinner)
1800-1900: Rest
1900-2100: Meeting

Everyone, both Chinese and European, seemed pleased with the idea. It would bring some degree of order to what in the past had been a rather disorderly bunch. The new programme was set to start in four days time on 5 December, which also happened to be Arthur's twenty-fifth birthday. He wondered for a time if there was anything symbolic in it, but couldn't see what and, in any event, by the time the day came around, the question became academic because it began to rain...and rain and rain.

The rain fell continuously for one hundred and thirty hours.. almost six days. It then stopped, for one day, and started again. During this continual downpour, Arthur became dangerously ill. It overtook him a couple of days after his birthday, which he and Bomber, as well as Roy, Pete and Scottie, had celebrated with rice pancakes and coffee for supper. It had seemed like a bad cold at first. Arthur complained of feeling 'heady' and nauseous with some aches and pains. These reasonably mild conditions persisted for a few days until suddenly Arthur found that he had to go to bed.

Although the temperature during the day was quite warm, despite the rain, he could not stop shivering. He asked for extra blankets and lay on his grass tikka mat in his shelter, alternately sleeping and staring out into the rain for two days. The small stream which normally flowed quite gently past their camp was now a raging torrent. Roy and two others had also come down with fever. No-one was really sure what it was, but it was generally accepted to be malaria.

Arthur had thought about it previously and had been surprised, considering the amount of time they'd spent living in swamps and in different kinds of jungle, and all the mosquitoes that had feasted on them over the past months, that he hadn't been badly affected by malaria earlier.

They were given quinine. There wasn't an enormous amount of it available, but there was sufficient for three or four of them to be given some for a few days. It seemed to have a beneficial effect on Arthur, although, if he improved for a day or so, he soon found himself flat on his back again, helpless and weak, alternately shivering and trying to cover himself with blankets to keep warm, and then flinging them off as his temperature rose alarmingly again and he sweated profusely.

For most of December, Arthur was ill with malaria but both he and Roy, who was also very sick, were well looked after. Medicine was brought in and they were given extra treats like tobacco, sugar and ginger, and even some oranges and coffee. At times, though, they were far too ill to appreciate anything.

Because of the rain, this was also a period of enforced inactivity for the rest of the camp, and for the Japanese. Trains were not running, many of the roads and villages in Johore were underwater, and twenty people had drowned in Senahkung.

By 23 December, Bomber also began to come down with something. He thought it was flu at first, as Arthur had done, but very shortly it became clear that it was the same illness suffered by Arthur and Roy. Bomber, too, was immobilised and fever-ridden on the floor of his shelter. Christmas Day 1942 found the three of them all sick with malarial fever, lying on mats in the shelters, watching the endless rain pouring down to turn everything around them into a mudbath.

Fortunately the roofs of their shelters, made of layer upon layer of attap leaves and grass, did not leak at all and with drainage channels dug all around them, no water came in. They were fortunate, too, that the rain came almost straight down-- had there been any wind, they would certainly have been soaked. As it was, all Arthur could do was lie on his mat, watching the rain make little rivulets of water which ran down to add to the torrent of water in the river at the edge of the camp. In the week between Christmas and New Year, his condition began to improve. His bouts of shivering became less frequent and he began to regain some of his lost appetite. They received another letter from Major Barry Couvin, the British officer who had written seeking information of their whereabouts shortly after Arthur and Bomber had met up with Jock Smylie's group. It had been many months since they had heard from Couvin and none of the Chinese in the camp could give them any news of him. They said they hadn't any, and Arthur and the others had no way of knowing whether it was true or not.

Couvin's letter was short and really asked more than it told. He was in one of the guerilla camps near Batu Pahat and was anxious to leave it to join up with Arthur's group. But he didn't know where they were. The letter had come via a very roundabout route, carried by several different messengers, and had taken nearly two weeks to reach them. They set about writing a reply. Several of them made suggestions about how Couvin could get to the camp and how he should approach the leaders of his camp in order to get permission to come. Scottie wrote the letter and it was sent off with a runner who was heading for Chaah on 27 December.

17

JANUARY 1943. THE TURN OF the year and a couple of anniversaries seemed to focus attention on the predicament they were in and on the question of how long they would be isolated like lost refugees in the jungle. Scottie had his forty-fourth birthday on 18 January and, the following day, they 'celebrated' the fact that twelve months had passed since the disaster at Bakri. There were no festivities, just some discussion and recognition of the fact that they were fortunate to still be alive.

Roy, Bomber and Arthur were recovering, but they never all seemed to be 'up' at the same time. Roy would rally and be in seemingly good health for a few days while Bomber was down with fever and Arthur still felt low and weak. Then Bomber and Arthur would recover somewhat and Roy would have a relapse.

At one stage during this period, Arthur had a strange dream in which he heard a deep voice speaking to him in the night about his shirt and how wet it was. He felt as if someone were grabbing hold of his shoulder. He woke with a start and found no-one there. His shirt, however, was sopping wet with sweat.

Arthur gradually recovered, although occasionally his pulse rate inexplicably shot up to about 110 beats per minute. He also found that, once again, he was beginning to get rashes in his groin and sores on his legs. During the weeks that followed, the sores on his legs became progressively worse although he was consoled by the fact that he generally felt in better health than either Roy or Bomber, who seemed unable to throw off the effects of their fevers. Others in the camp had also been very badly affected by malaria. Ah Yen, who had been suffering intermittently, had a relapse and had to be carried out on a stretcher to another camp where he could be treated more adequately.

As the weather changed in the latter part of January, with the north-east monsoon sweeping in over the southern part of Malaya, the camp became more and more cold, damp and dreary. The days were warm, if the sun came through the clouds, but the nights were often cold.

Sou Lim and LQ arrived at the camp together one day in late January. Sou Lim, as usual, was only visiting, but LQ had been sent to take over from Ah Yen, at least temporarily. A meeting was called to hear their news, including a disaster for the Communist Party which had occurred in the capital, Kuala Lumpur, on 1 September.

There had been a secret gathering of Party leaders from all parts of Malaya. It had been held in the area of the Batu Caves, just outside Kuala Lumpur. The Japanese had learned of the meeting through an informer and had surrounded the area in the early hours of the morning. They mounted a surprise attack on the guerilla meeting, killing seven Party members, including the head of the entire guerilla movement in Malaya. Many more were captured. The Party leader was beheaded and his head displayed prominently in Kuala Lumpur.

On the other hand, LQ and Sou Lim also reported that one hundred and fifty traitors had been killed by guerillas in Johore during the past month--fifty-three in one week-and that a Japanese troop train heading north had been blown up, killing a great many Japanese soldiers. Rifles, revolvers, and large quantities of ammunition and rice had been taken from the wreckage. Arthur and the others had actually heard the explosion two nights previously, coming from a long distance away, but didn't know what had caused it.

Other news included reports of major sea battles in the Solomons, in which four Japanese battleships were said to have been sunk. Another battle in the Mediterranean involved the sinking of three Italian warships. The Russians were pushing the Germans back from Stalingrad, the reports said, and there were now great food shortages in Germany.

LQ said that they would be getting a typewriter and a 'Roneo' machine for copying within a day or so. There were plans to copy off regular news-sheets which could be sold for three cents and distributed widely as anti-Japanese propaganda.

Within a few days the machines arrived and by early February the camp was regularly turning out large bundles of propaganda sheets which were disseminated clandestinely in the kampongs and towns nearby, much to the anger and annoyance of the Japanese.

Shortly after this, although the two events were not connected, Pete and Scottie asked permission from LQ to make a return trip to their secret supply cache near a kampong called Lenek. They had not been near it for many months and had no idea if it was still intact or if it had been discovered and completely looted, but when they'd prepared the site, after the Japanese invasion but prior to them overrunning Johore, they had hidden it so well they were both convinced it would be exactly as they had left it. Neither Arthur nor Bomber expected permission to be granted to the two Englishmen, but LQ agreed to the journey on condition that they be accompanied by a Chinese guerilla called Ah Kow who would take them to the closest kampong where they would be joined by a guide for the trek.

A day or two passed and then word came back that they had found the dump and that it was still untouched. The messenger who brought the news also carried a couple of revolvers and some .38 ammunition as well as several packets of Tommy-gun ammunition. It was almost a week later that Scottie and Pete finally returned to the camp, but all they brought back with them, among other odds and ends, was a bottle of whisky, a tin of porridge, a rifle and a few boxes of matches.

"The dump was there, all right," Scottie told them, "but all of the tins had rusted through. The ants got into one hundred and seventeen tins of food. They even ate through the corks of medicine bottles. But the worst thing that happened was that on the first trip, three or four Tamils saw us going into the area and when we went back the next day, the dump had been raided. So we scuttled back to HQ to tell them. They were even more browned-off then that we'd brought out seven bottles of whisky on the first trip instead of ammo and explosives, because, after that we couldn't go back. Apparently five truck-loads of Japs turned up pretty quickly and went through everything with a fine toothcomb."

"So what did you end up getting out of it?" Arthur asked.

"Just some of the arms and ammunition, but we had to leave them at HQ, along with six of the bottles of whisky." "Six bottles?!" Roy exclaimed. "Yeah. They weren't too happy about us bringing the whisky out in the first place. Anyway, they're keeping four bottles for themselves and sending two to Jock, back at the old camp near Senahkung. He's still in pretty bad shape, apparently."

None of them had heard from Jock for some time. Letters had been written, but there had been no reply. They had heard from others, however, that he was still alive, but suffering from recurring bouts of fever.

"That's not good," Arthur said. "I'm worried that if he doesn't pull out of this one, he'll keep going down."

During the last few months, Arthur thought Jock seemed to have lost the will to live. Ever since the fall of Singapore, he had often brooded on the fact that his wife had been in the city at the time of its surrender and had almost certainly been captured or killed. He knew nothing of her whereabouts or her fate. Nor could he have done anything if he did know. His dark moods had become more frequent in the weeks prior to the split-up of the Europeans and even before he became ill, Arthur had often observed him sitting alone, up against a tree or in his shelter, gazing into the sky or the surrounding jungle, lost in his own sad thoughts.

After Scottie and Pete had finished their unfortunate tale of the supply dump, they went off to bathe in the nearby stream. In just a few minutes, though, there was a terrified yell and Scottie leapt naked from the stream out onto the bank beside Pete. A seven-foot-long snake had swum into the small pool where he had been washing. Arthur, Bomber, Tom and Roy rushed down to the pool and managed to trap the snake and kill it. It was carried triumphantly to the cookhouse where it was boiled up with nebong for dinner that evening.

After the meal, Scottie produced his bottle of whisky. The J&B label had almost rotted off, "but the contents are okay", he assured everyone as he passed it around for all to take a tot. Arthur drained the small amount of amber fluid from the bottom of his mug. It burned his throat like fire but he revelled in the warm, glowing sensation it immediately brought to his stomach. He wondered, at the same time, whether Jock was having a tot from one of the bottles that had been sent to him.

He wondered, too, what else could be done for Jock. There was no medicine that could be sent to him but perhaps, Arthur thought, some of our food might be better. He spoke to LQ about sending him some porridge, sugar and coffee to cheer him up. LQ agreed to try to arrange it.

Early the next afternoon, Ah Kow came in from the headquarters camp with the terrible news that, after the Japanese had raided Scottie and Pete's dump two days previously, they had turned on the nearest kampong and, believing the inhabitants to have been involved in the secret cache, had surrounded all of the houses and set them alight, shooting the occupants as they ran out, killing a total of seventy-five men, women and children.

It was clear from their reactions that both Scottie and Pete felt a sense of guilt over what had happened and also considerable apprehension for themselves over possible repercussions, although they never came. Arthur was surprised that news of the brutal Japanese attack did not bring a tirade of abuse on Pete and Scottie, for having been the indirect cause of the massacre. It occurred to Arthur, and of course to Pete and Scottie, that the leaders might consider punishing them. But for some reason, known only to themselves, LQ and the others said no more about it.

For a few days after this, Chinese New Year, from 5 to 7 February, brought some lightheartedness to the camp. There were plays and singsongs, and the inevitable political speeches, but for Arthur and his friends, the best thing about Chinese New Year was the extra rations of food that everyone was Allowed-- curry puffs and cakes, and plenty of tobacco and coffee. Scottie, in an unusually generous mood, even shared an extra tot of whisky all round.

For a while after their visit to the supply dump, Scottie and Pete seemed more friendly and congenial towards the rest of the camp. But they still had their minds set on breaking off on their own. The boat plan had long since been shelved. Now they wanted to head north. They had convinced Roy that their plan of moving north and finding an escape route was feasible and he had told them that he would join them. Generally, however, their idea was looked on by everyone else, including Arthur and Bomber, as a bit of a joke. There was no denying that both Pete and Scottie had a good understanding and command of the Malay language, as well as some Chinese, but it was clear to everyone, except Pete and Scottie apparently, that the backing and help of the Chinese guerillas was needed if one was to travel and survive in the jungle for any length of time. So Scottie and Co. would need the blessing of the Communist Party if they wanted to attempt a trek north--the sort of approval that had so far not been forthcoming.

Despite their disapproval of Pete and Scottie's plan, both Arthur and Bomber also wanted to move, but within the framework of the guerilla organisation. They had spoken a few times with Stalin, the Marxist idealist who had become quite influential in the camp hierarchy, about transferring to the camp where the British officer Barry Couvin was living. Stalin's response was to suggest that Couvin come to their camp, and that Arthur and Bomber should send him a letter to that effect. Arthur and Bomber agreed, and set about writing the letter which included several questions about the conditions at Couvin's camp. It was sent with a runner two days later, but no-one could estimate when it would reach Couvin, or when a reply could be expected.

The question of Pete and Scottie's move was put in abeyance when Pete fell sick. Again, no-one could say what it was, although Pete said that it felt like malaria. Whatever it was, he was laid low and couldn't move. Bomber, too, was suffering again from beri-beri. His fever seemed to have improved but his feet were so badly swollen that he couldn't walk.

At the same time, the whole camp, or at least seventy per cent of it, seemed to be afflicted by sores and a terrible itch, either in the groin or on the hands and legs. Arthur's hands were full of open sores and it seemed that nothing could be done about it. They felt sure it was their diet, but they could only eat what they could get and it was rarely a balanced meal. For long periods they might have only potatoes, then only nebong and occasionally some meat. For a time, towards the end of February, they had great success with the homemade rat and squirrel traps they had fabricated. Whenever they scored a rat it was divided up as equitably as possible, which usually meant rat soup for breakfast. Squirrels, being a little bigger, provided more meat and, when they perfected their trapping techniques, they were able in one night to catch eight squirrels, which, when served with some nebong, provided a real feast for the camp at breakfast that morning. Everyone thought of it as something of a bonus, but then the same thing happened the following night--six squirrels, then seven the next--every night for a week, until the squirrel population was virtually depleted. They also had a couple of seven-and eight-foot snakes which provided meat and soup for the whole camp.

On 23 February they received a letter from Jock at the camp near Senahkung, saying that he was very sick and that he felt he was dying. "There is no quinine or other medicines here," he wrote, "and the porridge and whisky you sent has long gone. I don't think I'm going to last for too long. Nobody here seems to be able to do anything. Need help."

Arthur spoke to Stalin to see if any of the Europeans could go to see Jock, but he was told that it was too far to go. It would take almost a week of travelling on foot through the jungle, mostly at night, to get there. It would be too difficult to organise. "I am sure he will get well again soon," Stalin said to Arthur.

They managed to get together some more porridge and whisky, donated by Scottie, to be taken to Jock, but they had no way of knowing when, or even if, it would ever reach him. It wasn't until more than a month later, on 25 March, that they heard from LQ, on one of his visits, that Jock had died of his illness on 21 February at 3.30 am, two days before they had received his letter telling them how ill he was.

Arthur was struck again with the picture of Jock during the weeks prior to his illness, sitting up against a tree, brooding morosely on the fate of his wife. But whether or not this had contributed to his inability to survive the illness, they would never know.

This was also a very difficult time for the camp and Jock's death, although they did not know it, was only the first in a tragic series that followed over the next couple of months. And sickness, disease and death were not their only troubles. The Japanese now seemed more and more determined to flush the guerillas out of the jungles, and their stepped-up efforts began to make all in the camp increasingly uncomfortable.

A meeting was held to plan some sort of strategy to cope if the Japanese arrived in force. Roy, Scottie and three Chinese were detailed to go further into the jungle, about two miles east, into an area of very dense vegetation, to begin building another place in preparation for a possible evacuation of the present site. Other parties were detailed to make bamboo carrying-baskets and cups to carry the food supplies. There had been no definite decision to make a move, but everyone was to be prepared.

Later that evening, two guerillas came in with a Malay they had captured in the nearby rubber estate. He had been reported as a traitor. He was handled roughly and briefly questioned before being tied to a tree for the night. The young man, in his mid-twenties, was clearly terrified by the situation and sobbed and cried all through the night. In the morning, under the direction of Wing Lu, whom Arthur and the others had dubbed 'Cut-throat', because he was such a 'nasty-looking type', the captive was interrogated under pressure. Cut-throat was tall for a Chinese, about six feet two inches, and ugly. His face was covered with pockmarks and a jagged scar ran from the corner of his mouth across his left cheek. He taught Kung Fu to the other guerilla soldiers in the camp and was regarded by all as a very tough customer indeed.

Cut-throat hit the man several times and kept prodding him more and more firmly with his bayonet until the man finally broke down in terror and admitted that he had been receiving $30 a month and free rice from the Japanese for betraying any Chinese or Malays who gave food or aid to the Communist guerillas in the jungle.

Once Cut-throat had obtained the first confession, he did not let up. He pressed for more and more. And the man, either knowing he was done for or perhaps hoping, forlornly but mistakenly, that his openness might warrant forgiveness, kept talking. Already, he said, the Japanese had arrested five of the people he had betrayed and stopped eight bags of rice that had been intended for our camp. Two other people were due to be arrested on the day that he had been captured by the guerillas.

The interrogation lasted several hours and then Arthur and three other men were detailed to go and dig the man's grave nearby. Shortly afterwards, he was brought to the site by three other men and they began to tie him to a tree by the throat. Arthur and three young Chinese women were standing near Cut-throat, watching as the man was tied up, when suddenly, with a superhuman effort, the hapless prisoner tore himself free and tried to run past them in a bid to escape. Both Arthur and Cut-throat had been holding bayonets. Arthur lunged at the man catching his arm with the bayonet point. As he screamed and turned to avoid it, Cut-throat's bayonet plunged deep into the man's solar plexus. Quickly withdrawing it as the man fell to the ground with a gasp, Cut-throat repeatedly drove his bayonet into the terror-stricken man as he squirmed and contorted himself, desperately trying to avoid and parry the deadly thrusts. He was dead within minutes, but for him every second had been horrific.

As Arthur looked up from the gory scene, he caught the eyes of two of the young Chinese girls who had come in two days previously from the other camp. They had stood and watched the whole incident. One of them raised her eyebrows and nodded seriously. The other smiled slightly and said in Cantonese, "Ho! ho! (Good! good!)."

Arthur himself was stunned. Although he had instinctively thrust his own bayonet out to prevent the man's escape, he was repulsed at the way he had died. For some time afterwards, and he had experienced similar feelings after witnessing other executions, he found himself imagining what it would be like to be lying on the ground with a bayonet being plunged repeatedly into his body. It sent cold shivers running through him for several minutes even though, until that time, he had been sweating profusely from the humid heat of the afternoon.

The crumpled body was rolled into the shallow grave and, as a few drops of rain fell, they began covering it with earth. By the time they had finished, it was raining heavily. In the fading afternoon light Arthur sat gloomily in his shelter gazing out at the torrents of falling water and the rivulets running by, joining rapidly to form puddles and ultimately a small lake in the open space that separated his own shelter from the rest of the camp.

18

A WEEK AFTER THE YOUNG Malay was killed, reports were received that a new contingent of Japanese soldiers had arrived in the kampong area and was setting up a sort of headquarters there, presumably to direct a more thorough search of the district. Regular patrols by Malays and Tamils were to be established, with frequent reports made back to the Japanese.

Arthur became preoccupied during this time with the deteriorating condition of his feet and legs. Like Bomber's, they had suddenly begun to swell up like balloons again and were extremely painful. At the same time, the rash and sores returned to his groin and legs and he found it difficult to either walk or sit down.

One of the Chinese guerillas who was fulfilling the function of 'doctor' at the time, told both Arthur and Bomber that they should stop eating blachan, the river shrimps. Others told them it was a deficiency in vitamin D, but no-one really knew the cause or the cure, so for the time being they just endured it. Their main concern over the condition they found themselves in was that if the Japanese attacked the camp, they would not be able to escape.

Ah Yen, who had recovered from his illness, returned to the Camp at this time and resumed his role as leader. He ordered that all of those involved in administration, including the typing and printing of propaganda leaflets, should move further into the jungle, about a mile or so, to the site which Scottie and Roy had helped prepare a few days earlier. The women in the camp, as well as the sick and the five Europeans, would move also.

Although the site was not far away, it was a slow and difficult move which they began shortly after midday. The path was narrow and slippery and the undergrowth very close and thick, with thorny bushes constantly tearing at their clothes. It was also awkward because those who were sick had to be carried or helped for most of the way. Eventually, when they reached their destination, they found a cold, damp and dark place in a very small area, in which two tiny huts had been constructed.

There were, of course, no beds. This was always one of the first things they had to do at every new site. They carried their own tikkas, the woven mats, but these lay flat on the ground and provided scant protection from the myriad crawling and creeping insects that came in the night. On several occasions, in previous camps, they had found scorpions. Bluey found an enormous one--about six inches long, like a small lobster-- crawling around on his tikka one night. It was killed, but they then spent hours searching for its mate because they had all heard and believed the story that scorpions always come in pairs. The main feature about a bed, however crudely it might be constructed, was that it lifted its occupant a vital few inches above the floor, preventing most of the crawling things from reaching it. Many even went to the lengths of putting the legs of the bed into small cans of water, so nothing would crawl up the legs. But that sort of refinement only came after spending some time in a camp that was relatively well established.

Here, on their first night in what they all took to be a very dreary place, they had only the ground to sleep on. Arthur, having made the mistake of drinking two cups of strong coffee before bedding down, found that he spent half the night lying awake, pulling leeches off his arms and legs. Even so he missed two of the ugly creatures which fell, bloated and distended with his blood, onto the ground as he arose at dawn the next day.

They had news in from the main camp that the Japanese were beginning to step up their search programme. Parties of Tamils and Malays were said to be poking around the jungle verge, looking for tracks, although they apparently hadn't found any leading to the camp yet. In the twenty-four hours since they had left the main camp, another traitor had been brought in, questioned, tried and executed by Cut-throat with his bayonet.

The next two days were spent consolidating their new position: building new huts and shelters and making a small dam in the nearby creek. Arthur figured that they were quite close to the main north-south railway line as they could occasionally hear trains passing in the distance from the point where the dam was being constructed. This was more often at night; the Japanese fearing possible daylight aerial attacks on their rail transport.

During this time the most recent disappearance of a traitor from the kampong area apparently infuriated the Japanese. They issued a warning that if any more people went missing, the whole kampong would be killed. It was a difficult edict for them to issue without identifying those people who had been cooperating with the Japanese. They could hardly say, 'if this person or that person disappears, we will seek retribution,' because that would immediately mark that person as an informer or a collaborator. So, they could only issue the warning in a general sense to cover the whole kampong population of several hundred. In theory, this meant that even if someone sympathetic to the Communist guerillas decided to leave the kampong and join them in the jungle, the departure would also invite the destruction of the kampong by the Japanese.

As there were still several traitors in the kampong, the guerillas discussed alternative plans to deal with them. The approach which seemed to have the most support was to follow the individual whenever he left the kampong and then to kill him elsewhere, although this would not necessarily guarantee that there would be no reprisal from the Japanese.

There was an altercation during this time between Roy and one of the camp leaders they called Gert. Roy stayed in his shelter one morning, instead of getting up at the appointed time, so Gert had Roy's rifle taken from him. The incident developed into a shouting match with Roy telling Gert that he wasn't going to take orders from him. A meeting was held and the Allied soldiers were told that, as they were all in the one guerilla army, they had to obey soldiers' rules, or get out.

Scottie took issue with them. "When we joined you, we agreed to follow the leadership of the Malayan Communist Party while we were in the jungle," he said, "not of every ordinary soldier."

Roy said, "Sergeant Shephard is the senior-ranking Australian soldier in the camp. I take my orders from him."

Arthur looked up in surprise at Roy's comments, but then nodded seriously in agreement.

The Chinese then withdrew into a group to discuss this new development. Arthur, Scottie and Roy also went into a huddle. They knew they were splitting hairs, but now that the situation had blown up, they had to follow it through or they would lose status in the camp. "We're getting to be just like them," Arthur said, "worrying about losing face."

The end result of the confrontation was that Arthur was declared to be the kepala, the headman, over all the Australians in the camp, with the power to take their rifles away. In the meantime, to save Gert's face, Roy had to do kitchen fatigues for three days.

During the last week of March, the situation in the nearby kampong suddenly deteriorated. The Japanese suspected a Chinese man, originally from the kampong but living in the town of Kluang, some thirty miles to the south, of helping the Communist guerillas in that area. He had been warned and when the Japanese went to get him, they found he had left Kluang, making his way eventually to Bekok and then to his own kampong.

But through other collaborators, the Japanese soon found out that he was there and, on 24 March, they paid a visit to his family house. Once again, he had been warned and had escaped into the jungle to the guerilla camp. The Japanese then told the people of the kampong that, unless they produced the man by the following morning, they would burn down ten houses and kill all of the people in them. The result was that, at four the next morning, the entire kampong fled into the jungle to join the guerillas.

The Japanese hesitated only long enough to allow a group of one hundred Tamils to ransack and loot the settlement before burning it to the ground. The policy of intimidation by terror was becoming more and more common. They also heard of another incident, at Kulai, to the south of Kluang, where the Japanese had taken an eleven-mile stretch of road and burnt every house along it--over a thousand houses--and killed more than three thousand people. The guerillas couldn't find out why it had been done, but the report they heard suggested it was to do with the reluctance of the local populace to volunteer for either the military or labour forces which the Japanese were trying to raise in the district.

During the weeks that followed, Japanese troops remained in the area putting increasing pressure on the local people. At one stage they arrested a friend of the guerillas, a Chinese man named Hok Yuen who on several occasions had visited the main guerilla camp in the area. A report which reached the camp indicated that the man had been beaten and tortured, by having burning rubber dripped onto his chest, as his Japanese interrogators attempted to extract the location of the camp from him. He had apparently been able to withstand their torture, but he was taken away and no-one knew if he had survived.

The destruction of the kampong and the increased Japanese attempts to locate the guerillas in the jungle forced them to make yet another move, this time only four miles to the north, but through very rough and hilly jungle country. The move was very hard on the sick, as well as on those who were well, because they had to carry the sick. Whenever they came to a steep hill, Arthur found that he had to carry a fever-ridden Chinese soldier called Ah Lim. Although almost collapsing under the weight of the man, whom he carried piggyback fashion, Arthur felt nothing but relief at leaving the cold, wet and cramped conditions of the emergency campsite they had occupied for the past few weeks.

The new site, again one which had been occupied previously by guerillas, seemed at first glance to be a good one. It was on top of a large hill and, although protected from the view of any passing observation planes, was much more open and airy than the previous camp. The only problem, a significant one, was that the nearest water was almost a half a mile away, requiring constant water-carrying parties.

During the first few days in the new camp, as many people as possible were sent out on food-gathering forays, both for vegetables growing wild in the jungle and from a couple of other nearby kampongs.

Arthur spent the first few days working with the carrying- parties--sometimes on trips up to six or seven miles away-- chopping wood for building huts and for firewood, and collecting attap for the roofs of the shelters they were building. He found that he was beginning to feel fitter and healthier than he had for some time and the sores on his legs and bottom began to heal. But while his condition seemed to improve, Bomber became extremely ill, confined to bed with high temperatures and pulse rate. Pete was still having difficulty in walking, Scottie came down with fever and Roy became almost crippled with stomach cramps. Many of the Chinese were also sick and there was really no way to treat any of the ill with conventional medicines. Even when they could get the correct pills, lotions or injections, there was never enough to treat everyone who was sick. Various Chinese herbal remedies were tried on all of them and in many instances seemed to do a great deal of good--for example, Arthur had found that a lotion made of a particular type of squashed root had a beneficial effect on open sores, but nothing seemed to be an absolute cure-all.

Despite their illnesses, everyone agreed that this camp was far better than the previous one. Water was always a problem, but they began to get used to the carrying routine and, generally, they all hoped they would be able to spend a little more time at this place before moving on once more. They all knew, though, that was expecting too much. They lived in constant fear of being betrayed to the Japanese by traitors amongst the local populace, and yet they had to rely on locals for food and supplies and in this area there were several people on whom they had to keep a close watch--or get rid of. In early April, there were two forays, in which men from the camp participated, which were specifically to assassinate known traitors in local kampongs or towns.

During one such excursion to the Paloh area, two Malay traitors were captured by five of the Chinese guerillas and shot in the jungle. Unbeknown to the guerillas, two other Malays, who had been nearby and heard the shots, ran off to notify the Japanese. Two truckloads of Japanese soldiers appeared shortly afterwards and began mortaring the jungle, but did not enter to look for the guerillas, all of whom escaped.

A few days later, two of the men who had participated in the assassination, young men whom Arthur and Bomber had nicknamed 'Bucktooth' and 'Tugboat', went into Paloh again to pick up some more food from a supplier. Paloh, despite the traumas of the war, was a pleasant, tree-shaded little township on the main north-south railway. The main street of the town was lined on both sides with grocery, produce, hardware and clothing stores in the traditional Chinese shop-house style. The colonnaded balconies of each store, side by side, formed a continuous arcade along the footpath, onto which the proprietor usually extended the store and its wares.

Bucktooth and Tugboat were sitting in one of these stores, a small restaurant, drinking some coffee, when a Japanese soldier and a Malay came by. The Malay, a long-time resident of the town, immediately picked the two men as strangers and whispered to the Japanese soldier who turned and walked into the cafe towards them. Bucktooth and Tugboat tried to remain calm and to bluff it out. The Japanese soldier was small and quite young, probably in his early twenties. Bucktooth noticed, from the star and stripe on his sleeve above the elbow, that he was a corporal. He was carrying the new model 99 rifle, which Bucktooth found slightly comforting because he felt it would be more awkward for him to use it in a confined space like a coffee shop.

"Tunjukan surat jalan?" The soldier spoke in broken Malay, without a smile, holding out his hand to Bucktooth, demanding his travel permit. Bucktooth reached into his pocket and produced his forged pass. The soldier scanned the travel permit and then turned to Tugboat for his. Tugboat reached into his pocket for the pass but as he did so, the Malay caught a glimpse of the pistol in his belt and shouted a warning. The soldier dived towards Tugboat as he drew the pistol and the two fell scuffling to the floor. Bucktooth immediately drew his own pistol and within seconds, shot the Malay in the head at point-blank range. Tugboat, meanwhile, had fired one shot with his own weapon but had wounded himself in the foot, near the ankle. Then, as he manoeuvred for a second shot at the Japanese soldier, and fired, the pistol jammed. In the confusion of tumbling bodies, with the other customers trying to flee, the soldier jumped to his feet and ran from the shop shouting for assistance. Bucktooth and Tugboat then ran through the rear of the store escaping through a small field into dense foliage by the river.

From there they were able to make their way to a rendez-vous in the jungle where they met with three other comrades. Although he had managed to hobble on it immediately after the shooting, Tugboat's wounded foot became so crippled that he could no longer walk. When word of the fight arrived at the camp one day later, a party of men was sent out to carry Tugboat back, a procedure which occupied several dangerous days.

As a result of this incident, Japanese pressure started to build up on the camp again. Groups of Malays were seen with increasing frequency by the food-gathering parties. They were either gathering food themselves, or searching for clues to the whereabouts of the guerilla camp. They were never seen alone. There would always be at least three or four of them, for safety. And if ever they saw any camp members, they would always run. Arthur and the others knew that gradually the net would close in on them.

Several patrols were sent out to look for a new camp. It seemed to Arthur that the whole thing was a never-ending process. They could, of course, go deep into the trackless jungle of Pahang, but they would then be too far from their sources of food and supplies. And, from a military viewpoint, they would not be in a position to strike at the Japanese if and when they built up sufficient strength. But whenever they stayed relatively close to conventional sources of food, such as towns and kampongs, it was never very long before someone betrayed their location to the Japanese. And now, it was all happening again.

By the middle of April, groups of Japanese soldiers were working steadily around the jungle fringe not far from their camp, and on 14 April, a body of them was reported to be close to the point where the track from the camp led out of the jungle. A decision was made to move again, despite the fact that there were many who were too sick to do so. Arthur was reasonably well, Scottie and Roy seemed to have recovered sufficiently from their illness to make the trip, and Pete could just stagger along with great effort. Bomber, though, was racked with terrible bouts of shivering and could not move. His mind was wandering. It was difficult to make him understand what was happening.

They were told they had about six miles to cover and that there was a resting point, halfway, where the sick could stay overnight. Arthur and Roy took turns to carry Bomber. Whenever the track was wider, they supported him between their shoulders. Bomber hardly knew what was happening.

"C'mon, mate," Arthur kept saying to him. "It's not much further. You'll be able to lie down and we'll wrap you up to make you warm."

Bomber moaned softly, but said nothing. His face was deathly pale. His skin was cold and every few minutes he would shudder violently.

It took five hours for them to cover the three miles to the resting place. Long before they reached it, Bomber had collapsed completely and had to be carried. One of the stretchers that had been used to carry sick Chinese to the halfway point was brought back so that Bomber could be brought in. When they arrived, some of the group were already preparing to leave on the second half of the trek to the new campsite. Arthur and Roy stayed overnight with Bomber, so they could help to get him over the second half of the journey.

Arthur noticed a small group of guerillas standing around a black man, a Tamil, who had obviously been taken prisoner during the day. He learnt that the man and another Tamil had been caught spying on the guerillas as they made their way through the jungle. The other had been shot as he tried to run away, while this one had been brought in for questioning.

Arthur, Roy and Pete had laid Bomber down, wrapped up in a blanket to rest, and were all sitting down in a small patch of grassy, open ground when they saw the Tamil executed on the opposite side of the clearing. After about twenty minutes of rough interrogation, Stalin had simply walked up to the man, placed a pistol beside his head and fired it.

It seemed to Arthur that there was nothing at all unusual about this any more. Executions, he thought, have become a part of our daily life. What was unusual about this one, though, was that the man was not carried away for burial, or shot above his own already-prepared grave, but left lying on the ground for some time while a discussion was held around him. Arthur and the others could not hear the discussion and, in any event, were too tired to become involved. They simply watched the proceedings from a distance.

Suddenly, Stalin knelt down beside the body and tore open the man's shirt, baring his chest. A large knife was handed to him and he proceeded to carve deeply into the body.

"Jesus!" Arthur said. "Do you see that?"

"Yeah," Roy returned. "What the hell's he doing?"

They watched in stunned silence as Stalin deftly opened the dead man's chest and, after a few deep slices with the knife, plunged his hand into the man's chest and removed a still-dripping heart from the body.

The three Europeans watched the whole procedure in open-mouthed, silent amazement. Stalin held the organ in his gory hands for a moment, then handed it to Slim, one of the cooks.

"Christ Almighty," Roy muttered. "They're going to cook it."

Several of the Chinese from the group watched the process as Shorty, the other cook, who had already lit a fire and had water boiling away, chopped up the heart, fried several pieces of it with garlic and onions and then served it to two of the very sick Chinese who had been carried in by stretcher. A small but rich broth was also made from it and given to some of the others who were ill. The broth was offered for Bomber but, to the surprise of the Chinese, Arthur refused on his behalf.

As he lay in the darkness, trying to sleep, Arthur wondered whether he had done the right thing. In a situation like that, he thought, what's wrong and what's right? Who am I to refuse Bomber something, on ethical grounds, that might save his life?

In the morning, Pete had a relapse and was suddenly unable to move. Roy and Arthur were asked to help carry stores to the new campsite and then return to look after Bomber and Pete. It was decided not to try to move them or the other four seriously-ill.

A confused few days followed in which Arthur and Roy spent half their time living in one place and half in the other as they shuttled back and forth looking after Bomber and Pete. Eventually, with a number of stretcher-bearers assigned to the task, they managed to get Bomber, Pete and the other sick Chinese up to the new campsite, once again on top of a steep hill.

There were now almost seventy people in the camp, a large number of whom were suffering from various kinds of illnesses. Bomber and Pete remained seriously ill and were kept isolated from the rest of the camp with several others in a small area designated as a makeshift sick bay, down in a slight valley beyond the far side of the clearing. Bomber's feet and legs were grossly swollen and his mind kept wandering. It had been a long time since he had been able to speak sensibly, although he seemed to drop in and out of his delirium.

It was during this time that a guerilla leader called Sou Young arrived with several others from the old camp in the Pagoh area. They brought news of Mac, Tom, Les and Bluey, as well as Gaje but they had no news of the young Javanese soldier Smit. All had apparently been down with fever, although Mac and Tom were showing some improvement now.

Sou Young was the commander of the 3rd Headquarters group. He was referred to as 'Number Two', although who he was 'Number Two' to, Arthur could never establish. 'Number One' was mentioned from time to time, but never identified. Sou Young was however, of equal rank to LQ and senior to Ah Yen, whom he was to relieve. He was tall and slim and, Arthur guessed, about thirty-one or thirty-two years old. He had longer hair than was usual in camp leaders and, in the practice common throughout China, grew a number of long hairs from a black mole on the side of his left jaw. He wore rimless glasses which, combined with his friendly personality, gave him a generally academic air. He had, nevertheless, a reputation as a tough and brave guerilla fighter.

Sou Young and those who had accompanied him had travelled for six days and six nights from the Pagoh camp and, as they approached this area, their scouts had spotted a large concentration of Japanese soldiers establishing themselves on the jungle fringe close to where the previous campsite had been.

In the group with Sou Young was a young Chinese man called Ten Chen, whom Arthur remembered from the old camp at Pagoh. Arthur had referred to him at that time as a 'Bad Hat' in that he always seemed to adopt a surly and aggressive attitude towards Europeans, having been rude and abusive to Arthur and the others on several occasions. Arthur noticed he was wearing a Dutch pistol similar to the one which Smit had carried.

"Where did you get the pistol?" Arthur asked him in Malay.

"It was given to me," he replied.

"By whom?"

"By one of the Dutch Brigs," he said abruptly. Ignoring Arthur and Roy, he then began a conversation in Chinese with one of the other soldiers.

There was no way Arthur and Roy could dispute his answers. Later, when they asked him about Smit and the Dutch group, they received only vague and evasive replies. Of course, Smit had separated from the Dutch group not long after they had and there was no reason to think that he had rejoined them. In fact, until then, they had believed that Smit was still with Mac and the others.

During the last days of April, they were relatively free of the fear of a Japanese attack and once again they concentrated on the process of establishing camp and making themselves as comfortable as possible, even though Sou Young and several others had set off to find yet another 'permanent' campsite, possibly nearer to the major town of Segamat. Roy celebrated his twenty-first birthday and they had roast pork for dinner. They were given a letter that Barry Couvin had written to Jock before Jock's death. From it they realised that Couvin had received none of their letters and so was still completely in the dark as to their whereabouts and their wishes to join up with him. Arthur decided to try once again to make contact, although he felt depressed about the chances of a new letter ever reaching him.

On 29 April, a little more than ten days after they had arrived at their new campsite, they woke to find that Pete had died during the night. It came as a shock to Arthur. If any of the sick was going to survive, he thought it would be Pete. At every stage during the past few weeks, he had seemed stronger than Bomber. He had rallied on several occasions and never slipped into delirium like Bomber. He had been able to walk and talk sensibly until only a few days previously. Now he was dead. Scottie, who was grief-stricken, kept pacing up and down mumbling to himself, "...he was only twenty-six."

Scottie and Pete, despite their eighteen-year age difference, had been inseparable. Arthur had observed an occasional
argument between them, but generally their friendship had been
firm and one of mutual respect. Their association had had a sort
of exclusivity about it. Amongst the Europeans, they were the
only ones, or felt that they were the only ones, who really understood Malaya. In the beginning, Pete had often affected a rather
snobbish air and it was clear that they regarded the British and
Australian soldiers who had poured into Malaya before the outbreak of hostilities as Johnny-come-lately types. The fact that
they had stuck together, often isolating themselves from the others, and seemed to have their own sources of supply for things
like tobacco, sugar, razor blades and other little luxuries had often irritated Arthur and his companions. But they had grown
used to it and, partly because of Pete's sense of humour, they had
all come to accept them as they were and to generally get on well
together. Now, although Scottie knew he could rely on the continuing friendship of his other European comrades, he was now,
in a way, on his own.

Roy and Scottie and Arthur buried Pete on the slope of
the hill at the edge of the camp clearing just before a torrential
thunderstorm broke. For most of the day they sat under their
shelter, Roy and Arthur smoking and playing cards while Scottie
sat watching the rain and brooding on Pete's death.

As soon as the rain stops, Arthur thought, I'll go and say
hello to Bomber. Bomber was still in the sick bay in the valley,
with several of the other sick Chinese. The rain kept up until
around 5.30 pm and when it eased, Arthur left Roy and Scottie to
walk over towards the sick bay area. As he was heading down the
track into the small valley, he met one of the Chinese men who
acted as a nurse. Arthur sensed something was wrong.

"Your friend is dead," he said. "Bomber?" Arthur whispered. The man nodded. They stood facing each other for a minute with no more said. "When?" Arthur looked up at a small
break in the darkening sky. "Half an hour." His face was like a
mask. There was no emotion. "Half an hour?" Arthur's mind
raced. "But...but I could have come. The rain...did he...? How was
he? Did he say anything?"

"He just eat, makan, half finish. Then bad pains in stomach. Heart." The Chinese man touched his own chest, pressing his flat hand firmly across his heart. "Then calling out for someone called 'Shep'—are you Shep? And also Mr Roy. Then he die."

"Oh, Jesus...Bomber," Arthur moaned, turning away as tears welled in his eyes. "Bomber." He turned back to the man. "He died---quickly?"

The man nodded. Arthur turned away again to walk back to the others. It was too dark and wet now to think of burying Bomber, so after he had told Scottie and Roy, he returned to the sick bay and sat down on a makeshift bunk beside Bomber. He held his hand, which still retained some warmth. He felt it go slowly cold and stiff. He sat for an hour and then lay down beside Bomber. He lay awake, long after the camp had gone to sleep, staring out into the jungle, listening to the soft sounds of small creatures and insects, thinking of Bomber's life and his stories of the First World War, Gallipoli and France, and of all of the things they had been through together at Bakri and since then. In the darkness he reached out several times to touch him, but it was as if he was touching a board. He's gone, Arthur kept whispering. A good pal gone.

19

ARTHUR WASN'T SURE IF IT was a Chinese trait, regarding death more casually than is done in the West, or just an indication of how brutalised all their lives had become during their time in the jungle, but the deaths of Pete and Bomber caused barely a ripple amongst the Chinese in the camp. Immediately after several of them had helped Arthur and Roy to bury Bomber beside Pete, they leapt straight into preparations for the May Day celebrations planned for the next day.

Arthur recognised the fact they had all become somewhat inured to death. It was happening all the time, all around them. There were constant reports of dreadful atrocities being perpetrated by the Japanese on Chinese and Malay villagers who may have collaborated with the guerillas, while they themselves were executing, at a steady pace and often in a quite ruthless and brutal fashion, their own enemies--the Malay and the few Chinese traitors who collaborated with the Japanese. And yet, in the midst of this unreal world, where death was a possibility on any day, either from a Japanese bullet or from horrible jungle disease, Arthur found himself more upset and disturbed by Bomber's death than he would have believed.

After all they had been through together, Bomber's dying seemed to emphasise just how precarious their lives were. Arthur found that it left him deeply depressed for several days. He noted in his diary not long afterwards that it was Mother's Day, thinking at the time how different his world had been when he could celebrate Mother's Day with a card, some flowers or chocolates and a kiss. And back home, right now, people are doing just that, he thought. He sat beneath a gnarled old tree on the edge of the camp clearing, feeling desperately remote from the real world. He thought of his mother and his sisters and brothers. And he thought of Nancy. Strangely, although she had only come into his life in the last month before he had sailed from Australia, he found that she was often on his mind. I wonder if she's got another boyfriend, he thought. She might even be married. She probably thinks I'm dead. He felt enormously frustrated. I might just as well be on bloody Mars, he thought. The distance is no greater.

Because their situation was never really secure, there was, perhaps fortunately, never time to dwell introspectively on things of this nature. There were always shelters or beds to build, food to be gathered, guard duty or cooking to be done--or a new move to be made.

Once again, in early May, three weeks after their last move, they were aware that another was soon to be made. Sou Young and several others were off scouting for a new position where there would be, as the Chinese told them optimistically, 'plenty of everything'. They all knew from past experience that such predictions had to be taken with a grain of salt, but somehow, because they all wanted it to be true, it was difficult not to believe that such a place existed somewhere in Malaya and that their next move might just be the one which brought them to it.

It was during this time, while they were waiting for Sou Young and his party to return, that another traitor, a young Malay man, was captured and brought to the camp. He had evidently come to a nearby kampong and begun making enquiries in the village. Each house, under Japanese regulations, now had to display, on a box on the door, how many persons were living there. The newcomer, whose official capacity, if he had any, was not clear to the villagers, began questioning the fact that seven men were sitting talking inside one house which should only have had two people in it. This was an offence under Japanese law.

The newcomer was also enquiring about an amount of medicine that had recently been bought for the kampong and about two men known to be on the Japanese 'wanted' list. He also asked if anyone knew of several Australian soldiers who were living in the jungle. When he was brought to the camp at gunpoint by three Chinese guerillas, he was arrogant and aggressive under questioning, despite the rough treatment he was receiving from several of his interrogators, including Cut- throat who most frequently assumed the role of physical interrogator--or more correctly, torture--if no information was forthcoming from a prisoner through normal questioning. This one was particularly difficult. He was a young man, tall, well-built, with an almost aristocratic bearing. It was learnt later that his family were very wealthy and owned a rubber estate outside Bekok. On initial questioning, he neither revealed nor admitted anything. When queried about his reasons for making so many enquiries in the village, he more or less told his interrogators to mind their own business. Other Chinese people in the camp knew that he spoke English, but when Arthur questioned him, all he would say, in Malay, was "Sikit sikit tahoelah (little knowledge),"--meaning he knew nothing.

It was decided that he should be kept for the time being. He was offered a meal--rice with brinjel and kelame vegetables-but he refused it, demanding pork and fried rice instead. Cut-throat slapped his face and punched him in the stomach and told him to shut up or learn to be more polite. But he seemed unwilling to learn. He demanded a good bed and blankets and when he was given a hessian bag and told to sleep on the ground, he protested loudly. Cut—throat and several others proceeded to rough him up a good deal more and this seemed to have a chastening effect on him as he was quiet for the rest of the night, although tied up and under guard.

Next day he was subjected to severe torture, being hit repeatedly in the body with rifle butts and beaten with a rotan whip, before being strung out on the ground, to be put through 'the rubber torture'.

Arthur and the others found it difficult to deal with these torture sessions, which seemed to have become a regular part of their lives with the guerillas. More often than not they found themselves repulsed by the brutal acts of the guerilla inquisitors, particularly Cut-throat, who clearly obtained a degree of perverse pleasure in the power he wielded over these traitors--or suspected traitors. And yet they found that it was virtually impossible for them to protest about the process of torture. The Chinese regarded it as fitting treatment for traitors and, if any concern or dissent was expressed by anyone, they were either laughed at derisively or treated with suspicion, as if there might be some ulterior motive in their not wanting the prisoner to be subjected to just punishment. At the same time, they realised that their lives often depended on the weeding out of these 'traitors' and also of extracting information from them about other people who might be collaborating with the Japanese. It was the process they found abhorrent.

A ball of rubber latex on a stick was set alight, then held above the prostrate prisoner, so that the burning drops of liquified rubber would fall on his chest and face in an attempt to break his resistance, to get him to talk. The smell of burning flesh, which was inescapable throughout the camp, was terrible. It was as if he was cooking. Arthur, sitting in his shelter some distance away, found it difficult on several occasions not to vomit. And yet the young man refused to divulge the names of anyone who had collaborated with him.

Eventually, when Cut-throat and the others realised they would get no more from the man, who, almost delirious with pain, was slipping in and out of consciousness, they bayoneted him to death. At that stage, it could only have been a precious relief.

Sou Young returned a week later with the news that within three days the whole camp was to set off on the long trek to the new site chosen by him. Much of the time that he and his party of twenty men had been away was spent preparing the trail which the camp members would have to follow. A great deal of it was through virgin jungle and they had spent three weeks cutting their own path through it with machetes.

The move they were now to embark on was not one which Arthur was looking forward to. His legs and ankles had once again become so swollen and sore-covered that he had difficulty walking. The seriously ill, who now numbered twelve, including Scottie, would have to stay in the hilltop camp with several others who would look after them until they were well enough to attempt the journey. Scottie was suffering from what the Chinese called 'sakit ungin'. In Malay this simply meant 'wind sickness' and covered a multitude of illnesses that afflicted them, ranging from an upset stomach to dengue fever and beri-beri, which couldn't be properly diagnosed at the time. The true nature of his illness, no-one knew. He was just very ill, too ill to move.

Those who were fit to travel set off at around ten on the morning of 25 May. After breakfasting on soup made with a cat that had been brought back to the camp by Sou Young's party, they were issued with individual supplies of rice and flour to carry, along with other food and their own personal equipment. At first they followed tracks that had been used by woodcutters. Some of the time these were easy to follow, but for long periods they found the going difficult, clambering over fallen timber and up and down steep hills through thick vegetation.

By three in the afternoon, it was raining heavily and everyone was thoroughly drenched, but they had to keep moving in order to reach an area, some ten miles from their starting point, which Sou Young had prepared not far from the main north-south train line between Kuala Lumpur and Johore Bharu. They reached it by nightfall, finding a rough shelter had been built there by Sou Young's party. They were able to build a large fire to cook food and to partly dry their sodden clothes.

The rain stopped during the night, but everyone found it exceedingly difficult to sleep comfortably with most of their clothing wet and cold. So, at the first light of dawn, around 5.30 am, most of the camp was up and moving around, getting ready to eat and move on again. Within half an hour of setting off, they came out onto the railroad track which was edged on both sides by thick jungle. For a short while they walked along it. If any train or other vehicle had come along the track, they would have heard it through the rails in plenty of time to slip into the jungle, but nothing came.

After a couple of miles, they turned into the jungle, climbing two very steep hills, one at an angle of almost 70 degrees. Then, following woodcutters' trails again, they came close to a kampong where they had to move carefully through dense thicket. They passed without incident and pressed on along the rough trail for two more hours and then stopped, around one-thirty in the afternoon, to rest and eat. According to Sou Young, they were close to some small settlements, so they were not able to cook. Instead they ate dry rice and some ikan bilis.

After a long rest of just on two hours, during which most of them were able to sleep, they moved on again, working their way cautiously around the perimeter of a large clearing where timber had been cut and cleared away. There was no sign of life anywhere as they made the slow and difficult circumnavigation of the large open area. How much easier it would have been, Arthur thought, to just walk straight across, but he knew how foolish that would be.

Having bypassed the obstacle and moved on, they came, just on dusk, to a similar clearing in which timber had been felled and sawn up but not taken away. The group stood quietly on the edge of the clearing, listening intently for any noises, and then settled down for the night in the jungle. Before doing so, however, they placed themselves near to a reasonable track which could serve as an escape route in the case of an emergency.

It was a terrible night for all of them. The place swarmed with mosquitoes and sandflies, which made it all but impossible to sleep. Arthur had a blanket which he tried to pull to over his head, but somehow the mosquitoes found his hands, or arms, or a piece of exposed neck, which they attacked mercilessly. Even when he was able to stop them reaching his flesh, their constant droning around his ears prevented him from sleeping. No-one in the camp escaped the onslaught and when the moon rose at about 4 am, word was passed through the camp that they were moving on. Nobody complained. They would have accepted anything to get away from the mosquitoes.

Following the track from the clearing, they came onto a long, rough timber road which led them through another big clearing, then onto a second-class road which clearly carried regular vehicular traffic during the day. They made good time along it and shortly met the main tarred road to Labis.

Feeling excessively bold in the eerie, pre-dawn light of the moon, they ambled silently down the road for some time, past several old houses that were set back in the trees at the side of the road. It was risky, but Arthur and all of them felt a sense of elation simply to be walking down a main thoroughfare again. He wondered how long it would be before he could do it without fear.

Sou Young, who was at the head of the column, soon led them off the road and into the rubber, where they followed another rough track to the edge of the jungle. Here they rested until just after dawn, having covered some five miles. The going now became hard and slow as they travelled around and through large areas of swampy ground and then thick bush areas where they had to avoid groups of Malays who were out cutting rotan. Moving a mile or so on past them, they stopped to eat--again dry rice and ikan bilis and some bamboo shoots.

As the day wore on and they tramped successively through jungle, swamp and long grass, Arthur felt the lack of sleep beginning to tell. His shoulders were sore from the load he was carrying in his army pack and, after his blanket fell into a swamp and became heavy with water, even after it had been wrung out, he felt like lying down where he stood and not moving an inch further. His legs and ankles had been extremely painful to begin with, but now they had simply become numb. It was as if he was wearing a pair of lead boots.

Although he felt irresponsible, he threw the blanket away to lighten his load. He did at least offer it to a couple of Chinese men, but they refused, so, when an opportunity arose when no-one was looking, he dropped it in some bushes.

Fortunately they stopped not long afterwards, just before 4 pm, at a place where there was water. According to Sou Young, they would find no more water for several miles, so he decided they should spend the night where they were. There was no argument. It was estimated that they had covered around sixteen miles that day and everyone was feeling the effects of the long trek and the lack of sleep. As soon as the evening meal was finished, nearly everyone, except the guards, who would be rotated frequently during the night, fell quickly asleep. Fortunately there were no mosquitoes, so all in the camp slept soundly.

The next day was more of the same. Three hours through swamps, thigh-deep in mud and water, then onto a jungle track where the going was faster. They passed so close to a Malay kampong that Arthur felt he could have thrown a rock onto the nearest roof. They moved as silently as possible through the underbrush surrounding the kampong-they could easily hear the sounds of children's voices and chickens, so it was assumed those in the village would just as easily hear them. Once past the kampong, they followed a good woodcutters' track to an area where there were large patches of long lalang grass, through which they moved until they came to a river. Travelling beside the river bank for some time they came eventually to a minor road. They were about to walk out of the foliage and onto the road when they heard the sound of approaching vehicles. Everyone dropped to the ground and froze where they were, under cover, while two Japanese military trucks approached. As they passed, Arthur could see soldiers in the back of each of the vehicles. The trucks turned a bend in the road, but Sou Young signalled everyone to remain where they were for some moments, listening to the sound of them travelling on. They heard the trucks slow and come to a stop.

Arthur, who lay close to Sou Young in the foliage by the roadside, heard him curse sharply in Chinese as he heard the trucks come to a halt.

"What's the matter?" he asked.

"We need to go along the road towards them," Sou Young muttered, "to get to our next track."

There was a hurried debate about whether they should wait until the Japanese trucks went on. Perhaps the trucks would be stopping just around the corner at some house, or military location, for some time. A decision was made that they should go carefully along the road and try to make it to the track as quickly as possible without being seen. They filed out of the thicket on the edge of the road and then ran quickly down the road towards the bend. Arthur felt it was strange to be running towards the enemy, who were probably less than a quarter of a mile ahead of them. Fortunately, after little more than two hundred yards, and just before they reached the bend in the road, Sou Young slowed his pace and, pointing to the right, motioned everyone off the road and onto a narrow track, the entrance to which was virtually invisible from the road.

They followed the track for some time, hearing, on one occasion, woodcutters working some distance to their left. They crossed a small river several times, when its winding path blocked their way, by jumping from rock to rock and scrambling over boulders. For part of the afternoon they stuck to game tracks, narrow paths made by jungle animals, probably seladang (buffalo) or ketchang (deer). Shortly after 4 pm, they came to a very pleasant spot by the river. Sou Young and the others decided it should be their stopping place for the night. Several of the group, including Arthur and Roy, bathed in the fast-moving stream and then ate their fill of what food there was. Supplies were running low and they were virtually living on flour and water and whatever jungle vegetables they could find.

Unfortunately, just as they settled down for the night, it began to rain very heavily and everyone was drenched. All except one, that is, who inadvertently started a major fracas in the camp. One of the Chinese had set to, as soon as they had arrived at the site, making himself a crude shelter so that, when the rain started, he was well-protected and dry. But, when several other Chinese tried to barge into the tiny shelter, not just to share it, but to push him out, he fired a shot from his rifle to warn them off. Several of the leaders, including Sou Young, became involved in the heated argument which followed and the man's rifle was taken away from him for three days. However, the other men were instructed to stay out of his shelter, so at least he managed to have a dry night.

The next day was one of the group's best--they made fast and steady progress through easy country, consisting mainly of long grass and established tracks through areas where there were few people. They stopped at noon by a river to have a swim and cook the last of their rice, which had been saved and carried separately. They also took the opportunity to cook up the evening meal while they were there, because, according to Sou Young, they would be camping quite close to a Malay kampong, so it was considered prudent not to light any fires in case they might be noticed. Another relatively easy walk during the afternoon brought them to the place Sou Young had selected. They had covered just on twelve miles since the morning. Sou Young was in a good mood when they arrived and told them that the next day would be the last. They should reach their destination by late afternoon.

As it turned out, they arrived ahead of time, having made an early start and travelled the fifteen miles fast, over easy terrain: flat country with long grass and a few disused and deserted rubber plantations, for most of the way.

When they arrived they found others already there. Arthur knew several of them, including Kok Ching from the Pagoh camp and some from a women's platoon. They found a big, well-prepared camp which, with their group, would total about seventy people. They were surprised and pleased to find several fair-sized shelters and huts already half-constructed for them and a good meal of rice and steamed vegetables waiting.

"This is Sou Lim's Headquarters camp," Sou Young told Arthur and Roy as they began to settle in. "He is not here at the moment, but he will return in a few days."

Arthur and Roy felt positive about the camp from the moment they arrived. It was evidently in an area near the towns of Buloh Kasap and Segamat, although Arthur couldn't establish which town was closer. In any event it meant that they had now virtually retraced the route the 2/29th Battalion had taken by truck on that day in January 1942, some seventeen months previously, when they had driven from Buloh Kasap to Bakri to meet the Japanese.

Many of the people already in the camp were from Segamat, which was a much bigger town than Buloh Kasap. One of them, a young Chinese boy, sixteen years old, called Wong Tek Chiong, befriended the two Australians immediately. He spoke excellent English, having been to the English school next door to the 2/29th Battalion's billet in Segamat.

The following few days were spent settling in to the new camp and during this period they all realised that their new location was quite different from any of the previous ones. People seemed to be coming and going all the time. The camp had a much more aggressive feel to it than any they had been in before. Guerilla soldiers went out frequently on harassing raids against the Japanese and to capture traitors from nearby towns, kampongs and plantations. There was also a heavy training routine, often with full pack, as well as weapons instruction. Kok Ching seemed to be in charge of the training programme and he would cajole and bully and shout at everyone to get them working, exercising and training. "We have to be ready," he said, "for a Japanese attack. There have been reports of a Japanese build-up nearby."

On a morning following one of these heavy training sessions, while the camp was having breakfast and preparing to face another bout of training, a warning whistle was suddenly heard from the direction of one of the guard posts, followed, almost immediately, by several shots and loud yelling. The whole camp burst into action, with people running in every direction, grabbing their arms and racing to positions which had been allocated to everyone for the defense of the camp.

Everyone was alert and ready. The camp seemed to be totally deserted, but scores of people were hidden in positions in the jungle around it, with their lines of fire directed so that they could shower a devastating hail of bullets on anyone who approached the camp from either of the two main tracks leading to it.

A few more shots were heard from the guard-post area, about half a mile away, then silence. For about twenty minutes, no-one moved. They listened and waited. Then Kok Ching's voice was heard from just down the main track. He called out saying that all was clear, but that everyone was to stay exactly where they were. He entered the camp with Sou Lim, whom Arthur and the others had not seen since January, almost five months ago.

Both Sou Lim and Kok Ching now made an inspection of all the defensive positions and the people occupying them, criticising some and complimenting others on various aspects of their preparedness for an attack.

There had been no danger, they told everyone. This had only been a dry run to test the camp on its alertness. The general feeling, however, was that it had been successful and that everyone had reacted as they should.

During the first ten days or so after their arrival, the young student, Wong Tek Chiong, had left the camp for several days to return to his home in Segamat. On his return, he brought several English books, some notebooks and a Japanese newspaper. He also brought a letter written by the two British soldiers, Bennett and Stewart to Sou Young. According to Tek Chiong, the two men were only a couple of days' travel away from this camp. Arthur sat down immediately to write a note to them, to let them know that he and the others had arrived at the new campsite and asking the Englishmen to join them here. He gave the note to Sou Young, asking him to try to get it to Bennett and Stewart as soon as possible. He hoped they might receive it within the next few weeks, but from past experience he knew there was no guarantee they would ever receive it.

Not long after, one of the guerilla groups which had been away from the camp for several days returned with two prisoners, both Chinese. One was perhaps twenty-five, the other in his mid-thirties. They had apparently been collaborating with the Japanese. The older of the two was regarded as a particularly important catch as he had been instrumental in the capture and execution of several guerilla members. Both men were held in the camp for a couple of days during which time they were interrogated and put on trial. At the end of the trial, both were sentenced to death, but the main traitor, the older man, was subjected to a terrible beating--two strokes of the rotan from every member of the camp, at that time around sixty people. '

By the time it was finished, the man couldn't stand, yet he had not made a murmur throughout the whole awful procedure. He was cut loose from the tree to which he had been tied and then dragged away to a place beyond the fringe of the camp where two graves had been dug. There the two men were shot and buried.

Two days later, in the early hours of the morning, another group of soldiers returned with two more prisoners, one of them an elderly, grey-haired Chinese man who protested his innocence vehemently. The two men were questioned intensively during the day. It seemed that the guerillas had considerable evidence against the younger man, but nothing on the older man, who said that he was a doctor. He had been found near one of the group's older camps, abandoned because its location had been betrayed to the Japanese. The old fellow insisted that he had only been collecting jungle vegetables for his family. He was a friend of the Communists, he insisted over and over, and he would never betray them. Kok Ching and Sou Lim were inclined to believe him, although they decided to send out for more information on the man. In the meantime, he would remain alive but under surveillance. The other man was executed.

For several days, about this time, Roy had been feeling ill. Externally, he was suffering from very bad sores--tropical ulcers on his legs--but now he also began to feel extremely weak and tired. He was running a high temperature and felt generally very ill.

That evening, at mealtime, Arthur wandered down to the kitchen hut to see if he could get some soup to take to Roy, who said that he was too ill to go to the normal mess parade. Arthur noted a delicious aroma as he approached the mess hut and, as he stepped inside, asked what was being cooked. The two cooks looked at each other and smiled.

"It's pig tonight, for you and everyone else. But something special for the sick--seladang heart and liver."

Having told them that Roy was ill and could not come to the meal, they put a small slice of liver and heart onto his tin plate from a bowl of cut meat which was to be divided amongst the sick.

"You want some?" Slim asked, offering a piece to Arthur.

"It smells very nice, but I am not sick."

"Never mind," the other whispered conspiratorially, "there is enough to go round."

Arthur took the piece of meat, about as big as two fingers, and ate it. He nodded appreciatively. "Good," he said. "Very nice."

They had been getting meat quite frequently since they had arrived at the new camp, but it was usually pork or chicken, so Arthur felt it a treat to have something which tasted a little 'gamier' than usual. He munched away, savouring the taste as he took the plate of meat and rice up to Roy.

Roy managed to eat one of the pieces of meat and some rice, but left the other. Arthur finished it for him. Later that evening, when they were gathering for a meeting on the parade ground, Slim, Shorty and several other Chinese guerillas approached Arthur. The cook asked, "How did you like the seladang tonight?"

Arthur looked at him curiously. "Very good, very good," he replied. "Why do you ask?"

The man laughed and so did his friends. "That wasn't seladang heart," he said, "that was traitor's heart."

Arthur's mouth dropped open in amazement. The Chinese laughed even more uproariously and then turned amongst themselves in a babble of excited Chinese conversation which Arthur did not understand.

"But, but I ..." Arthur began, but then could find nothing to say. He remembered how much he had enjoyed the meal and thought, my God, I'm a cannibal!

The cook smiled at Arthur's confusion and then, as if to reassure him, said, "It is special food for the sick, not for everyone. Man's heart and liver can save life of sick man. It is very powerful medicine."

Saying nothing, Arthur walked away, his head filled with a turmoil of thoughts. While they seemed to find it perfectly reasonable to cut another human being apart and eat him, Arthur found it difficult to accept, even with the justification that only the vital organs were being used for the sick.

Shortly, he was to see that the procedure was not as widely acceptable to the Chinese as the cook and some of the others would have him believe. A little more than a week later, three more prisoners were brought into the camp. They were questioned during the afternoon and executed in the evening, but, although there were still people ill in the camp, the three men were buried without their heart and livers being removed. Arthur asked Slim and Shorty why they had not done as they had with the previous prisoners. Shorty gestured towards a group of kampong people, dozens of whom had been arriving in the camp during the previous few days after being forced to leave their homes by the Japanese.

He shook his head. "They would not understand," he said.

No, Arthur thought, I don't suppose they would! He felt relieved, to some extent, to know that eating human parts was not some longstanding Chinese custom.

.

20

EVER SINCE JAPANESE TROOPS HAD moved into the area and arrested nine villagers, the people of the nearby Selumpoh kampong had been swelling the population of the camp rapidly. The Japanese had told the rest of the villagers that they would not be permitted to live as close to the jungle as they were and would have to move to the bigger towns. They were told that anyone staying in the village and not obeying the ruling would be killed. The result was that over one hundred villagers, including women, children and even small babies, with as much baggage and as many animals as they could take with them, fled into the jungle to the guerilla camp, swelling the camp population to over two hundred.

An enormous amount of food was being brought in all the time, with ducks and fowls being killed on a larger scale for meals. Three dogs which came with the villagers were also killed and chopped up for soup. During this period, which was rather chaotic, Arthur caused something of a stir amongst the new arrivals. He had been detailed, with several of the other Chinese camp regulars, to move a pile of rice bags down to an area next to the kitchen shelter. The sight of Arthur carrying rice bags brought a crowd of the newcomers, the village people, to a standstill. A buzz of whispered conversation ran through the group as they stood watching him work. He smiled and waved at them. They smiled back, with looks of astonishment spread across their faces. Then they laughed and called out friendly and encouraging comments. Arthur realised they had never seen a white man doing manual labour before, and probably thought they were incapable of it.

It was clear to the camp leaders that, in the long term, the number of new arrivals would pose serious problems for them all as far as food provision was concerned. Some sort of more permanent and regular supply system would have to be worked out and it was suggested that a new site be found, further in the jungle, where the villagers could plant and grow their own crops.

While this was being investigated, another party was sent back to check their vacated village to see if any more food and supplies could be salvaged. They reported that there was a man there who had appointed himself as some sort of leader and had gathered thirty or forty people from the towns of Segamat and Buloh Kasap to ransack the houses of the kampong, taking whatever goods and furnishings they could collect away with them. Some members of the camp knew who he was, so a small group was sent out to see if they could capture him.

In the meantime, the one prisoner they had been holding for some time, the old doctor, had been cleared of suspicion. All of the checks that had been made of him had shown him to be strongly anti-Japanese and a supporter of the guerilla cause. This was borne out when he was told that he was free to leave. He asked if he could stay and work with the sick in the camp and when Sou Lim gave his approval, the old man then asked if his three wives could come to join him.

Sou Lim was slightly taken aback but agreed to the request because so many in the camp were ill. Almost half the kampong people had come down with some sort of illness in the short time they had been in the jungle. Arthur found it hard to believe that the food had made them ill because there was such a variety and so much of it.

Sou Lim was concerned about how he could arrange for the old man's wives to be collected from Segamat where they, and all the remaining people from the kampongs on the edge of the jungle, had been taken. The latest reports indicated that, in addition to the hundreds of local people now crowded into Segamat, some three thousand Japanese soldiers were also in the town.

The Japanese plan was evidently to keep up the pressure on the several guerilla camps in the area by clearing out the kampongs close to the jungle and keeping them clear. Groups of up to three hundred Japanese soldiers would now regularly tour the kampongs and villages from which people had been moved. If they found anyone still there, they would be killed immediately.

The news of these events came to Arthur's camp from a party of six men sent back to the Bekok camp to check the condition of the sick, including Scottie, who had been left there. According to the report, Scottie was now fit and well again and, in a message sent by him, he said he would be making the journey to join the rest within a few days.

Arthur thought that it would be good to see Scottie again. Although he had often been difficult to get on with in the past, Arthur felt the need for European company. During the past few weeks, Roy had been too ill to communicate, although he was now showing some signs of improvement. His legs, however, were still covered with sores which no treatment seemed to cure.

A large number of the kampong people--about eighty, mostly men--left the camp a day or so later to move to a new campsite which had been prepared some four miles deeper into the jungle. It was felt they would be safer there in the event of a Japanese attack. The women and children remained in the main camp another three or four days, until additional huts and shelters had been built at the other site. Everybody noticed the difference their departure made. While they were in the camp there was always movement and noise. Now, suddenly, there was peace and quiet. Arthur had often wondered how the Japanese hadn't heard them from Segamat, which, they had been told, was only a matter of a few miles away.

Now, the remaining regulars set to work to clean the place up. Young Wong Tek Chiong turned up during the clean-up process with various items he had brought from the nearest town, including a couple of English books for Arthur: Rosa Luxemburg and Farewell France. Arthur began reading them immediately and, although he found Rosa Luxemburg dry, he was greatly pleased to get them as they were normally starved of any English reading material.

With the kampong people gone, their days began to settle once more into a routine. Sou Lim had returned from one of his long forays or patrols--Arthur never knew exactly what Sou Lim did to keep him so long on the road. He had seemed like a sort of roving ambassador in the past but now, in the camp, Arthur realised that he also played the role of conventional guerilla leader.

Sou Lim asked Arthur to become an armourer. There were a few unusable weapons in the camp and he felt that Arthur should be able to repair them. He knew Arthur was a signaller, but he felt the Australian was somehow better qualified than anyone else in the camp to fix guns. Arthur accepted the fact that he might well be, but didn't think that was saying much for the others.

His first job was a jammed Lewis machine-gun which had no legs. He set to work on it one morning, laying the whole gun out in pieces on a groundsheet on the edge of the parade ground. Although he wasn't very familiar with the Lewis gun, having seen it stripped down in a demonstration only once before, he found he was looking forward to the job. It was a beautiful day, the sky was clear and the jungle was quiet, except for the sounds of a few birds and distant monkeys in the trees. Everyone was busy doing their own jobs, some out foraging for vegetables, others cooking lunch or building new latrines and food storage shelters. Sou Lim, Sou Young and several of their senior aides were in conference in the headquarters shelter, while a small group on the far side of the clearing were being given drill instruction by Kok Ching.

Arthur began to enjoy himself. He had plenty of time. He took a bottle of gun oil and carefully oiled each part as he cleaned it and laid it down on the groundsheet. As he took the weapon apart, and examined each piece, he began to understand how it worked, but he couldn't work out what had been making it jam. He picked up the main breechblock and slid it back in its track to expose the barrel. He slipped a shell into the beginning of the breech to see how the transfer of shells from the magazine was working. Suddenly the spring-loaded block slipped from his grip and slammed forward, pushing the shell fully into the breech, the firing pin hitting the shell. With a deafening report, a bullet hurtled through the trees on the far side of the clearing.

The camp exploded into action, with people running everywhere, shouting in surprise and concern. No-one was more surprised than Arthur. The weapon had gone off in his hands, while most of it still lay in pieces on the ground. After the initial panic had subsided, Arthur reassembled the gun and gave it to Sou Lim, who had rushed over with several others to see what had happened.

"It seems to be in reasonable working order," Arthur told him, "but the movement is very touchy. Once it's cocked, there's no way of knowing whether it's going to go off on its own, or not."

Later in the day, the gun was leaning against the table in Sou Lim's shelter when someone walked by and brushed against it. The magazine fell off with a clatter and the gun fell to the ground. There was no ammunition in it but the three or four men who were sitting near it and saw it fall dived to the ground for cover. After that the Lewis gun was stored away in the arms shed and relegated, in effect, to the 'too-hard basket'.

That night, after the evening meal, six men left the camp for Buloh Kasap on a mission to capture a particular traitor. As was the case on most of these occasions, word had come in about this person helping the Japanese and betraying the Communist guerillas. A plan had been made to snatch the man as he rode his bicycle to a certain house to play mahjong, as he did every Friday night. He was successfully captured and brought under guard back to the camp at about 11 pm. However, some of his belongings, including incriminating documents which the guerillas had hoped to get with him, had been left at his home. Almost immediately, the six men left to raid the man's home before he was missed there. Again they were successful, returning in the early hours of the morning with two small cases of the man's belongings and papers which clearly indicated his collaboration with the Japanese.

One item in his possession instantly attracted Arthur's attention, alarming him. It was a photograph showing two Australian soldiers, both of whom he recognised as being from his own battalion: Private Mickey Sharpe, who was in Arthur's platoon, and a corporal from C Company called Launder, who Roy knew quite well. The photograph showed the two of them standing naked in a courtyard, with two armed Japanese soldiers standing nearby. Neither of the two men were bound but they were clearly prisoners and about to face either torture or execution. Both Roy and Arthur desperately wanted to know when and where the picture was taken, but the man denied any knowledge of what the photograph was about, or what had happened to the two Australian soldiers. He was questioned further on other issues by the Chinese in their usual manner, which became increasingly aggressive and brutal as the interrogation proceeded. The man finally broke down, admitting his guilt and giving information on some of his activities and on other collaborators, but he would say no more about the photograph of the two Australian soldiers.

He was sentenced to death, executed and buried within ten minutes of the interrogation and 'trial' ending. Despite all Arthur's efforts in the future, he was never able to find out what happened to Mickey Sharpe and Corporal Launder.

Later the same week, a letter arrived in the camp from an Englishman called Maurice Cotterill. He had heard Arthur and Roy had moved into the area from Bekok and had written ten days previously from his own camp near Palong kampong to make contact. In his letter he explained that he had been manager of the Kuala Reman Rubber Estates near the east coast town of Kuantan, in Pahang. Arthur found his letter full of interesting news from outside, including both an Allied and a Japanese version of the struggle for Europe, as well as the sea, air and land battles raging through the islands of the South Pacific. He also said that he was in contact with Major Spencer Chapman, the British officer who was leader of an Allied commando unit called Force 136, which had also been operating behind Japanese lines with the Chinese guerillas.

Cotterill's letter was accompanied by four books which he said Chapman had sent to him. "I shall be glad to have any reading you can supply," he wrote, "as it is lonely on one's own, especially without books, as I have been for most of the time." Arthur wrote in reply immediately, attaching the letter to a small parcel containing the two books which Tek Chiong had brought him.

A regular correspondence began between Cotterill and Arthur over the next few weeks. The letter he wrote on 1 July didn't leave for a day or two, but Cotterill received it within a week and, on 16 July, Arthur received a note back from him which had been written on the 10th, shortly after receiving Arthur's letter. Arthur felt six or seven days in either direction wasn't too bad under the circumstances.

There wasn't a great deal of information they could put in their letters other than local news and whatever outside news or rumours they had heard, plus the occasional personal item. It was clear that Cotterill was lonely for European companionship because in each letter he asked if it would be possible for him to join Arthur's camp.

Roy, whose health was rapidly improving, had taken a keen interest in Arthur's correspondence with Cotterill. "We should try to get the poor bugger over here," he said. "We'll have to start some sort of campaign to get him transferred from Palong."

Their first attempt to organise a move for Cotterill was inconclusive. At this time both Sou Lim and Sou Young were away on separate missions and the camp was under the command of one of the younger guerilla leaders, Cheung Loong Lee, or LL as Arthur dubbed him. LL said that he wasn't sure about a transfer for Cotterill. He thought he might have to go 'higher up' to seek approval for the move. Two days later, when they raised the subject again, he told them that he would definitely have to ask headquarters before any move could be made.

At this time both Roy and Arthur became involved in a dispute with other members of the camp because they had objected to having to sit, almost every night, through three or four hours of patriotic speeches in Chinese. There were a few comments made to the effect that they were willing to eat the cakes which were passed around at the speech meetings, but they weren't conscientious enough to listen to what the Chinese called 'important messages'.

After one confrontation along these lines, LL called Arthur and Roy to a meeting the following morning to ask why they could not see eye to eye with the Party.

"We can't understand seventy per cent of what is being said," Arthur told him. And then, thinking 'In for a penny, in for a pound', he said, "But also, we're very unhappy that we are being prevented from meeting with our friends and compatriots, like Maurice Cotterill."

LL looked embarrassed and nodded. "Yes, it is difficult, I know. But we must make arrangements that are best for all." He hesitated and seemed for a moment undecided.

"But it is best for everybody," Arthur said. "He wants to come here and we want him to come here. Why shouldn't he come?"

"All right," LL said, "as far as I am concerned, he can come. I am going to visit his camp. I will talk to the leaders there."

Arthur and Roy left the meeting elated. They had gone to it expecting a lecture and a dressing-down and had come away gaining what they felt was a major concession.

Two days later, after Sou Lim returned to the camp, they were told that Cotterill would arrive within a week. A few days after this news, however, LL returned from his trip to Cotterill's camp with the message that the leaders there wanted to have a meeting before they would consent to Cotterill leaving. It had seemed to Arthur, from Cotterill's letters, that there was no problem in him leaving, yet now, suddenly, he didn't have permission. Both Arthur and Roy were concerned and suspicious that this situation arose only after LL's visit to the camp.

About a week later, Arthur wrote to Maurice Cotterill suggesting that they try it the other way around, that he ask camp leaders if Arthur and Roy could come to his camp. None of them felt there was much hope that the plan would be accepted, but, Arthur thought, at least it was worth a try.

Five days later, a runner arrived at the camp with a message that Maurice Cotterill would be allowed to leave his camp and would be arriving within two or three days. Three days later, another message arrived, passed on by LL, saying that Cotterill would definitely not be coming. He was not allowed to leave his camp, the message said, because he was needed there.

Arthur and Roy complained strongly, telling LL that they were being messed around and that they were getting heartily sick of it.

LL said he was sorry, but there was nothing he could do.

Arthur and Roy didn't really believe him, but they had to accept what he said. Arthur and Cotterill continued corresponding over the following months but, although they were separated by a relatively short distance, it seemed they would never be able to meet.

Their position during this period, or rather the Chinese attitude towards them, was possibly affected by other events which they had no knowledge of at the time. These events revolved around Scottie, who, as far as they knew, was still at the Bekok camp despite the report they had received in late June that he was well enough to travel and would soon be joining them. This was not to be.

On 14th July, Ah Yen and another Chinese man arrived in the camp having travelled from Bekok. When Roy and Arthur heard of their arrival, they quickly sought them out in Sou Lim's shelter to ask about Scottie. But from the moment they saw the two men, Arthur realised that there was something wrong. Ah Yen was smoking Scottie's pipe, which Arthur would have recognised anywhere. It was an old briar with a curved stem. It had been like a dummy for Scottie. Often he'd have it clamped between his teeth for hours after he'd run out of tobacco. It was something he never would have parted with readily.

Neither he nor Roy mentioned the pipe at that stage, they were both so amazed to see Ah Yen smoking it. Arthur felt he would see what Ah Yen had to say first. "How is Scottie?" he asked.

"Scottie run away," Ah Yen replied to Arthur's initial query.

"Run away?" Arthur asked. "What do you mean? Where to? What happened?"

Ah Yen gave a little derisive laugh. "Ungmor Quoi (the red-haired devil) was on guard duty. Japanese came. He run away. Our camp surprised by attack. Two men killed, one injured." "When was this?" "One week ago." "Where is Scottie?" Ah Yen shrugged his shoulders. "I do not know." "You mean he didn't come back?" "No." "Did you look for him?" "Of course." Arthur and Roy asked a few more questions which Ah Yen answered peremptorily and aggressively. It was clear that they were not getting the full story, because Ah Yen simply was not going to tell it. Something had gone very wrong for Scottie.

As they left the shelter, Roy tapped Arthur on the shoulder and glanced towards the other Chinese who had come to the camp with Ah Yen. He was closing a wallet into which he had just placed a folded piece of paper. It was Scottie's wallet. Again, Arthur and Roy would have recognised it anywhere. Of all the Europeans with whom they had started their sojourn in the jungle, Scottie was the only one who ever had any money. He had come into the jungle with a large supply and guarded it well, either in his pack or a money belt. No-one really knew where he got it from but whenever he wished to pay for some small luxury, which he had asked a runner to bring from a kampong or a nearby town, he would produce a few dollars from his calfskin wallet. Now, this young Chinese guerilla was carrying the very same wallet. And to cap it all, Arthur now noticed that Scottie's rifle was leaning against the wall of the shelter.

Arthur paused to turn and ask about the rifle, the wallet and the pipe, but Roy pulled him aside. "Leave it, Shep," he said. "Leave it for a bit. There's nothing we can do now. They don't want to tell us anything, but we'll find out in time."

"But they're lying," Arthur said. "If he ran away, how did they get his rifle and his wallet? He'd never have left them anywhere. Nor his pipe. I reckon the bastards have shot him."

They heard nothing more of Scottie for some weeks. Ah Yen and his companion moved on quickly to some other assignment, so they had no further opportunity to question them. Sou Lim had also gone off to a series of meetings, one of which, they learnt, was in the Bekok area. Shortly after he returned, Arthur and Roy cornered him briefly to ask again about Scottie and finally heard a story which, knowing Scottie, they felt might have been fairly close to the truth.

"Scottie gave much trouble to the Party," Sou Lim explained. "He always told our men not to work so hard. Some of them followed him and formed a separate group to work against the Party. He was warned many times not to do this--all must work together. He was a dangerous influence."

Sou Lim pulled a battered metal tin from his pocket and extracted a hand-rolled cigarette from it. He lit it, inhaled deeply and blew out the smoke with a long sigh.

"On 6th July, Scottie was on outer perimeter guard duty from 1800 to 2000. He came back to the camp, without orders, after one hour. The Japanese attacked the camp twenty minutes later. Our men were lucky to escape, but still two of them died."

Sou Lim paused, taking a couple of puffs on his cigarette. Arthur and Roy waited quietly.

"Scottie was put on trial," Sou Lim said softly, "for deserting his guard post. He was executed." He looked away from them.

"But why did he come back from his guard post?" Arthur asked. "Did he say the Japanese were coming? Did he come back to warn the camp?"

"No, he did not warn the camp. I do not know why he left his post. I only know what I have told you."

They all sat in silence for a few moments, contemplating Scottie's death.

"How did he die?" Roy asked. "Was he shot?"

"I do not know--probably."

"Could we get his diary?" Roy continued. "Just for his family. And for the record, after the war."

"Maybe. I will ask if it is possible. Perhaps it has been destroyed, who knows?" '

Sou Lim stood up and moved to do other things, signalling the end of the conversation.

During the following days and weeks they asked several times about the diary, but received only the same vague kind of answers. Whenever the opportunity arose, they also asked other people who came from the Bekok area for any news of the Scottie incident. The only variation on the story they had received from Sou Lim confirmed that Scottie had run from the guard post back to the camp, but he had done so only when fired on by the Japanese and to warn of their attack.

Of all the stories they heard, there was none they could believe totally. The truth apparently lay somewhere in the middle and it seemed that, whatever Scottie had done, the Party hierarchy had seen it as an opportunity to rid themselves of someone who had become a worrying thorn in their side.

Towards the end of July, they were involved in another move. It was not forced on them by Japanese manoeuvres, but by the need to keep camp sizes down. More and more civilians were fleeing to the jungle as a result of the Japanese oppression of the villages and towns, and those who fled came naturally to the guerilla camps. The swelling numbers meant that more camps had to be created. Within two months of Arthur and Roy's arrival at their present camp, there were already five new camps established close by in the jungle.

Arthur, Roy and about half of the existing camp were sent off to a new site about four miles away and about three miles from the border of Pahang State. The old doctor was part of the group, as a free man now. Arthur found that he liked the man and the two got on well together. He spoke reasonable English and, as his three wives had not been able to get to the camp yet, Arthur felt that he welcomed the opportunity to spend time with someone who wasn't constantly spouting Communist Party dogma.

But even the new site was quickly filled by the arrival of additional civilians. A great deal of work was required to make the new site livable, but everyone set to with a will, clearing the trees, making dams on the stream to ensure a constant water supply, and building shelters. All the while, mountains of supplies seemed to be coming in, with everybody carrying as much as they possibly could.

Arthur and Roy were out every day chopping firewood. Arthur had put on considerable weight and felt fitter than he had in years. They were getting meat frequently and their general diet had been reasonably balanced for some time.

The men who went out on hunting expeditions would often get the big seladang buffalo, as well as small varieties of deer. There was also wild pig and the kampong people nearly always brought their own domestic pigs and chickens. A few elephants had been shot, producing enormous amounts of meat--three to four thousand pounds--which would be distributed as widely as possible amongst the various camps in the jungle.

Whenever an elephant kill was reported, a team of carriers had to go out immediately to bring back as much meat as possible, usually five hundred to a thousand pounds for Arthur's camp. It had to be cooked and eaten over a period of two, perhaps three, days before it went off. On the occasion of the second elephant kill, in early August, the camp numbers were up around three hundred, so the meat did not last long anyway.

Arthur and Roy both found elephant meat very pleasant. It was tough when fresh but after two or three days it seemed to them much better, with a taste unlike anything they had ever eaten.

Their woodcutting excursions were now a regular routine. With so many people in the camp, the firewood they brought back was quickly used up by the kitchen. One day when Arthur and Roy and some others were out chopping firewood, an enormous spider ran up the handle of Arthur's axe. He dropped it with a yell, but it had already run onto his left arm. He swiped at it instinctively with his right hand, sending it flying to the ground where it stood for a moment, glaring back at Arthur--at least that's what he felt it was doing. Fortunately it hadn't bitten him, for which he was thankful. It was the biggest spider he or Roy had ever seen. Its body was gunmetal grey, about an inch and a half thick and four inches long. Its legs extended a further two inches all around it. It had large pincers and, from where Arthur and Roy stood looking at it, they could see they were bright red. Roy took a swipe at it with the head of his axe, but it scuttled out of the way into the undergrowth.

They had become fairly used to the various creeping and crawling inhabitants of the jungle over the past eighteen months, but something as big as that was an exception. Since the snakebite of the previous year, Arthur had been able to avoid being bitten by anything other than mosquitoes and a scorpion which had put its claws into Arthur's big toe while he was lying in his shelter one day. In surprise, he jumped so high off the bed and so quickly that the scorpion was sent flying. Arthur then hit it with his sandal. The scorpion was a big one, about five inches long, but fortunately it had grasped Arthur's toe with the claws at the front of its body, not the poisonous pincer on its tail.

As the size of the new camp continued to grow, people would be split off to form new camps further into the jungle. Arthur found it astounding to see how quickly places could be transformed with gardens and shelters, and all the while the Japanese unable to prevent it happening.

Reports came in telling of the continued Japanese efforts to deal with the jungle camps. The pattern was always the same. They would attempt to get the village people to move to the major towns from the kampongs that were close to the jungle edge. The villagers would invariably flee to the jungle. The Japanese would then loot and destroy the village, often razing it to the ground and then attempt to flush the villagers back out of the jungle. But the Japanese were evidently unhappy about sleeping in the jungle, so any forays they made towards the camps were never very prolonged or very deep. They would always withdraw and cover the various known exits and entrances, but that was all. They were unable to flush anyone out of the camps, which flourished with a great degree of immunity.

At first the camp leaders were worried when the kampong people began flowing in, in such numbers, without any arms. But then a flood of arms and ammunition also began coming in, so there was no longer any need to worry. One hundred and fifty rifles, Bren, Lewis and Tommy guns, plus plenty of ammunition, were brought in from the Pagoh area and the men and women civilians began training programmes that would equip them to defend themselves and perhaps join the guerilla army.

The Japanese were beginning to feel their lack of complete control over Malaya. Thousands of troops were tied up, just in the area of Arthur's camp, trying to track down and clear out large numbers of Communist guerillas who just would not go away. And that situation was repeated all over Malaya. From the end of June, all of Malaya was subjected to nightly black-outs because of heavy Allied bombing raids which could strike anywhere from Singapore to Penang. But most unnerving for the Japanese was the fact that they seemed impotent in trying to prevent or deal with the increasing number of daring raids and ambushes being carried out by the Communist guerillas.

But the difficulties faced by the Japanese in Malaya affected the civilian population badly. Prices for food and commodities were ridiculously high, often up to ten times the pre-war price, although wages had not increased. Some scarce items were outrageously expensive--leather shoes, which cost M$1 before the war were now M$80; a fountain pen which had cost M$5 was now M$100; a mosquito net or blanket was now the same, M$100. A bottle of cod-liver oil, which had sold pre-war for M$1.50, was now M$100, the same as a bottle of whisky. Staple foods were also priced beyond the reach of the poorer workers who were receiving little more than fifty cents a day under Japanese rule.

11. Examples of English language propaganda sheets prepared in the guerilla camps.

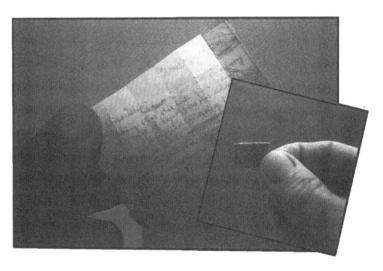

12. Jungle letters were often folded into tiny squares for easy concealment

13. Guerilla currency, hand-printed and numbered by Arthur, sometimes on exercise book paper, was accepted by the Allies at the end of the war as legal tender.

14. Arthur's guerilla force armband.

In addition, the Japanese imposed a series of crippling taxes on the most simple things. For every person living in a house, there was a flat fee of M$1.50; for all persons over the age of fourteen, a M$1 road pass, which was little more than permission to come out of the house onto the streets; for every dog, M$5 and for every cat, M$3. For farmers there was a land tax which, if they were growing vegetables, imposed a flat tax of M$1 for every acre under cultivation, M$3 if they had fruit and M$5 if they were growing rubber. To own a bullock cart, a fee of M$10 had to be paid to the Japanese authorities. A bicycle required a fee of M$1.30 and to operate a shop, M$400. To buy rice, a person was required to hold a card which cost ten cents and an additional five cents tax had to paid every time a purchase was made. Most of the taxes were supposed to be paid yearly, but the Japanese collected them whenever they felt like it.

At the end of August, Arthur and Roy had their first news in months from the old camp which Mac, Bluey, Tom Percival, Les Taylor, Gaje and Smit had gone to when they had all split up. The person who brought the news, a Chinese runner, had only heard it second or third hand from someone he'd met several weeks previously, so Arthur was not sure how to react to it.

"The Indian (Gaje) and the young Eurasian (Les) had a big fight with bayonets," the runner told Arthur. "Both of them were injured."

"What was it about?" Arthur asked.

"I don't know. Just a fight."

"Are they all right? I mean...no-one was killed?"

"I think just hurt, not killed."

"And Tom," Arthur said, "what about Tom Percival?"

"Is he an old man? An Australian?" the young runner asked.

"Yes, that's right."

"I think he is the one who died, an old man I think."

"Died?!"

"Yes. I think it was an older man, an Australian."

Arthur and Roy could get no more from the young man. It was clear that he was only relaying the story as he had heard it. But four days later, they heard more direct news from a Party official who had been to the camp in question only ten days previously. He confirmed that there had been a fight between Les and Gaje, but, as violent as it had been, their injuries had been superficial and they were apparently on friendly terms once again. To their sorrow, the man also confirmed that old Tom had died. He had suddenly fallen ill and unlike the succession of severe illnesses they had all suffered over the months, this time Tom had reacted particularly badly. He had been ill for a week and then simply died in his sleep.

21

THE NEXT SIX OR SEVEN weeks were reasonably stable for the guerillas in that there seemed to be a slight lull in Japanese interest in flushing them out of the jungle. During this time Arthur and his comrades managed to make their lives somewhat livable. He and Roy were now quite expert in constructing comfortable and rainproof shelters and, while some of the others were often prepared to make do with a leaky lean-to, the two Australians always made it their first priority on any site to get their sleeping quarters set up properly right from the start.

This period was also quite a successful one for them as far as food was concerned. There seemed to be no shortage of meat, whether it was from domesticated animals like pigs and hens, or wild ones. On three occasions they had musang, a wild civet cat. Two of them were shot in the jungle, while the third was caught trying to get at the camp's chickens. They also killed a tapir, a curious animal, distantly related to the rhinoceros with three toes on each of its back feet, but four on the front two. As they are nocturnal animals, it was something of a fluke that this one was caught. It was a large animal, providing the camp with over one hundred and fifty pounds of meat, smaller amounts of which were kept for several days after the main meals were eaten, to provide flavouring for soups.

At the beginning of October, after days of heavy rain, the creek which flowed past the camp began to flood badly. A young girl of eight, the daughter of one of the kampong families, was tragically drowned in the rushing stream when it first began to rise. She had gone to collect some water and had slipped on the muddy edge, falling into the fast-flowing waters. Not being able to swim, she was swept away before anyone missed her. Her body was found some hours later, caught in a tree downstream. The girl had been an attractive and happy child who Arthur and Roy liked and spoke to frequently. They were both upset by her death.

A development which served to take Arthur's mind off the tragedy was the arrival of a radio. It had been saved from one of the kampongs which had been razed by the Japanese and, although it wasn't working, they were assured by Lem King and Ah Lian, who brought it in, that only a good battery was needed.

Lem King was something of a secret agent. He was a Party member but had a job outside, driving a truck for the Japanese. He had the opportunity to travel to several parts of Malaya and would regularly report on his travels to the guerilla authorities. The radio had been given to him by another Communist agent, Teo Ee Lim, who worked as the chief detective under the Japanese in Segamat. He also used his position there to report on traitors and if any Communist guerillas were captured, he would do his best, without endangering his own position, to set them free.

The radio that Lem King and Ah Lian brought in was an ordinary home receiver, a Philips model with a basic short-wave capacity, which had been converted to run off a six-volt car battery.

Several days elapsed before they were able to get a car battery into the camp, but much to Arthur and Roy's surprise and everyone's delight, once the radio was hooked up to the battery, it worked perfectly and they all sat up until midnight listening to whatever news they could hear:

One of the sessions they tuned in to was a broadcast by the Japanese authorities, in English, which included a segment in which Emperor Hirohito spoke, through a translator, for a few minutes. Italy had entered the war because of Germany, he said. They had fought like brothers, but now that Italy had been defeated and was out of the war, it would make no difference to Japan.

During the following day, Sou Young and others in the headquarters shelter listened to the radio for the whole morning, with the result that the battery went quite flat and it was several more days before they could get it recharged in a nearby village and back to the camp again.

When it was reconnected, they managed this time to tune in to what seemed to be a French station, probably a Japanese-controlled station in French Indo China. One of the Chinese men, who had lived in Saigon and who spoke French, translated for the listeners. He said that the broadcast was about how Britain was being crippled by strikes--a walkout on the docks, an electricity strike and the greatest coal strike of this century. Arthur found it difficult to believe that this could happen in a country so hard-pressed by the war, and dismissed it as propaganda.

The problem of recharging or replacing the battery became increasingly annoying, as it left them out of touch with what was happening in the outside world. Of course, previously, without the radio, they hadn't been able to get the news anyway, but now that they had the means at their disposal, they became frustrated and impatient as they waited for the return of the battery from its frequent recharging.

They even devised a complex, Heath-Robinson affair with which they tried to charge the battery. Someone had brought a small generator to the camp, so it was rigged, with makeshift belts, to a bicycle wheel. With someone pedalling like fury, sufficient electrical current could be generated to recharge the battery, but it took so long, and so much effort on the part of a succession of totally fatigued pedallers, that it was abandoned. The old system of using the battery up and then sending it out to a local village for recharging, despite the effort involved in carrying it back and forth and the inherent dangers, was reinstituted.

But even this intermittent access to the radio was not to last for long. Arthur and Roy spent the evening of 12 October with members of the headquarters group, under shelter from the pouring rain, listening to various radio broadcasts, including one from Australia which gave details of the war in Europe and the Pacific. It said that a huge barrage of artillery fire was devastating the German city of Aachen, Soviet forces were crossing into Poland, Churchill and Stalin were meeting in Moscow and over one thousand bombers had made a massive air assault on Formosa.

But what pleased and excited them most was an item that told of a number of Chinese from Singapore who had somehow managed to make their way by sea, and then overland by devious routes, to reach the Nationalist Chinese forces in Chungking with reports of the activities of the Communist forces in the jungles of Malaya. The report mentioned that there were a number of Allied troops living in the jungle with the Communist forces.

"You hear that?" Roy exclaimed excitedly. "At least they know we're in here."

"I wonder if Mum or Nance heard that?" Arthur said. "Of course they didn't say any of our names, but at least it might give them some hope."

The news delighted and encouraged the two Allied soldiers and they both went to sleep that night thinking fondly of home. They were awake again at 3.30 am, trying to monitor a BBC broadcast. There seemed to be something wrong with the atmospherics, perhaps a thunderstorm in the south, because the reception was so bad they could hardly hear it.

They broke briefly from their listening vigil to have breakfast and were just settling down again to try to pick up some news when shots were heard from the direction of one of the camps below them on the hillside. The camp was about a mile away but, to Arthur, the shots seemed to be much closer.

In these situations they were used to reacting with lightning speed, carrying out a predetermined set of plans which varied depending on how much firing was involved, how far away it was and so on.

A couple of shots in the distance would have everyone grabbing their arms and belongings and being ready to run, but not actually moving from the campsite until word came back from the guards.

On this occasion the firing was heavy and continuous, with many automatic weapons involved. It was clearly an all-out Japanese attack on one of the camps. Roy, Arthur and Tek Chiong had instructions, in a case like this, to head for a particular clearing in the jungle about two and a half miles away with the radio, their rifles and whatever farming equipment they could carry. Things were happening quickly. People were rushing in every direction and there were shouts that the Japanese were coming.

Arthur, Roy and Tek Chiong slithered down towards the creek, which had risen some four or five feet during the past thirty-six hours. They had to cross it, via a log, to strike the path that would take them to the clearing. Roy went first. Tek Chiong followed, carrying the radio, but halfway across he slipped on some mud left on the log either by Roy or one of the others who had also been running across it, making for the escape route.

Tek Chiong plunged into the muddy torrent with his pack, radio and all, and disappeared from view for several seconds, surfacing some yards downstream, struggling with the radio as the water carried him along. He reached out with one hand and grabbed the branch of a dead tree lying in the creek and, with Roy's help, was able to clamber, spluttering and choking, up the muddy banks on the far side.

Arthur made it across and scrambled downstream to help.

"You take the radio and his pack," Roy said. "I'll give Tek Chiong a hand. We'll follow you."

With Roy and Tek Chiong behind him, Arthur, struggling under the additional weight, joined a couple of Chinese who were pushing up through thick bamboo to reach the path. The shooting continued. Low commands were given as several of the guerillas ran by in the dense undergrowth. Within minutes, Roy and Tek Chiong had become separated from Arthur and the others. When they arrived at the clearing, Arthur waited anxiously, but there was no sign of his companions. He asked the others if they had seen Roy and Tek Chiong, but no-one had. After a while, when the firing seemed to have stopped, he began to make his way back to try to find them. Moving carefully and quietly, he covered the whole distance to the campsite where, from the sound of voices he heard there, it was obvious that the all-clear signal must have been given. Roy and Tek Chiong were already back there, none the worse for wear, which was more than could be said for the ruined radio.

The Japanese had not reached their camp but, according to the reports that came in later in the day, they had been led in by two Malays, first to an old camp, then on, by jungle paths, to the camp just below their own position. Normal guard posts had been established around the camp at a distance of about half a mile from the camp itself.

The exchange of fire between the guards and the Japanese were the first shots they had heard. According to the report, the Japanese had disregarded the automatic weapons firing at them and charged directly on, sustaining casualties but by-passing the guards' position, to reach the camp area within five or six minutes. There the fighting continued in earnest while the camp members, including large numbers of kampong people, scattered into the jungle. The raiders burnt down all of the huts and whatever clothing and equipment that was left behind.

Fortunately, the Japanese did not continue on to the next campsite and, despite the chaos and panic, only three guerillas were wounded, not badly, while three or four Japanese soldiers were killed.

From the sound of the shooting, both Arthur and Roy had expected much worse casualties on both sides. Apparently, none of them could shoot straight.

Sou Lim, who had been away from the camp for several days with a Sakai guide they called 'Jungle Bird', had a lucky escape from the Japanese. The two men were returning to the camp and knew nothing of the attack. The firing had stopped and the Japanese, on their way out of the jungle, had stopped to rest briefly on the track. Rounding a bend, the unsuspecting Sou Lim and Jungle Bird almost walked right into the Japanese. When the Japanese saw the two men, who hesitated briefly on the path, they beckoned to them to come forward. Sou Lim and Jungle Bird naturally turned and ran, diving into the jungle to flee as fast as they could. The Japanese loosed a hail of bullets in their direction, but then let them go without mounting a chase, something they would not have let happen if they had known how close they were to getting one of the Communist Party's key guerilla leaders.

Back in the camp, Roy and Arthur were now instructed to take the sodden radio and some other gear to the safe clearing to try to repair it. When it was eventually taken apart, they found that, in addition to being very wet, a small valve had been broken.

Fortunately they had several hours of clear sunshine in the early part of the day which was sufficient to dry the parts out. But when heavy clouds gathered in the mid-afternoon and it began to rain steadily, they gathered the parts together and reassembled them under shelter, in the hope that, with a new battery, they might at least get some reception from the damaged set. But two days later, when they had an opportunity to hook up a freshly charged battery, there was no response from the radio and they had to accept the fact that they would have to try to obtain a new valve, or a new radio.

Not long afterwards, two Malay traitors were captured. Although they were not the two that had led the Japanese into the guerilla camps, they seemed to be implicated in the attack in some way. There was enormous animosity towards them from the camp population during their brief trial, and their execution was particularly gruesome. One was bayoneted to death while the other was paranged! Tied with his back to a tree, the horror-struck man could only shut his eyes as a heavily built Chinese guerilla, wielding a large, razor-sharp parang, literally split the unfortunate man down the middle with one blow. An explosion of blood and gore splattered both the executioner and the bystanders.

Later, in what the guerilla leaders treated as some sort of ritual, the two men's hearts and livers were taken and fried up with onions, flour and pepper, and small pieces were handed around to camp members.

Both Arthur and Roy felt more than reluctant to participate in the procedure, but that evening, in the darkness of the jungle, broken only by the flickering light of the campfire, they became caught up in what somehow became a base re-enactment of one of the most primitive of human actions, each partaking of the proffered meat. Both men later agreed that it tasted no different to the heart and liver that one might purchase from a suburban butcher.

The following day, they went about their business almost as if nothing had happened. For a while Arthur tried to think his actions through and found no real way of explaining them to himself. He and Roy, and of course the other guerillas, had seen so much death and destruction, so many dead bodies that had once been living people, that he felt largely inured to the sight of it. He told himself that death, for all of them, was just around the corner, whether from a Japanese bullet or from starvation or disease. Life had become cheap, their own lives as well as those of their adversaries. It now seemed quite natural to take the life of anyone who threatened their lives, either directly or indirectly, and, although they clearly didn't need the food value the hearts and livers might provide, it was a relatively simple step to join the others in the camp in what he later saw as a dark and inexplicable rite.

Fortunately, for many of the months that followed they did not have to confront their consciences with moral dilemmas of this kind as there were no more executions of captured traitors for almost a year, at least in the camps in which they found themselves. There was, however, a particularly upsetting execution of one of their own men, Lem Pin.

Lem Pin had been a good friend to Arthur and Roy. He was the one who had brought Tom Percival, Gaje and Roy to the deserted Sakai camp, back in March of 1942, to meet up with Arthur, Bomber, Jock, Mac, Bluey, Les, Scottie and Pete. Over the long months since then, although he had not always been in the same camps at the same time, he had appeared every now and then to greet Arthur and Roy as old friends. He had apparently worked well for the Party on many missions, but then had got mixed up with another Chinese guerilla called Ten Chen who, in retrospect, turned out to be a bad influence on Lem Pin. Ten Chen had been the man who had arrived in their camp carrying the Dutch pistol which Arthur had recognised as Smit's.

Ten Chen and Lem Pin had begun working against the Communist Party, or so the Party claimed during Lem Pin's trial. When leading other soldiers out on various missions, they had worked a sort of protection racket on villagers and others, persuading them to donate pigs, fowls and other food supplies which they did not hand over to the Party. They sold the livestock elsewhere, keeping the money for themselves and storing the tinned food supplies in the jungle in a hidden cache which also contained twenty rifles and ammunition.

Lem Pin was sentenced to die, but before the sentence was carried out, he asked to be allowed to make a speech. Arthur felt a wave of pity sweep over him as he stood watching Lem Pin, listening to him speak. He had always been a happy, good-natured man and Arthur found himself feeling that the events that led up to this moment had not really been Lem Pin's fault. In a strong voice, he said he knew that he had done wrong and that he hoped his death would be a profit to others. He said that he only wanted to make two final requests. He asked firstly that the Party write to his mother to say that he had died of sickness and, secondly, that he be given a last good meal before he died. Both requests were granted. He remained affable and friendly to the last, cracking jokes with the men who dug his grave and even with those who tied the rope around his neck to garotte him.

Apart from Lem Pin's execution, there were a couple of trials of other camp members, on charges such as leaving a patrol, or going to sleep on duty. The man who left the patrol had simply cooked himself a small meal and gone to sleep. He was sentenced to die, but several people pleaded on his behalf, saying that as he was only an uneducated workman who had been in the Party only a short while, he knew no better. He had been working in carrying-parties and had not been instructed in the correct procedures and responsibilities while on patrol.

To their credit, at least in Arthur and Roy's eyes, Sou Lim and the other leaders granted a reprieve to the young man, giving him, instead, two months hard labour, mostly in the kitchen. The men caught sleeping on guard were also given hard labour.

In the days following the Japanese attack, they prepared for another move. Although the enemy had not penetrated as far as their camp, apparently unaware of its existence, the camp leaders still considered it prudent to move further away. Not much further, as it happened. Again, like their last move, it was only about four miles, but in country like this, four miles often seemed like four hundred.

The track was terrible but Arthur felt it was worthwhile because it would be equally difficult for any Japanese attackers to come the same way. They found on their arrival, though, that the new site was hardly worth the trouble. There was almost no water and food-collecting would be difficult. Nevertheless, they set themselves once more to the task of making the situation livable. There were a couple of deserted huts, left by previous guerilla occupants. Arthur, Roy and some others began to clean them up and nearly wrecked them in the process. They had been cutting down some trees in order to let more light into the clearing when one which Arthur had chopped through fell the wrong way, directly towards one of the huts. Fortunately, a strong creeper, attached to another tree, was growing from it and swung it a little so that, instead of falling squarely in the middle of the hut, it just hit one corner, hurting no-one. The result was one slightly tilted, but at least still-standing house.

Once they had settled in and the food supply system had been sorted out, they began producing the first partisan currency with a small, simple printing press, carried in not long after their arrival. As Arthur had demonstrated his ability in drawing up a series of war maps of Malaya and a large-scale map of Johore over the previous weeks, he was put in charge of designing and printing the first guerilla banknotes; one dollar bills, supposedly equal to Malay currency.

It was very basic: a piece of white paper with a few Chinese characters, three red stars and a serial number stamped in one corner. The Communist authorities then made it known that they would pay a salary to soldiers in the guerilla army, and that all camps would now pay for their purchases with the new banknotes. Of course, the money was of no use in Japanese-occupied Malaya--in fact it could be extremely dangerous to have. Anyone seen or suspected to have the money in their possession would immediately be arrested and interrogated and would probably not survive. The guerilla authorities promised, however, that when the war was over, the Allies would honour the bills and exchange regular Malayan currency for it on a dollar-for-dollar basis.

It was a rash promise, but to their credit, at the war's end, the liberating forces did honour the commitment of the guerilla army leaders. Of course there was no way of knowing they would in advance and yet, somehow, the people of Malaya who helped the Chinese guerilla army believed it would be so and they accepted the new money readily. The rest of the soldiers in the camps did also and when, towards the end of November, they all lined up to receive their first month's pay of one dollar per man, all were genuinely pleased. It was, in a small, strange way, Arthur felt, like re-establishing a link with the real world.

Later, as the currency became more widely used and accepted, they began producing five and ten dollar notes as well as the smaller denominations of fifty, ten and five cents. For Arthur, this entailed many hours of numbering, which, unlike the process of printing, had to done by hand, changing the number on the stamp each time.

It was during this time that a number of confusing reports came into the camp about the Javanese soldier Smit, who had left with Mac and Bluey and the others. One of the leaders from another camp, on a visit, said he'd heard that a Javanese called Smit had turned traitor. His story was that Smit had been on guard over a Malay traitor and somehow the man had escaped. Smit had been put on trial for allowing this to happen. He was placed under guard but, making the excuse that he had diarrhoea and needed to go to the latrine, he managed to escape, making his way to Pagoh where he informed the Japanese of the camp's location before leading them to it.

Two weeks later a different story emerged when a man from Pagoh camp arrived. He said that Smit had been sick for several weeks and seemed, for a time, to be mentally unbalanced. During one period he had fired a shot at one of the Chinese camp members. He was grabbed by others and restrained. The camp leaders told him that they realised that the reason he had fired the shot was because of his illness and let him off without any punishment. Two days later, in the same camp, two traitors were put on trial and executed. Smit became quite agitated at the sight of the execution and became frightened that the same fate was in store for him. So he fled the camp and made for Pagoh where he was picked up by the Japanese. They took him to Muar, where, if the other reports are accurate, he died, though whether from his illness or Japanese interrogation, no-one knew.

Although they were without a radio in their new camp, they still seemed to get a reasonable flow of news from the outside world even if it was mostly unverified reports which came to them either third- or fourth-hand, or sometimes even more removed from the original source. But occasionally they received first-hand reports, such as those from Lem King, who had brought them the radio in early September. He had been down to Singapore, travelling on forged papers and posing as a businessman from Segamat. While in Singapore he saw Japanese soldiers herding a large number of Chinese people into an enclosure in the Katong district, an area on the waterfront to the east of Singapore's town centre. He had no idea, nor could he find out from the few questions he asked before moving quickly on, what was happening. While in Katong he also saw part of the enormous hulk of a Japanese warship that had been either torpedoed or bombed some ten days previously and had burnt out or sunk.

Some of the local news they received included information that large numbers of Allied prisoners of war had been brought up from Singapore and put to work building an aerodrome near Senahkung. Both Arthur and Roy wondered, when they heard the news from Ah Lian, who had come into the camp with Lem King after a period outside, whether any of their mates from the 2/29th might be among the men working on the project.

And there was overseas news, news that the Allies had re-taken New Guinea and that the Germans had run into trouble in their campaign in Russia and were bogged down in the snow around Moscow. Surprisingly, both of these reports, which were encouraging to the guerillas, came from Japanese news-papers in Malaya.

But if the tide seemed to be slowly turning as far as the war as a whole was concerned, to Arthur and Roy it appeared to be having little effect on their situation in the jungle. The Japanese were renewing and increasing their pressure on the guerilla camps. In mid-November, thirteen trucks carrying some four hundred Japanese soldiers arrived in Selumpoh to gradually move in on the surrounding camps.

A series of reports coming in to the camp over the next few days indicated that the Japanese now had a firm plan and were about to make a determined effort to find the guerilla camps and root them out. The first reports Arthur and Roy heard were that over one hundred Japanese had arrived in each of the nearby areas they called '80 acres' and '120 acres'. As a secret track led from '120 acres' to their present camp, they could only hope that the Japanese would not find it. Next they heard that twenty-six truckloads of soldiers had been taken to Lun Ching

Ching kampong, near Selumpoh, and had been busily engaged in cutting tracks into the jungle.

Sou Lim told Arthur and Roy that the Japanese wanted to reach the creek on which they were camped, because they knew that the camp existed somewhere along the creek. "They can only have been told by traitors," he said. "They want to cut around through our forward camps and to block our avenues of escape in those directions."

Then they heard that one of the forward camps, which had been abandoned about ten days previously, had been burnt out and destroyed. Only smouldering ruins remained, surrounded by many Japanese footprints.

Arthur and six others were detailed to prepare a new camp-site. It was little more than half a mile away, but the camp leaders thought it to be safer than their present one. Safer or not, Arthur found it to be a much more pleasant position on which a great deal of work had already been done. There were five huts already complete, with four more half-finished. Built in two rows, a hundred feet apart, the huts on the site covered a large area. Over a period of some days, they felled more trees to let the sunlight in and cleared more of the land, gradually making the place more livable. By the time they had made the move to the new camp and everybody had shifted in, they were all very pleased with the place. It seemed one of the best they had been in so far.

Arthur's twenty-sixth birthday came a few days after the move. He was still occupied with drawing maps and printing the new currency, but he was now also giving morning and afternoon lessons to new guerilla recruits on the use of arms-in particular the .303 rifle, the Tommy gun, the Bren and hand grenades, of which they now had a few different types.

Both Roy and their young Chinese friend Tek Chiong had been sick during the move and the settling-in period. Roy had been having more trouble with his kidneys. Nobody could be sure what was wrong, and the old doctor couldn't diagnose it properly either, but Roy was very ill and experiencing bad pains in his kidneys. Tek Chiong had dysentery and was constantly vomiting. They were concerned at one time that he may have cholera and that he would dehydrate so rapidly he would die. But he gradually came through and his health slowly improved.

Then the old doctor was laid low after an unnerving experience with a centipede, a huge one, some ten inches long, which crawled onto his face while he was asleep and bit him. As he came awake screaming, the centipede bit him three more times before he could brush it away. The old man almost passed out from the pain alone, which was terrific. He couldn't speak and his whole face began to swell up like a football. For a few minutes no-one knew what to do. Then Jungle Bird, the Sakai who knew more about survival than all of the rest of the camp put together, called for cigarettes, or tobacco. As people pulled their precious tins of tobacco from their pockets, Jungle Bird gathered together a handful of tobacco and soaked it in a little water then squeezed it in a handkerchief until a thick, brown, nicotine juice came through. He rubbed it swiftly over the old doctor's face. Although there was no immediate relief, after several applications, over a period of hours, the pain lessened considerably and, by the middle of the following morning, the old man was feeling much better and recovering rapidly.

During this time, in mid-December 1943, they experienced what seemed to be a slight respite from Japanese pressure, although they later learnt that there had really been no let-up at all: the Japanese had simply turned their attention to other nearby areas where they felt the chance was greater of more immediate gain against the Communist guerillas.

On 14 December, one of the outer camps received news that a party of about two hundred and fifty Japanese were coming along one of the jungle trails. They cleared the camp, laying in wait in the surrounding jungle.

By terrible chance, a party of five guerillas, out on patrol and knowing nothing of the impending Japanese arrival, came onto the main camp trail from another track and entered the deserted camp before the Japanese arrived. As several of the patrol group were wearing khaki caps similar to those of the Japanese, one of the men hiding in ambush mistook them for the enemy and fired on them. Before the mistake had been realised, three of the patrol had been killed and two wounded, one with his leg badly smashed.

The Japanese, only a short distance away, heard the shooting and thinking that it was directed at them, made for the nearby river, also firing away, but only at imagined targets. Eventually, realising that the element of surprise in their own intended attack had been lost, they withdrew, but not before killing an unfortunate civilian, one of the kampong people they found as they rushed towards the river. The poor man's body was found later, tied up to a tree and horribly hacked by dozens of bayonet thrusts.

The whole incident had been a case of bad luck, but it resulted in a firm order being issued forbidding the wearing of any khaki caps similar to the Japanese uniform.

As their new camp was some distance from the outer camp where the incident occurred, the group was not sufficiently concerned to begin planning an immediate move. Instead, they began to prepare stronger defenses. Over the period leading up to Christmas and the New Year, considerable time was spent digging weapons pits at strategic locations around the campsite and by the river, where clear lines of fire could be found along possible avenues of attack.

In the meantime the Japanese continued to use the area around '120 acres' as a base from which they made numerous sorties into the jungle, using a variety of techniques in an effort to achieve surprise. Arthur's group learnt that the Japanese had been informed that the guerillas had a track running out of the jungle to Selumpoh village, and another to the small town of Tunkutiga, and were secretly trying to cut their own track through the jungle to intersect one of the guerilla paths which would then lead them to the camps.

Another approach they tried was to move about eighty Japanese soldiers disguised as Chinese labourers, into the area between Tunkutiga and '120 acres'. They were carrying chunkels (small shovels) and other work instruments, wheeling along a couple of carts containing their rifles and other arms hidden in bags or between sheets of latex from the rubber plantations. The guerillas never learnt what the Japanese hoped to achieve by this tactic, other than to take a few villagers by surprise, because nothing came of it. Any group that size entering the jungle area, away from the rubber plantations, aroused immediate suspicion regardless of their clothing.

On this occasion, after they'd spent a reasonable amount of time pretending to be labourers, they seemed to realise that they were fooling no-one, so they gave up and returned to their base. Arthur noticed, however, a general increase in the pressure tactics on the guerillas. The ten to fifteen miles between Jementah and Segamat were patrolled by Japanese soldiers and conscripts who had been warned that they must increase their vigilance and report any person carrying anything at night. The penalty for failing to do so was death.

During this period, Arthur had resumed his correspondence with Maurice Cotterill, and with Bennett and Stewart who were in a separate camp. But for some reason it now took up to six weeks for any letter from them to reach him. He could only presume that it was because of the increased activity of the Japanese. As the two men were still keen to join up with Arthur's group, he raised the question once again with Sou Lim.

"They can come here," he told Arthur and Roy, "but one part of the journey is very difficult, through a big rubber estate." He lit a small, blackened pipe and puffed a few times to get it burning properly. "There is one day travelling through a place where there are plenty of Tamils and Malays. If our men pass by they pretend not to see, but if white men come through, they may talk. Dangerous." '

"But is there no other way?" Arthur asked.

Sou Lim paused a moment, thinking. "Yes, there is. It might be possible, but they would have to travel some distance by river. We are trying to get a boat from some Malays to make use of this route ourselves. It has already been discussed with headquarters and a runner is checking the route at the moment. If it is okay, then I suppose the two men could come that way, or even return with the runner."

"How long would it take?" Roy asked. They had both heard that sort of promise before, and seen nothing come of it.

"Perhaps two weeks," he looked down at the ground, nodding slowly, "perhaps longer."

There was no more that Arthur or Roy could say or do except wait, once more, to see what happened.

A couple of weeks later, two days before Christmas, a letter arrived from Bennett and Stewart indicating that they were halfway there. And then, on Christmas Day, which was also Tek Chiong's birthday, they received word from a runner saying that the two men would be arriving within a week. When they had still not arrived by the middle of January, Arthur and Roy heard from a messenger that the two men were both ill and could not travel. They would come as soon as they were well enough to travel, according to the runner's message.

Was this just another of the interminable excuses they had been given for months? They had no way of knowing. In the weeks leading up to that Christmas at the end of 1943, Arthur's health had improved markedly. The lump and pain in his stomach had disappeared and his right shoulder seemed to have straightened itself up again. In addition, he had put on more weight. The food supply was better organised at this Camp than at previous ones, so that if someone wanted extra ladles of rice at the end of a meal, they could have them, as well as more ubi chips and other vegetables.

Arthur found that, unlike any other time in the jungle, he was putting on more weight than he wanted to. He now weighed about 195 pounds. Neither Arthur nor Roy were particularly worried, however, as the general feeling amongst the guerillas was that if one could make up a bit of weight during good times then it was wise to do so, because there was no guarantee that those good times would last. Arthur was to discover how true this was just a few weeks later.

For Christmas dinner, by way of celebration, they were allowed to stuff themselves with five bowls of vegetables each. By contrast, New Year's Eve was comparatively quiet. The only excitement was the extensive planning and preparation for a major attack on the Japanese in Buloh Kasap scheduled for 1st January. Over one hundred armed men and a similar number of carriers were to be involved, including thirty men from Arthur's camp. Both Arthur and Roy volunteered, as they had for other missions on many previous occasions, but were once again refused on the same grounds as always--as Europeans, they were too conspicuous.

So, on the first day of 1944, while the attack operation was underway, Arthur and Roy spent their time fishing, lying around reading, smoking a new supply of tobacco, and talking.

The guerillas attacked Buloh Kasap in several areas simul-taneously. While one band of men closed in on the area of the town's police station, which the Japanese were using as a local headquarters, another group prepared to blow up the railway line beneath a train carrying Japanese soldiers. As the train drew closer, the men, hiding in the jungle verge, prepared to press the plunger which would blow the line under the engine. They had placed themselves strategically on both sides of the track to deal with the Japanese soldiers and police who were expected to be in the first and last carriages of the four-carriage train. When they had been eliminated, the cargo in the centre carriages could be looted and carried off.

As the train approached the mark, however, they noticed that it had what looked, in the darkness, to be a fifth carriage on the end. The charge of gelignite went off under the engine as planned, derailing it and throwing it on its side, bringing the rest of the train to a sudden grinding halt. With smoke and steam issuing from the stricken monster, the surprised Japanese soldiers poured from the first and fourth carriages, as expected, to meet a hail of automatic fire from the darkness.

Many of them stayed in the carriages to try to return the fire, but the wooden sides of the carriages offered them little protection and many were killed without ever seeing where the bullets were coming from. As the firing from the train began to die down, with the guerillas feeling they might be close to achieving their objective, something unexpected happened. One soldier, or railway-man, had managed, in the darkness, to creep between the derailed first carriage and the second, and uncouple the two, so that suddenly the whole train began to pull away, back in the direction from which it had come. The fifth 'carriage' had been another engine!

The tactic of using two engines, one at the front and one at the rear, enabling escape from unexpected situations in either direction was to be used extensively by the Japanese throughout Malaya from that time on.

Meanwhile, at the first sound of explosions and firing on the track, a mile or so out of town the other band of guerillas had let go with everything they had, including grenades, at the police station in Buloh Kasap. This also resulted in a pitched battle which went on for some time. Only a few individuals ran from the station when the shooting began--as they were quickly cut down, the rest remained inside to try to return the fire from there. The fighting continued for some time, with the station being all but demolished, until a party of Japanese soldiers arrived by truck from Segamat, less than five miles away. The guerilla band then pulled back quietly into the jungle and disappeared.

The third aim of the attack on Buloh Kasap had been to eliminate a notorious traitor who had betrayed many sympathisers, turning them over to the Japanese. His house, which was on the outskirts of the town in a small grove of palm trees, was surrounded before the other attacks had begun. It was essential that he be killed before the other two attacks took place, because once any shooting began, he would be on his guard. So that no shots would be fired, it was arranged that the man be 'paranged' as he opened the front door of his house.

When one guerilla went to the verandah of the house and knocked, the traitor came to the door. Before opening it, though, he enquired who was there. Posing as someone else, the guerilla, who knew the traitor in pre-war days, told him through the door that he had come because a friend of the man was sick. The traitor, also carrying a parang, opened the door. Both men struck at the same time. The guerilla hit the traitor in the chest, splitting him wide open in one sweep, but at the same moment, the traitor's swinging parang caught his attacker in the head, splitting his skull and killing him instantly.

The traitor fell to the floor, still alive and screaming for help. Another guerilla leapt forward quickly and with one stroke of his parang almost severed the traitor's head to finish the job. The guerilla party then fled into the jungle while the dead man's family cowered inside the house expecting a similar fate.

The raiding parties finally returned to their camps three days later. Although a total of three guerillas had been killed during the raid on Buloh Kasap, including the one who had been paranged, there had been no casualties from the contingent that had left from Arthur's camp.

At almost the same time as the return of the raiding party, another small group came into the camp carrying the young man whose leg had been hit during the incident in December when a returning guerilla party had been fired on by mistake. The man was in a shocking condition. He had sustained a terrible wound which, because of the conditions in the jungle, had not received adequate treatment. It had been a herculean task to get him to this camp over a long distance through rain and mud. Somehow the bleeding had been stopped but nothing had been done about the smashed bones in his leg. The wound, wrapped in bloodstained and muddy bandages, gave off a foul stench and it was clear to Arthur and Roy that gangrene had set in.

Rain had been falling, almost without pause, for some time, turning the whole camp into a quagmire. It was no place to handle a situation like this. The young man was conscious, but his face had a deathly grey pallor and, although he made no sound, his eyes stared almost beseechingly at the old doc and others who attempted to minister to his needs. They talked of trying to amputate his leg at mid-thigh, but no-one had ever done such an operation and there were no facilities. Nevertheless preparations were made to try it.

But they were too late. The man's long and arduous journey to the camp had been to no avail. Shortly after two in the afternoon, two days after his arrival-a bleak, grey day of torrential rain-he closed his eyes and died.

22

THE SUCCESS OF THE RAID on Buloh Kasap generated wild and ambitious plans in Arthur's camp. Perhaps the most audacious in those first few days of 1944 was one put forward by Lem King, the secret agent. He wanted to rob a bank in Segamat. According to Lem King, who had put some time into planning the job, it would be set up as a daylight robbery during banking hours, so that one of the bank clerks who had access to the vaults would assist him and then leave Segamat to join the guerillas. Once the robbery was completed, Lem King had arranged for a fast car to be waiting nearby with an Indian driver ready. After much discussion, during which it was suggested they might scoop some $50 000 to $60 000 from the vaults, approval was given for Lem King to attempt the robbery. Within a couple of days, he set off for Segamat.

During the next few days, as they waited to hear the results of the venture, Arthur was also busy making money, thousands of dollars-worth of their own jungle currency, all of which still had to be laboriously numbered individually.

Another example of the Party's gradual organisation of what was a rather ramshackle army was that all the members of Arthur's camp were now issued with armbands which sported three red stars, as an indication of which unit the wearer belonged to, as well as an individual number. Arthur's was 594, Roy's was 593. Everyone wore them for a while, but in time they became tattered and torn, or lost, and within a matter of months, the order that everyone should wear an armband was pigeonholed and no-one wore them.

At this time Arthur was working under a painful handicap. Although he was generally in good health, another huge boil had developed, this time on his left eyelid. It took several days to build up to its full and agonising glory, puffing up and completely closing his eye. It stayed in that condition for three more days before eventually bursting one morning as Arthur got out of bed, sending large amounts of pus running down his face. The relief was immediate, however, and once he had washed and cleaned himself up, he felt much better. There was a large hole where the boil had been, much larger than would be thought possible in that part of the face, but with a small amount of sulphur powder which they were fortunate enough to have in the camp, it quickly began to heal and the swelling to subside.

Coinciding with Arthur's boil bursting--at least, on the same morning--all camp members were given a pay rise: two dollars, instead of one dollar a month. Not bad, Arthur thought, one-hundred-per-cent pay rise in one month!

To add even more to Arthur's sense of good fortune, Tek Chiong returned from a trip outside with four books and a letter for Arthur from Tek Chiong's older brother Tek Liong, a teacher living in Segamat. Arthur immediately sat down to write back and thank him. This was the beginning of an irregular but long-running correspondence between the two of them.

On 28th January, nine days after he had left camp, Lem King returned with great commotion and celebration, accompanied by his bank clerk accomplice in crime. They had pulled off their robbery, almost without a hitch, escaping with $20, 000. The only drawback in the whole operation, in Lem King and the clerk's view, was that the haul was less than the $60 000 they had hoped for. The clerk, whose name was Ten Chu, felt that, either through traitor's information or Japanese intuition, there had been an increased sense of caution in his bank and possibly in other banks in the area. It had not extended to the use of armed guards, but for several days the amount of cash that was readily available to the bank staff had been less than usual.

The robbery had taken place within a matter of minutes, with no shooting and no injuries on either side. Of course Ten Chu, who left with Lem King once the money had been collected, immediately became a wanted man, but he was happy to join the guerillas as many of his friends and relatives were already in the jungle and he had made elaborate arrangements for the rest of his family to flee on the previous night. The robbers' escape by car with the Indian driver also went smoothly and, after they had left the car and made for the jungle, the

Indian had stayed at another guerilla camp near the small kampong of Tenang, where he had several friends.

Despite their disappointment at not bringing home as much money as they had expected, the headquarters group--Sou Young and company--were ecstatic and there was a great celebration that evening with cakes and coffee, and even some chocolate that had been brought in for special occasions.

Headquarters was so pleased with the success of Lem King's cheeky, yet apparently simple, exploit that they felt similar coups could be attempted in the future. Arthur and Roy, though, felt that the considerable lack of training and competence of all but a few of the men in the camp would hamper their potential for success. Arthur was convinced that there was too much politics in the Communist army and not enough training and preparation. On several occasions, he had added up the hours spent talking about rules, regulations and politics, and averaged it out to around seven hours a day-compared to three hours on drill and weapons training.

"Some of these jokers have been two bloody years in the jungle," Arthur complained to Roy, "and they couldn't even hit a flaming barn door with a rifle. Some of them can't even do a left or right turn!"

And yet their instructors, like Kok Ching, were not at fault. By far the best instructor in Arthur's camp, having been through the Chinese military academy in Amoy before the war, he was the only one in Arthur's camp who had had any formal training in weapons or military tactics and strategy. Yet, because he was not a Communist, he was given no rank and therefore no authority.

"I do not care about all their talk, talk, talk," he said to Arthur and Roy one day. "I joined to fight, not talk."

Unfortunately the other instructors, most of whom had only primary school education, were given rank and authority simply because they were Party members. They then attempted to teach politics first and military tactics and weapons second, to people who couldn't read or write.

Arthur found it crazy that there were more officers than private soldiers. If one was a Communist and could reel off some of the dogma, he would be made a kepala, or chief. Frequent, ridiculous situations developed where one kepala would order another to do some menial task because he thought it was beneath his dignity to do it. The other would refuse, for the same reason, and an argument would ensue over who was the more senior kepala. The dispute would finally have to be settled, after much wasted time and a great deal of acrimony, by one of the camp leaders.

Towards the end of January, there had been an influx of more fighting men into the camp to strengthen their position and to establish a more aggressive patrol system. On the 29th, under this new system, seven of the men from the camp were on patrol in a nearby rubber estate when, from an unseen position, they spotted a party of Japanese troops coming towards them. They counted a total of thirty-five soldiers. In quickly improvised ambush positions, they waited until as many of the party as possible was in a vulnerable position, and then opened fire with a Bren gun. Three or four Japanese fell and the rest went to ground. After a few moments, on an order from their officer, the Japanese rushed for new and more advantageous positions. Several more were cut down by the guerillas' automatic weapons. However, as it seemed the Japanese would soon find better positions and be able to regroup and counterattack, the guerilla patrol withdrew after a brief exchange of fire, disappearing into the jungle. The Japanese did not follow but stayed to look after their dead and wounded. According to later reports from locals, there were six Japanese casualties. One of the guerilla soldiers was also killed during the fight.

The action angered the local Japanese intensely. Apart from stepping up their anti-guerilla campaign, they called every male aged sixteen to forty-two together on the town padang in Segamat to deliver a long harangue about the guerilla fighters and how they were destroying the peace and stability of the area.

One Japanese officer, speaking excellent Malay, told the crowd of hundreds of men that the Communist guerillas and anti-Japanese parties were the only ones who were disturbing the peace in Malaya and that everyone should cooperate to destroy this cancerous menace. At the same time, orders were issued to the Japanese forces in the area for an even more intensified campaign against the jungle camps.

For some days, however, all seemed quiet. During the early part of February, Arthur was again occupied drawing maps of Johore. The weather was hot and muggy and a period of continual rain, although temporarily cooling, had turned the camp into a messy quagmire.

On 10th February they received reports that there had been continual fighting for three days between guerilla forces and the Japanese in the region of Tenang. Then there was word of more Japanese arriving at Selumpoh and, closer to home, a report the following morning from '80 acres', where Arthur's camp still did most of their food-collecting, that a large number of Japanese had been observed coming out of the jungle and into the nearby '120 acres' clearing. The friendly observers who passed on the information didn't say where the soldiers had come from, but a later check showed that they had cut their own path through the jungle from Tunkutiga.

At midday, Sou Young ordered Sung Poo, one of the young lieutenants in the camp, and seven other men out on a patrol to try and establish what the Japanese were doing and what chances they might have of successfully penetrating to the guerilla's innermost camp. But Sung Poo had another secret mission, the details of which Arthur would not learn for more than a month.

Around midnight, a runner arrived in the camp with a message from Sung Poo giving details of serious Japanese penetration of the jungle camp trails. Coming on to the Selumpoh track they saw a great many recent Japanese boot prints in the damp soil leading further into the jungle towards several disused camps which the guerillas had called Camps 5, 6 and 7. They had no sooner come across the footprints and realised their significance when sounds from further down the track made them slink quietly and quickly into the jungle to hide. They watched a further eighty Japanese soldiers come silently by in single file. Most were armed with rifles, but many carried automatic weapons. There were also several light machine-guns in the group as well as three mortar crews. Sung Poo had no idea how many more had gone ahead, but it was clear to him that this was a major Japanese attack against the guerilla bases. After waiting several minutes to be sure there were not more soldiers coming up the trail, he sent an urgent message back down the track to Number 5 Company (at Camp 8), explaining the situation and asking for an ambush at a point further down the track, to block the Japanese exit route.

That was all Arthur heard. The messenger had been sent before there had been any further developments and was unable to give any further details of whether there had been a battle between the Japanese and the two ambush groups led by Sung Poo and Number 5 Company.

There was, however, more news a few hours later which was even more disturbing. Another large party of Japanese had apparently entered the jungle from '120 acres' and was making its way along the track towards the old camps where they had first used the now-defunct radio and which were only a relatively short distance from their present position.

Sou Young and several of the other leaders appeared worried. The Japanese moves were obviously developing into a major threat. One of Sou Young's main concerns was the large camp of civilian refugees which lay between the two prongs of the Japanese thrust. Their camp was also only a short distance to the north of Arthur's camp and more immediately vulnerable. There were only five or six guerilla soldiers stationed at the civilian camp and they were the only ones with arms. Sou Young ordered another six men to go quickly to the camp and to prepare everyone there to flee into the jungle if it became necessary.

The following morning, after a day of tense anticipation and preparation, Arthur, Roy and the rest of the camp were up at 5 am, ready to move at a moment's notice. At 8.30 Tek Chiong and three other men left camp to carry out a careful reconnaissance of all the approaches to their camp and to see if they could establish where the Japanese were and what they were doing.

At 9.30 they suddenly heard several sustained bursts of machine-gun fire. It was difficult for them to judge the distance in the jungle, but the shooting was heard quite plainly and it was generally felt that the sounds came from about a mile, or perhaps two, from their own position.

It was immediately thought that Tek Chiong and his party had come into contact with the Japanese, but, as they listened further, there were no sounds of rifle-fire and, as Tek Chiong and his men had no automatic weapons, they had to assume that the shooting did not involve Tek Chiong.

An air of extreme tension enveloped the camp, but Sou Young did not order an evacuation. They waited. At 10.30 they heard mortar fire much closer, sufficiently close to hear the sound of the mortars being ejected, a delay and then terrific explosions. But again, surprisingly, no small arms fire.

Sou Young ordered all the women in the camp, as well as the sick and injured, to be taken further into the jungle on one of the escape tracks. Two prisoners were also sent off, with Roy and a Chinese soldier as their guards. If there was to be a general exodus, Arthur was to stay with four others to await the Japanese arrival. The plan was to greet them with some fire-power when they first arrived, and then disappear into the jungle. They had three rifles and two Lewis light machine-guns, and felt ready to give the Japanese soldiers a bit of a shock. But for the time being, Sou Young delayed ordering a complete evacuation of the camp.

The mortar fire continued sporadically for about an hour, with no sound of any fire being returned, and then it stopped completely. Half an hour later, however, the sounds of a more distant battle, with mixed firing from both sides, reached them and they thought that perhaps the Japanese had gone back down the trail and met up with Number 5 Company and the ambush that had been set for them. But a report that came in towards the end of the afternoon, when the shooting had stopped, told them that the Japanese were still at the old 'radio camp' in quite large numbers, and it appeared as though they might be planning to spend the night there.

With this information they relaxed a little, reasonably secure in the knowledge that at least there would be no more danger until the morning. The Japanese would not be making any attempts to break new ground in a move towards their camp at night. Even in daylight, the track in to their position was difficult enough to find, but in the pitch darkness of a jungle night, it was all but impossible. Sou Young and the others also felt reasonably sure that the Japanese did not actually know they were there, even though there was only about a mile of track, and probably less than half a mile in a straight line, separating the two positions.

Late in the evening, four guerilla soldiers arrived with more news. The firing of automatic weapons in the morning had been at Tek Chiong and his reconnaissance party, of whom there had been no sign since. There were now fears for their safety. The mortar firing had been from Camp Number 3, the civilian camp. The Japanese had apparently entered the camp to find it only recently deserted and so began firing mortars indiscriminately into the surrounding jungle, thinking that perhaps the inhabitants of the camp were hiding around the perimeter of the camp clearings. Their firing was fruitless, however, as the civilians had fled much further into the jungle.

Arthur and the others settled down for the night rather uneasily. Although they felt reasonably secure, they had never before had such a substantial Japanese force camped so close to them. Extra sentries were posted as the camp bedded down for the night, and all were ready to move at a moment's notice. Arthur managed to get some sleep, but kept waking with a start at the slightest sound.

Everyone in the camp was up before dawn for an early breakfast. A patrol was sent out towards the Japanese encampment to check what was happening and the guerillas again prepared for action. At around 9 am, Tek Chiong and his party of three men arrived back in camp. All of them were safe. They had met the Japanese on the trail the previous morning, but had escaped into the jungle without mishap. After reporting their news, they were sent to get some breakfast. The kitchen was set up by a small stream, a hundred yards or so from the centre of the camp. While they were there, being served rice from some four- gallon drums which were used for cooking, a sudden burst of machine-gun fire caused them to drop their bowls and race, with everyone else in the camp, to defensive positions.

The sound of the shooting came from the direction of the track leading to Number 2 Camp, the 'radio camp', but it was difficult for anyone to say exactly how far away it might have been and, after the first burst, there was no further sound. After half an hour or so spent hiding around the edge of the large camp clearing, Kok Ching, one of the men in Tek Chiong's ambush party, suggested going back to the kitchen to get the rice that was left in the four-gallon drums to carry back to their hiding place. Arthur, who was lying next to him in the jungle verge, volunteered to join him and one other Chinese soldier to make their way carefully down the short track leading to the river.

Within only four or five minutes of having collected the rice drums and returned to their hidden positions they were amazed to see the first members of a Japanese raiding party picking their way quietly up the same track leading towards the camp clearing. There was absolute silence as they watched the Japanese soldiers moving cautiously into the camp, unaware that there were rifles and Lewis guns trained on them from all around.

"Let them come, let them come," Arthur whispered to Kok Ching, hoping that the others around the camp perimeter would do the same, so that as many of them as possible could be taken by surprise. But by the time only two or three Japanese soldiers had begun to edge carefully into the camp, one of the guerillas on the left of the clearing became nervous and fired. A single shot hit the leading Japanese soldier, more by luck than good marksmanship, hurling him to the ground. Two others with him dived for cover unhurt, as a fusillade of shots from the guerillas followed the first bullet.

Within seconds, the Japanese were returning the fire and others were rushing up to support the first three who had been fired upon. From Arthur's position, where they had one Lewis gun and half a dozen rifles, they had a good view of any soldiers approaching up the kitchen track and they were able to direct some heavy fire-power into the second group that tried to come up that way. Of course, their position also attracted heavy automatic fire from the Japanese and Arthur heard several bullets whistle past his head and felt one tear at the shoulder tab of his shirt. It was only later when he noticed blood on his shirt, that he realised that the bullet had actually nicked him. It was only a scratch but for a while he kept thinking, 'if that had been an inch or two lower. . .?'

In the chaos that developed, there was little time to think clearly. Suddenly the Japanese began firing mortars, though only for a few moments, because this tactic went drastically wrong for them. Their first shot hit the canopy of leaves above them and exploded, sending shrapnel bursting back over them, injuring their own men. From then on, they used only small arms.

Arthur could hear their yelled orders and the subsequent movements they made. Concluding that the Japanese were going to begin an encircling manoeuvre to try to trap the guerillas, he and Roy, along with Kok Ching and a few others, collected their gear and weapons and melted further back into the jungle, following some narrow and hardly discernible tracks which led to a small clearing. There they awaited further developments and orders from Sou Young, hoping that others from the camp would also meet there.

Sporadic firing continued for about half an hour, then there was silence. After a further half-hour, they heard loud shouting in Japanese from the direction of the camp and, after a short while, terrible screams from someone in pain. They could only guess at what was happening, although Arthur and Roy had no doubts. "The bastards have got one of our blokes," Roy swore, "and they're torturing him."

After discussing possible action, they decided that, as there were only six of them together at that time and the Japanese probably numbered around sixty or seventy, they had to sit it out.

"They'd have got a good few more of us if they hadn't fired that machine-gun earlier," Arthur said. "There were a lot of our blokes down in the kitchen area. Coming up the back way like they did, they'd have got all those blokes by the kitchen."

"But how could they get onto that trail? It's almost impossible to find, even for us!" Roy said.

"It must have been a bloody traitor. No-one else could have led them that way."

They lay in the undergrowth, talking softly and listening. There was no more sound from the Japanese force. They continued their wait. Hours went by and, as the afternoon wore on, they decided to make their way carefully back towards the camp. On the way, only four hundred yards down the track, they met two men from the camp who told them that the Japanese were still there. The eight men then decided to bed down in the jungle where they were and to await further developments.

In the early dawn they heard a single rifle-shot from the direction of the camp. As there were no further shots heard, they concluded it was just reveille for the Japanese soldiers. Later in the morning, when they'd heard sounds of the Japanese moving, Arthur left the group to make a wide circle around the camp, through the jungle, to try to pick up a small trail he knew of to see if he could get closer to the camp. He spent some time searching along small, hardly visible tracks, one of which gave him a partial view of the camp area through the bushes on a low hillside. The first thing he saw was a column of smoke rising into the sky. Then, after shifting his position and climbing into the branches of a small tree to get a better view, he was able to see that it was the camp's hospital hut that was going up in flames. From his vantage point, he could see no sign of any Japanese soldiers.

While Arthur was sitting in the tree watching the camp hospital go up in smoke, rain began to fall in torrents. He tried to find cover temporarily under a larger tree, but he was quickly drenched to the skin. He turned back up the small trail, walking in what felt like a warm shower, with the intention of retracing the route back to the spot where he had left Roy and the others. Shortly he heard sounds of people moving quietly through the jungle in his direction. Cautiously hiding in

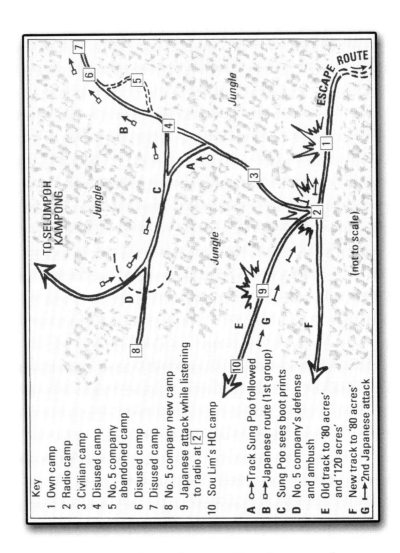

Map 6. *Approximate layout of jungle camps from May 1943 to the Japanese attacks during February 1944.*

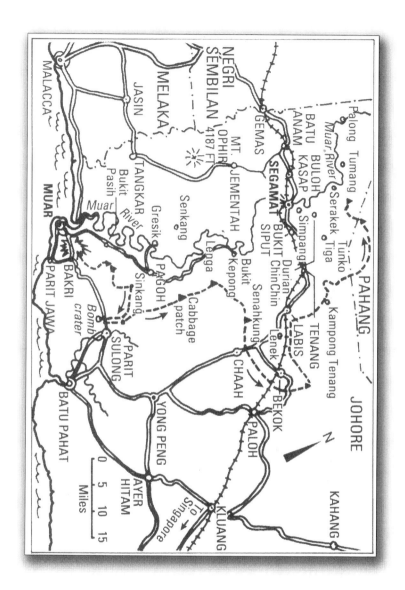

Map 7. Route of Arthur shaphard's jungle journey through Johore from January 1942 to September 1945

bushes to one side, he waited and watched and was relieved to see that it was three guerilla soldiers from the camp on a patrol. They told Arthur that a number of other members of the camp had set up a small bivouac in an area nearby where they were cooking up some rice. They said that the Japanese had left the main camp, but that it had been burnt to the ground.

Soon, after following directions from the guerilla patrol, Arthur arrived at the small bivouac to find Roy and the other six men already there. When the rain stopped half an hour later, they managed to light a small fire to dry out their clothes.

The following morning, after an uncomfortable night on wet ground, they returned cautiously to their camp to survey the wreckage. The Japanese had done a thorough job. There were books and papers strewn everywhere. All of Arthur's books, which he had kept in a small case and had carefully concealed in the jungle near the hut in which he and Roy slept, had gone, but his most precious possession, his diary, was safe in the small cloth wallet which he always wore around his neck. Searching through the sodden mess of paper strewn around the campsite, he managed to salvage two English-language books--one on algebra and one on English-Chinese conversation.

All of the main building structures were destroyed, burnt to the ground, and all around was strewn the garbage and remnants of the Japanese soldier's meals. Tinned bully beef from Australia, salmon from the USA and powdered milk from China!

"The bloody little bastards!" Roy fumed up and down what had been the parade ground, kicking at the ration cans. "Here we are in the jungle, scraping a living out of anything we can lay our hands on while they eat all our bully beef and Yankee salmon. Jesus!"

A shout from the hospital area interrupted Roy who, along with Arthur and several others was called to see an ugly sight--the shockingly burnt remains of a young civilian man who had been a member of the camp. He was tied down to stakes in the ground.

"Look at his stomach," Roy said in horror. "It's all swollen up." '

Arthur knelt down beside the man's disfigured and charred body. "They must have given him the water torture. I wonder how they got him?"

"He was the one with bad feet, remember?" Roy said. "He couldn't run at all. He probably didn't get far enough into the jungle to hide properly and they found him. Poor bugger."

Sou Lim came across waving a piece of material which had been tacked up on a tree. It had his name and that of another camp leader, Lou Sheng, as well as several others on it, with warnings written in Chinese beneath the names saying what the Japanese would do when they caught them. After everyone had looked at it. Sou Lim laughed and stuffed it in his pocket as a souvenir.

They salvaged what little they could from the wrecked camp-site and then left to return to the small bivouac area which would be a temporary camp for them until they decided where to go next.

The Japanese raid had been more successful than the guerilla leaders wanted to admit. If the Japanese had known how much they had thrown the camp organisation into disarray, they might have had even greater success. As it was, they were keeping the guerillas busy in several areas. People kept coming in to report that fighting had been going on at nearly all of the various camps in the region. There had been several close escapes--young Tek Chiong, who had been at another camp when a Japanese attack was mounted, had a bullet part his hair without breaking the skin on his scalp!

They set to work on the new bivouac site, enlarging it and making it more livable, and preparing its defences against any further attack by the Japanese. But in the days that followed, they saw no more sign of them. Messages coming back from Segamat indicated that the Japanese campaign against them had involved some seven hundred soldiers and they were now back in Segamat giving their versions of the attacks on the guerilla camps in glowing terms. They described the camps which they had attacked, including Arthur's, which they said they had wiped out, killing nearly everyone there. The truth was that only one man had been caught and tortured to death, while in other camps, many more Japanese had been killed than guerillas. At least twenty Japanese were killed near the Tenang camp when they raided it, another eighteen were killed near Bukit Pasih and at least seven at Se-lumpoh.

Nevertheless, the effects on the guerillas had been substantial. They were now short on arms, ammunition and, most importantly, food. At the time of their move to the temporary camp, they were left with sufficient supplies for only three more meals. Carrying-parties were sent out to collect jungle vegetables and also food from neighbouring villages. In the afternoon of the fourth day after the Japanese attack, a group of men from the camp arrived back with a tapir they had shot. It was a big one, about six feet long, and required a lot of carriers to get it back to the camp. Tapirs, being nocturnal herbivores, can hide very effectively from potential predators during the day, so the carrying-party was particularly lucky to get it.

The animal was cut up and a pickul (about 130 pounds) was sent out to another nearby camp. The balance was cooked up, providing everyone in the camp with two ladles of meat per person as well as soup, with enough left over for flavouring for the next day.

Despite their luck with the tapir, it was clear to the leaders of Arthur's camp that they could no longer remain where they were. Once again, what had become a very workable network of relatively safe and secure camps would have to be abandoned. But no move could be made until a good alternative campsite could be located.

23

DURING THE FIRST WEEK AFTER the Japanese raids, a runner arrived bearing, among other things, a letter from the British soldier Stewart. He had apparently arrived alone at Tenang camp just before the Japanese attacks, but had not been brought to Arthur and Roy's camp because it had been destroyed and their present camp was only a temporary one. It also seemed likely that they would be moving towards the Tenang area. Stewart's letter contained no word of his companion, Bennett, other than that, because he had still been ill and could not travel at the time of the move to Tenang, they had had to separate. Bennett was apparently still at the camp not far from Bukit Kepong.

During the period before the move, the monsoon rains began to sweep in over the jungle with monotonous regularity, drenching the camps and turning any cleared ground into a mud bath. There was little they could do except stay under cover as much as they could and watch the sheets of water falling from grey skies.

This was also a time for the guerilla leaders of Arthur and Roy's camp to reorganise. They decided to split the existing camp population and restructure it into four separate entities: a headquarters group and three out-station groups with twenty or so men in each. The out-station guerillas would occupy separate camps not far from each other while the headquarters group would be more mobile and ready to move from place to place at a moment's notice. Arthur was told by Sou Young that he would be needed in the headquarters group, for mapmaking as well as printing money and anti-Japanese propaganda.

Kok Ching had been made a sergeant in charge of one of the outstation camps and both Roy and Tek Chiong, who had been promoted to corporal, were to join Kok Ching's camp.

359

Because of Kok Ching's apolitical sentiments, his group was made up of what Sou Young and the other guerilla leaders considered 'rejects'. But Kok Ching knew that most of them had been 'rejected' because, like him, they did not like the continuous diet of politics and Communist dogma they were being fed most of the time. They said they would rather fight than talk and that suited Kok Ching perfectly. He was happy with his 'rejects'.

The camp leaders eventually grew tired of waiting for the right weather and on 22 February, Arthur and the others were told that, come what may, they would move the following morning. None of them was looking forward to a long trek in the rain but by about nine it had begun to ease and by ten when Arthur said goodbye to Roy and set off with the nine others in the Headquarters group, it had stopped, almost miraculously it seemed, after days of continuous downpour.

Despite the absence of rain, the going on the trail was sodden, slippery and steep, and all of them found it tough. In some places there were almost sheer cliffs to scale. They had to stop frequently to catch their breath and when the sun came out for brief periods during the morning and the humidity rose, they felt as though they were trekking in an oven. Nevertheless, by early afternoon they were halfway to where they were going, according to Sou Young.

With immense, dark rain clouds forming, they stopped for a lunch break at a small, abandoned Sakai hut in an overgrown clearing on the top of a ridge. As they settled down to eat a meal of cold rice and ubi chips, the rain started to patter down, increasing in intensity until it was a great roar and, looking out from the shelter of the hut, they could see no more than ten feet through the curtain of falling water. They sat for an hour and a half, unwilling to try trekking in such a torrential downpour. Finally the rain eased and they set off once again, this time in a fine drizzle, along a slippery and dangerous track, only to meet, within minutes, something infinitely more dangerous--a huge tiger!

Arthur was third in line as they walked in single file along the sodden track. The path widened slightly at one point and suddenly, as they passed a large tree, there was a movement in a small clearing to their right. Not twenty feet from them was one of the largest tigers he could imagine.

Malayan tigers can grow up to eight or nine feet in length (including the tail) and this one seemed to Arthur, in that one frozen instant of recognition, to be every bit as big as that. For a few brief seconds they stood transfixed, staring at the animal as it glared back at them, equally surprised. Before any of them could turn and flee, or whatever else sheer terror might have prompted them to do, the enormous beast turned and, in the same movement, bounded off into the jungle, leaving them momentarily stunned and breathless with relief.

They pressed on, crossing thigh-deep through several creeks which had grown to small rivers. By three-thirty in the afternoon, they'd crossed a ridge which Sou Young said was the borderline between the States of Pahang and Johore.

The rain came down again, making the going very tough and slow, and then, finally, impossible. The track they were following became such a quagmire, with mudslides in some places, that they had to abandon it and try to make their own detour. In the process they became lost, facing the prospect of a rain-soaked night in the jungle. According to the plan, they should reach the new campsite by about 5 pm, but when the hour came, they were still struggling through dense thickets of vine and thorny bush in the pouring rain, with hardly a clue where they were. Suddenly, however, they broke out into a small grassy patch which Sou Young recognised and which he said was only about a mile or so from the camp. They reached their destination, looking for all the world like a collection of drowned rats, just at nightfall. Fifteen minutes later, they would not have been able to see anything.

The following morning, after a good night's rest under cover, Arthur looked the place over. It seemed to him a pleasant position: a small, open area, surrounded by thick vegetation. A stream ran by, forming a nice swimming pool at one end of the clearing, and there were three huts--a fowl house, a cookhouse and one hut for them to sleep in. There was a camp of guerilla soldiers about two miles away and, Arthur was told, the British soldier Stewart was already there, although exactly where his friend Bennett was, no-one seemed to know.

It was some time before Arthur managed to pay a visit to the 'soldier camp', as they called it, because the rain continued to come down in torrents for several days, causing the stream to rise by more than fifteen feet. The rain effectively confined them to their hut, and once more they spent monotonous hours gazing out at the sheets of water which fell without a break. For a few days it would stop and start spasmodically every few hours, and during this time the level of their stream fell and the flooding generally subsided. Then, about a week after their arrival, the sun came through and began to appear on what seemed to be a reasonably regular basis.

Three of them, including Arthur, went to collect potatoes from a plantation near the 'soldier camp'. They gathered some small ones, going rotten because of the flooding, but were disappointed by not finding any decent-sized ones to take back. Following a different return route, they passed through the 'soldier camp' and Arthur finally met Douglas Stewart.

Arthur found him to be a short, pleasant-looking man, about his own age, with mousey-coloured hair and the sort of skin that Arthur could only think of as English: incredibly clear, blooming, with a constant blush on the cheeks. Stewart, who would not have appreciated hearing his skin described as 'English' was, in fact, a true Scot--a member of the 2nd Battalion , Argyle & Sutherland Highlanders.

"Ah, God, man, am I glad to meet ye at last!" he said, clasping Arthur's hand with unusual fervour. He seemed quite moved and at first Arthur was a little taken aback at the strength of Stewart's emotion. He wondered if perhaps Stewart had been ill, but it seemed that it was simply that, since he had separated from Bennett, he'd had no-one to communicate with. In all the time he had been in the jungle, he had not managed to learn any Malay or Chinese, either through lack of effort on his own part, or lack of interest and help on the part of the Chinese with whom he had been living. He'd become quite lonely as a result.

As they sat talking in the shade of a large tree, Stewart told the story of his epic three hundred-mile journey south from the Slim River in Perak State, eventually arriving in much the same area between Segamat and the coast that Arthur and his companions had been moving through in August 1942. It had taken until now, February 1944, for them to meet.

After Japan first invaded Malaya, Stewart's battalion, the Argyle & Sutherland Highlanders, had been amongst the British, Indian and Ghurkha units which had fought a losing battle against overwhelming odds as the Japanese Imperial Guards swept across northern Malaya to the west coast. Stewart's battalion had met a larger Japanese force at a small town called Titi Karangan, in the far north of Malaya. In the series of engagements which followed, it had been forced to retreat over two hundred miles through Lenggong, Kuala Kangsar and Telok Anson, to make a final stand, with Ghurkha and Punjabi units, on 7

CHAPTER TWENTY-THREE

January near the town of Slim River, about seventy miles north of Kuala Lumpur.

"We were supposed to be defending the bridge at Trolak, just north of the town, the railway line and the road through the Cluny rubber estate," Stewart told Arthur. "But the Japs suddenly came down the road with four medium tanks and..."

"Probably the same bastards that we met up with ten days later," Arthur said. "We knocked ten of them out."

"Did you now?" Stewart laughed. "Well, I can't think of anyone I'd like to have seen that happen to more than those chaps. You see, we didn't have any anti-tank guns, so they made mincemeat of us. Their infantry was right up with the tanks. In no time we were completely surrounded and we had to fight our way out. It was every man for himself--they got all but about a hundred of us." '

''That's exactly what happened to us," Arthur said. "What did you do after that?"

"Well, it's a long story, but there were six of us altogether. We'd been separated from the main group and, after a day or so hiding out in the jungle, we decided to make our way south towards Singapore. We thought we'd do it in about six weeks, but it took us months just to get this far. In the beginning we stuck to the edge of the jungle and the plantations and just kept moving south. We met up with Chinese who helped us along the way with food and on several occasions we stayed for some time in one place, either through illness or because it was dangerous to move on.

"Inevitably we met up with the Chinese guerillas and they began to control our movements. We were separated into different groups and at one stage, after we first arrived in this part of the world, when John Bennett was too sick to move, I was sent with one other chap from the Argyles to a camp near Tangkar. The Japs raided us there and we were taken on a bloody long hike to Jementah where I met up with John again. Then we were raided there once more--that was a hell of a situation. I had terrible fever from malaria as well as beri-beri and my legs were all swollen up. I was a dead loss. So when the Japs came, the guerillas managed to get me into the jungle and hide me, but John and the rest of them continued on the run until they got to the camp at Bukit Kepong. Some other guerillas eventually came back for me. I was in pretty bad shape after a couple of days in the jungle on my own, but they found me and managed to get me to Bukit Kepong, even though it took about four or five days."

"So where is Bennett now?" Arthur asked.

"Still at Bukit Kepong, I think. At the time we were to make a move to Tenang, he came down with fever again and couldn't move. Last I heard he was getting better, but I'm not sure if he's ready to travel yet."

They talked for a while longer before Arthur had to leave to take the potatoes he had collected back to his own camp.

"Can you ask Sou Young if I can join you in your camp?" Stewart said, pressing Arthur for an assurance that he would at least try to get him out of his present camp.

"I'll do my best," Arthur promised, "but Sou Young can be difficult. He has his own ideas about who goes where and it's not easy to change his mind. But I'll try."

"Please, please do." Stewart insisted. "Anything to be with someone I can talk to, or listen to."

On his return to camp, Arthur spoke to Sou Young on Stewart's behalf, but, as he had expected, the Chinese leader was not receptive. Arthur had felt for some time that Sou Young had been trying, for reasons Arthur could not fathom, to avoid having Stewart join the same camp as Arthur and Roy.

"He is of no use to us," Sou Young said coldly. "He can do nothing. He cannot speak to or understand the people he is with now. What good would he be here?"

"But I am sure he could learn quickly," Arthur insisted. "He is an intelligent man. He would be a great help to us, I'm sure, before too long."

"He has been a long time in other camps," Sou Young said, "and they say he has not tried to learn the Malay or Chinese languages at all. This is a small group here, specialising in propaganda. He would not fit in." The Chinese leader, who had been sitting, stood up and turned his back on Arthur. "He can join your friend Roy and Kok Ching's group if he wants to, when the flood waters go down." He turned briefly to look at Arthur but, without waiting for a reaction, strode off to join some other Chinese members of the camp.

There was not very much Arthur could have said in response anyway, and although he knew Sou Young thought little of Kok Ching's group of 'rejects', he also believed that Stewart would find that situation infinitely preferable to the one he was in. At least he would have Roy to talk to.

Arthur saw Stewart the following day to give him a spare pair of shorts and a shirt to replace his own which were falling apart. He also gave the Scot three books to read. In passing on the information that Sou Young was reluctant to have Stewart join the propaganda camp, Arthur did not elaborate on the reasons. He told Stewart that he thought it was likely that he would be able to join Roy's camp instead. This seemed to please the Scot considerably.

Two days later, he heard that Stewart had left the 'soldier camp' to join Roy and Kok Ching's group and, a short while later, a letter from Roy confirmed that he had arrived and that they were getting on well together, with Stewart much happier in his new situation. The news somehow made Arthur feel unsettled and lonely. He suddenly wished that he, too, was with Roy and the other group. He was fully occupied and busy most of the time in the small propaganda camp and was held in reasonably high regard by his Chinese companions, but he began to feel the lack of company of people of his own race and language.

His feeling were more than likely exacerbated by the beginnings of some sort of malaise. Several days passed during which he felt extremely weak. He was hot, but without any perspiration. Arthur thought that he was in for a bout of malaria but, after a few days, he seemed to recover and found himself almost too busy to be ill. He worked non-stop producing new maps of Johore, which were reduced in scale from a much larger map which Sou Young had procured.

During this period, Arthur and the others in the small group were able to eat extremely well. Hunting parties went out every day and almost always returned with something so that over a week they would have quite varied fare; a good-sized pelandok (a small deer), a couple of parrots, a furry-faced, long-tailed monkey, a goanna, a snake and, of course, rice and jungle vegetables, topped off each night with curry puffs and coffee. Arthur could not remember a time in the jungle when the food had been so consistently good. His spirits rose.

It was also around this time that he became aware, by piecing together comments from different people coming into the camp, that Cotterill, of whom he had not heard since the previous November, was in some sort of danger, not from the Japanese but from the Chinese guerillas themselves. Apparently this was because the people he had been camping and travelling with were not Communist guerillas but robbers--opportunists who, up until now, had been tolerated in the jungle by the regular Chinese guerillas, mainly because the targets for their robbery and murder attacks were nearly always the Japanese.

But now the situation seemed to have changed. There had been a series of negotiations between the Communist guerillas and the robber group which led to some sort of agreement. The guerilla side was to supply the robber camp with rice on a regular basis, in return for which they would consent to co-operate with the guerillas and their overall anti-Japanese strategy. A representative of the guerilla side was placed in the robbers' camp with authority over them, but after less than a week they seemed to have second thoughts about the arrangement and threatened the Communist overseer with a pistol, telling him to leave. They then continued with their own independent operations of robbery and plunder.

Arthur recalled that a group of guerilla soldiers under the leadership of Sung Poo had left Arthur's previous camp, at the time of the big Japanese attacks, for the Palong area where Cotterill and his robber companions were camped. At the time it had no real significance for him as he and the others were preoccupied with the Japanese all around them. But Arthur now learnt from Sou Young that their mission had been to 'clear out' the robber camp.

"But what about Cotterill?" Arthur asked immediately. "What will happen to him?"

Sou Young shrugged his shoulders as Arthur tried urgently to impress on him that Cotterill was not one of them. "He is not a robber," Arthur insisted. "He is only staying with them because he has to."

"We cannot be sure," Sou Young replied coldly.

"But many times he asked to come here, to join me—to join us," Arthur said vehemently. "Many times I have asked for him to come, and each time nothing has been done."

"This is true," Sou Young nodded and then walked away from Arthur without a further word.

Two days later, word came to the camp that Sung Poo's mission had been successful. But there was no news of Cotterill. For two more days Arthur pressed Sou Young for information, with no result, until one morning, after a group of men had arrived from the Palong area with food supplies and outside news, Sou Young came over to where Arthur was sitting eating a bowl of rice and some vegetables for breakfast, to inform him that Cotterill was alive and well.

"He will be going to join your friends with Kok Ching very soon," Sou Young said. "I think he will be happier there."

"But couldn't he come here?" Arthur asked. "I'm sure he could be a help here."

The separation from Roy, and the fact that Stewart had been sent to Roy's group, were beginning to have their effect on Arthur. He, like Stewart, was now feeling the need for the companionship of someone who spoke his own language. Even though he could converse very effectively in Malay and Chinese, it was not the same. He felt he needed to be with his own kind. He recognised it as a very primitive response, but he felt it strongly.

Sou Young, however, would only give one of his standard replies: "We will see. It is difficult now. But perhaps soon."

During this period they received news that a concert party was being sent off from the 'soldier camp' below them to several of the other camps in the area, including the one where Roy and Doug Stewart were now based. Arthur asked Sou Young if he could join the concert party just to visit the others. "I really would like to see them," Arthur said. But his request was denied by Sou Young on the grounds that the party would be away for at least fifteen days. "You are needed here to draw maps," he said.

Arthur felt depressed and lonely and this refusal, coupled with the fact that his feverish illness seemed to be returning, only increased his sense of isolation.

A couple of weeks had passed since his last bouts of fever, which he had dismissed as some sort of stomach upset. Now, in mid-April, it returned with a vengeance. On the first day, Arthur was simply laid low, feeling sick and absolutely weak. The symptoms were the same for several days--tremendous bouts of extreme heat and terrific perspiration, followed by shivering and shaking with cold. During those few days, Arthur lost an enormous amount of weight. By the time the fever had stripped it from him, he felt like a rake and there was no food that he could eat without throwing up.

After the first week he managed to hold down a bowl of goanna soup and some meat for breakfast and, either because of that or the fact that the fever was passing anyway, he began to feel a little better. The bouts of fever continued for the next week or so, with diminishing intensity, and although he was not feeling as desperately ill as he had been, he was nevertheless extremely weak and very thin, weighing only about 110 pounds. He had lost 85 pounds since Christmas. Towards the end of April, the illness began to ease until, finally, it went away completely, leaving Arthur like a wraith.

At this time there were also two welcome additions to the small numbers at Arthur's camp. The first was Sou Lim, who Arthur had not seen for almost four months. Sou Lim greeted Arthur with the news that the Englishman Cotterill had finally made it to Kok Ching's outstation camp and was there now, with Roy and Doug Stewart. Although Arthur was pleased to hear the news and anxious for more details, Sou Lim had no more information to give than the bare facts. He had not actually been to Kok Ching's camp, but had simply heard that Cotterill had arrived safely.

Since the big Japanese attacks on the guerilla camps in February, Sou Lim had been doing what he described as 'a lot of travelling'. He had taken part in many raids on the Japanese, most of which were successful. Arthur had little opportunity to question him further because he remained closeted with Sou Young and a couple of other leading members of the group for most of the day, but he felt sure that the details of his travels would emerge over the next few days.

The second arrival in the camp was a young Sakai man called Chling. In general, the Sakai, or native jungle people, had been friendly to the guerilla side and were strongly anti-Japanese. But they were a very independent race who took orders from no-one and avoided the concept of organisation and regimentation which could have befallen them had they formally joined the guerilla forces. Even if the Chinese guerilla army had wanted to, they could have done little to force the Sakais into that sort of situation.

The Sakais were 'lords' of the Malayan jungle. No-one knew that complex, twilight-green underworld better than they. They lived in it permanently in a semi-nomadic state. They knew all of its vagaries. They knew how it killed the unwary or the stupid, and how it could nurture and support those who were clever and careful. The Sakais had no need of support or aid from anyone and, as they had no racial or ethnic ties to the existing Malayan population, they could have given their support to the Japanese occupiers or the Chinese guerillas. The fact that they chose to help the guerillas, when needed, was good fortune for the guerilla side, but the Sakais rarely participated on a full time basis in the activities of the guerilla groups.

Chling seemed to be an exception to the rule. He came to stay and work with Arthur's small group. He was about twenty years old and, unlike his fellow tribes-people, who invariably spoke only the Sakai languages, he spoke Malay and four Chinese dialects as well as his own language. His multilingual talents were the result of his parents sending him out of the jungle at the age of five to live in a Chinese village near Kluang, to be educated there. He had been with the guerillas in several different camps for some time now and was well versed in the way things operated.

He had a pleasant personality, with a ready smile, and in the days when Arthur was recovering from his bout of malarial fever, Chling befriended him, encouraging him to get up and about as much as possible. Arthur went for short walks with him while he collected jungle vegetables and fruits, including leaves and berries and roots which Arthur would never have thought worthwhile to collect as food. He made others in the camp look incompetent in the way he could catch fish after fish in the stream when no one else could catch one.

24

DURING MAY, ARTHUR'S PHYSICAL AND mental condition began to improve slightly. Two books had been sent in by Tek Liong and he found he could concentrate sufficiently to read and enjoy them. But what was probably more important, he became hungry, which everyone treated as a good sign. The kitchen cooked up special meals of chicken for him, trying to bolster his strength, and he found that he could now eat it without throwing up and, more importantly, enjoy it. He ate steadily for several days and began to feel considerably better. This seemed to please the camp officials and it was not long before they began feeding him with work as well as chickens. More maps of Johore were needed and Arthur had to produce them.

He managed to do the job that was required, but it was clear to the camp leaders that he had still not recovered completely. Deciding to take advantage of the situation, Arthur again raised the question of joining Kok Ching's group, now part of Number 5 Company. Arthur's continual requests, together with the fact that most of the sick people from several camps were sent to Number 5 Company, because the food and general environment were better there, turned the tide in his favour. At the beginning of June Sou Young agreed to Arthur going with the next runner in two days' time.

Arthur spent the next morning walking, trying to get his legs in shape for the long walk to Number 5 Company. It was crazy, he knew, to expect them to be ready in one day, but at least he felt he should do something.

Just prior to leaving the next morning, Arthur was given four months' back pay--a grand total of six dollars (two dollars had been deducted for some chickens he had been given when they first arrived at the 'Radio Camp' many weeks ago). A fit person could have made the trip in one day but the messenger had to slow down considerably in order for Arthur to keep up. He found it very tough going. Up and down steep jungle hills with heavy rain falling most of the time, drenching them to the skin. It made their progress a continual series of muddy slides downhill and almost impossible climbs uphill. Arthur thought his heart would burst at times. By 4.30 in the afternoon, they reached a camp called Q Camp, occupied by guerilla soldiers, where the messenger said they would spend the night. Number 5 Company was still another three or four hours' march further. They would complete the trek in the morning. ,

Arthur was surprised to find Roy living in Q Camp.

"Too many arguments," Roy said, when Arthur asked why he wasn't still at Number 5 Company.

"Arguments? You mean with Kok Ching and the Chinese?"

"No. With bloody Cotterill and Stewart!" He held his arms up in despair. "We couldn't see eye to eye on anything."

"But I thought you got on all right with Doug when he first arrived," Arthur said.

"Yeah, that's right," Roy muttered. "But I feel better away from them."

Arthur pressed him for details but he was reluctant to spell out what their disagreements had been about, other than to say, "They're too bloody uppity."

Arthur now found himself in something of a quandary. He had been keen to move from the propaganda camp in order to meet up with Roy again, but now it seemed that they would not be in the same camp. He would have to continue on the following day to Number 5 Company where most of the sick were cared for and the food was better. There was no way he could make an arbitrary decision to stay at Q Camp with Roy without approval from Headquarters. So, the following morning, after having some breakfast, he set off with the messenger on the four-hour trek to Number 5 Company's camp, which Roy had told him was only three or four miles from Segamat. They arrived around midday, with Arthur as weak as a kitten and his legs almost collapsing under him.

Both Douglas Stewart and Cotterill--John Maurice Cotterill was his full name, although he preferred to be called Maurice— were there to meet him. They sat under a tree together so that Arthur could recuperate a little. Arthur found it strange to meet Cotterill in the flesh after having communicated with him by mail for so long, and the sight was quite a surprise. Cotterill was just about the thinnest man he had ever seen. He was over six feet tall, which tended to exaggerate his thinness, but clearly malaria had wreaked the same sort of havoc with Cotterill as it had with Arthur.

Arthur had brought the two men some English books which they fondled reverently and excitedly as they sat talking in the shade. Cotterill was a very soft-spoken, quiet sort of man, about forty years of age. He had mousey-coloured hair and blue-grey eyes set in a rather angular face. Arthur realised his face would almost certainly have been somewhat rounder in pre-war days when, as a relatively affluent rubber planter, he would certainly have had more weight on. He struck Arthur immediately as being a likeable sort of person, as had Douglas Stewart, and he found himself wondering what it was about them that had rubbed Roy up the wrong way.

He asked Cotterill about his experiences with the robber group and for the first time heard an account of how the guerilla group, led by Sung Poo had 'cleaned out' the robber camp.

According to Maurice, the robbers had agreed to cooperate with the guerillas against the Japanese on condition that they were supplied with an amount of rice that would provide four tahils (about five ounces) per person per day. When this arrangement was not adhered to, they complained and, when they still got no reaction, they quit the arrangement. When Sung Poo and his group arrived at the robber camp on 15 February they made out that they were friendly towards the robber group and were treated well. On 4 March, after Sung Poo and his soldiers had spent more than two weeks at the camp, a small concert was held with people taking turns to sing or recite and to make small speeches. This was followed, as was usual in many of the camps, by cakes and coffee and then bed. But at midnight, Sung Poo and his men went around to each hut in small groups, waking up the robbers and demanding their arms. Some of them refused and scuffles broke out. Shots were fired and three robbers were killed. Eventually all of the robbers, except Maurice, were collected together and tied up. A trial was held immediately, with Sung Poo officiating. Fourteen of them, including the robber chief, were condemned and shot there and then. The rest were permitted to join the guerilla band. There was hardly any choice. They either joined or died.

It seemed that Cotterill was regarded as being a member of the band only through force of circumstances and his claim that he had never participated in any of the robbers' raids was evidently accepted by Sung Poo and the other guerillas. Certainly there was no stigma attached to him at the time of his arrival at Kok Ching's camp.

Arthur found that, indeed, the food was considerably better here and the general treatment he received also began to work wonders. He was given medicine and allowed to rest and recuperate so that, within a week of his arrival in the camp, he was feeling sufficiently better and strong enough to take himself off the sick list.

He was put to work very shortly, repairing a torn and damaged map of Johore. Maps were his specialty but, by the second week, he was launched into a quite different direction as a concert performer. The previous concert party, which he had heard about while still at their temporary bivouac in March, had been a success and Sou Young and the other leaders were now contemplating a touring group.

During the second half of June 1944, a couple of concerts were organised in Arthur's camp at which various people gave speeches, sang, danced or performed in some way, either as acrobats, jugglers or magicians and, on the occasions when the concerts weren't rained out, they were regarded as a great success. Similar, equally successful concerts were held in some of the other nearby camps. The plans for a touring concert party now began to take shape. It would travel to other camp locations and to places nearby to civilian settlements which were known to be friendly to the guerilla cause. The concerts were felt to have excellent potential as fund-raisers and although there was always the danger of the Japanese discovering a concert, the risks were not considered sufficient to prevent the plans from going ahead. A concert would only be held in a place that was considered secure and would go ahead only on the last- minute advice of locals who had an up-to-date knowledge of Japanese movements in the area.

When Doug and Arthur were invited to join the concert party which was being formed, they both jumped at the opportunity because it offered possibilities of moving around. Maurice Cotterill was not included in the preparations, at his own request: "I've never been any good on a stage," he said.

"Oh, don't be a shirker," Doug laughed. "You can't get out of it. Anyway, I'm sure you'd be a star if you gave it a go."

But Maurice was adamant. He did not want to join them in the concerts. For several days Arthur and Doug tried to change his mind, impressing on him that there was another attractive aspect of concerts, for the participants, as well as for the audience--the food that came at the completion of the performance.

"It's like a party," Arthur told him. "Cakes made of minced chicken, fried pineapple, sugared peanuts, all sorts of other fruits, and there's always plenty of coffee."

These treats alone were sufficient attraction to entice Doug and Arthur into the concert business, but Maurice still said no.

Once they gave up trying to convince Maurice, the more immediate problem for Arthur and Doug was to develop some acts. They began by learning some Chinese songs and then they translated Australian and English songs into Chinese and Malay. Doug, in true Scots tradition, began perfecting a Highland fling routine which he said would 'lay 'em in the aisles'. Others in the touring party were busy learning their parts in various political, as well as humorous, plays.

For the next ten days or so they held a concert almost every second night, perfecting their routines, polishing their performances in readiness for their first show 'outside'. Although they knew it would be somewhere close by, no-one was sure exactly where it would be. Nevertheless, excitement was running high in the camp.

During this time, Roy returned from Q Camp to join them as he had become ill and there was no medicine at his camp. There was also concern during this period about possible Japanese attacks and on several occasions they were subjected to special 'alerts'--false alarms, given on purpose in the middle of the night to see how quickly they could react in case of an emergency. The first occasion had everyone leaping from their beds to scatter into the pitch-black jungle, scrambling around for half an hour--or, in some cases, for the rest of the night. It was so chaotic that the camp superiors decided more practice was needed.

So, in the morning they practised getting up and running from their sleeping positions along various escape routes. After doing it with normal daytime vision, they had to do the same thing blindfolded, as if it were night. Although they had always felt secure at night because it was considered equally difficult for attackers to move in the dark as the people they were attacking, several of the camp leaders seemed convinced the Japanese were planning night attacks. Fortunately nothing happened before the time came for them to take off on their first concert tour.

It was on a Monday evening in early July. They had an early meal at about 3 pm and then, accompanied by some riflemen, headed for the clearing called '80 acres' a few miles from the camp. Lee See, one of the leaders from Headquarters, and several other guerillas were there in advance to make sure it was safe and also to make some arrangements for staging the concert. An old deserted house at one end of the large clearing was to be used as a dressing room, its verandah forming the stage.

There were over one hundred in the audience, all sitting around on logs or on the grass, clearly keen to see the show. This, Arthur learnt, was not the first guerilla concert that had been staged in the area. There had been several performances by other guerilla groups and they had proved to be very popular. The civilian population was generally impressed with the guerillas and the anti-Japanese struggle they were carrying on, and they did everything possible to support them at other times.

The concerts had proved to be an excellent fund-raising avenue for the guerillas as everyone who attended had to have a chit, a piece of paper indicating that they had donated something to the cause. It could be a dollar or less, depending on the person's means, but some of the more affluent traders had given ten dollars or even one hundred dollars and there had been many occasions when concerts such as these had raised over a thousand dollars in a night.

Arthur's first concert began at 8 pm and ran through until midnight. It began with the political and propaganda speeches, then progressed to songs, dances and entertainment. Arthur gave a speech in Malay which seemed to please the audience more Arthur felt, because he was a white man speaking their language, than for the content, which he considered pretty boring. It dealt with the need for the civilians to cooperate with the anti-Japanese forces and the fact that the Allies--the British, Americans and Australians who were fighting the Japanese in the South Pacific--were also their friends.

The entertainment section of the concert was understandably the most popular, and Doug and Arthur's version of 'Mother McCree' and 'Auld Lang Syne' in Malay, and then Arthur's 'Waltzing Matilda' in Chinese, were great successes. When Doug danced the Highland fling, the laughter and applause were loud enough to make a couple of the guerilla leaders glance nervously around, as if the sound might carry to distant Japanese encampments.

After the concert Arthur, Doug and the other performers socialised with the local audience and plunged into the plentiful supply of cakes and coffee. Then they packed up what gear they had and set off, at two in the morning, to return to their camp, arriving dog-tired an hour and a half later. They were allowed to sleep during the day, but both Arthur and Doug found it difficult because of all the noise and normal activity that went on around the camp.

The groups often felt very nervous about the proximity of the concert sites to the centres of population and, therefore, to possible large Japanese military groups. One particularly arduous daylong trek had taken them through stretches of jungle, across rubber plantations and wading armpit-deep across rivers, to reach the concert location after dark. They were well into the performance, with lots of cheering, shouting and laughter in the air, when someone mentioned to Arthur that they were only two miles from Buloh Kasap, a town of several thousand people that was used regularly by Japanese Army units as a base for their anti-guerilla forays into the jungle.

This information made Doug and Arthur extremely edgy, although they noticed that no-one else seemed greatly concerned. They had a network of guards and lookouts posted well out from the concert site itself and that seemed sufficient to keep everyone happy. As it happened the concert went well, in the usual manner, finishing up, very nicely as far as Arthur and Doug were concerned, with plenty of large cakes, bananas, sugar-cane and coffee.

After Buloh Kasap there was only one more concert for Arthur's group, near the jungle camp called Number 21, near Serakek. From there they left the following morning to make for their own camp. They passed near to Selumpoh, collecting some six hundred tobacco leaves from a farmer there, and then went through the villages of Mangan and Durian Chin Chin, eventually arriving at their camp around dusk.

Settling down to exchange news with those members of the camp who had remained behind, they learnt that after their close call at '80 acres', when the Japanese patrol had arrived less than an hour after the end of their concert, the Japanese had been back in the area in numbers every day and sometimes at night. The concert group had obviously been extremely lucky to have missed them.

During the week they had been away, the other members of the camp and guerillas from nearby camps had also been busy. Tek Chiong and several other men had formed a special group, successfully blowing up several rail and road bridges. Four men from Arthur's camp had been into Segamat township to carry out the assassination of a man the guerillas regarded as the chief traitor in the area. The Japanese gave the local man an official funeral with riflemen firing shots over his grave. This was taken as a fair indication that the guerillas' assessment of the man as a top traitor had been accurate.

Five prisoners had been taken on this and another excursion, and the morning after the concert group's return to camp, the trial of two of these prisoners was held. It was another of the long, drawn-out affairs that Arthur had seen so often during the years he had been in the jungle. The questioning, under extreme pressure and torture, took most of the day. Finally, as they were being questioned separately, one gave the other one away. Once this had happened, the second one capitulated and gave details of the first one's treachery.

One of them had operated in the Tunkutiga area on a salary of five hundred dollars a month, trying to obtain information about the Communist guerilla forces in the jungle and the people in nearby villages who collaborated with them. Whenever he obtained information, he reported directly to Japanese headquarters in Singapore.

The second traitor had trained for almost a year in Singapore on different methods of working clandestinely in an area collecting information, which he would then pass on to his accomplice, who would forward it to Singapore. This information would invariably result in raids, arrests, torture and often execution of people supporting the guerilla cause. During 1943 and 1944, these two men had been responsible for the torture and death of many people. Before their own death sentences were carried out, they were subjected to an additional punishment of two strokes each with a rotan whip from every member of the camp.

During Arthur and Doug's absence on the concert tour, Roy and Maurice Cotterill had been sent back to Q camp, where Roy had been when Arthur passed through on his way to Number 5 Camp. The only reason given for the move was that they felt a Japanese attack was likely and they'd prefer Maurice and Roy to be at Q Camp. Fresh from their triumphant tour, Arthur and Doug were disappointed. There was no-one to meet them, nobody to listen to their tales. They had been looking forward to telling Roy and Maurice of their adventures.

As it happened, in a short time they, too, were instructed to move. Twenty-three of them were called up and told that they would be going to a deserted camp called 22 Camp near Mangan village. Arthur and Doug had passed by it on a couple of occasions during the concert tour and, when the place was described to them, Arthur didn't like the idea very much, particularly as the Japanese had evidently been to the Mangan area many times before and had cut trails through the jungle in order to attack it.

The guerilla hierarchy had decided that, as considerable time had elapsed since the Japanese had operated in the area, it was reasonably safe to reactivate the camp. Neither Arthur nor Doug could accept the reasoning behind it, but that was what had been decided and there was no arguing.

It took them four days to get there, not because of the distance but because of delays caused by uncertainty about Japanese movements in the area. They reached the camp at Durian Chin Chin by one in the afternoon on the first day and decided to wait until the following morning before pressing on because of a report that some seven truckloads of Japanese soldiers had been off-loaded in the district not long before they arrived. Two full days were then spent sitting around waiting for an all-clear report from a reconnaissance group that had gone on ahead to the 22 Camp area.

They finally set out at seven-thirty in the morning of the fourth day, keeping to jungle trails for the first part, then through disused rubber plantations for some time and back into the jungle for a short distance to the camp. Although the Japanese had not been there for some time, they could see quite plainly the results of their last visit-- bullet holes in just about every tree, some almost cut in half. They set to work to try to get the place back into workable shape, although for the first few days, most of the group were out collecting food. They dug potatoes from a large patch near their concert site only two miles from Buloh Kasap. They collected large quantities of the fruit growing in the area: papayas, huge pineapples, bananas, breadfruit and coconuts. There also seemed to be plenty of wild pigs, as well as domestic pigs provided by friendly locals.

Although the food in the camp was entirely satisfactory, Arthur had nagging fears about the Japanese attacking the camp. He felt that the leaders of the new group seemed a little too sure of themselves and of the presumed security of the camp. A good deal of shouting, blowing whistles and even singing went unchecked, and Arthur felt it was pushing fate too far. They were getting over-confident and both he and Doug felt nervous about it.

Arthur had begun to sense during the concert tour that there had been a marked change, over the past months, in the

attitude of civilians who had not previously been guerilla supporters, particularly the Malays, who had thought early in the
war that the Allies had been permanently defeated by the Japanese and that the Chinese guerillas in the jungle would also be
beaten eventually. It was now abundantly clear to the civilian
population that the guerillas were there to stay and had become a
real force to be reckoned with--a thorn in the Japanese side that
was becoming sharper with each passing month. While the Japanese were still well in control of large areas of South-East Asia,
there was plenty to indicate that they could not hold on forever.
And, when a patrol returned to camp the following day, they received a piece of news that, if it was true, added considerable
weight to the idea that the war might be turning.

A messenger arrived with a report that Hitler had been
killed. A bomb had been thrown by someone during a meeting of
his top generals, several of whom had also been wounded. With
that report--which, of course, they later learnt was only partly
true, as Hitler survived the blast--there were two others, the first
untrue, the second partly true. The messenger said that Tojo and
the entire Japanese Cabinet had resigned and that in Singapore,
a building in which the Japanese occupation authorities were
holding a meeting had been blown up, causing hundreds of casualties. Naturally, by this stage of the war, Arthur and the others
understood that even their own propaganda was often exaggerated, and in some cases untrue, but even if these reports were
only partly true, they still gave reason for hope.

25

ARTHUR'S MAIN PREOCCUPATION NOW WAS to get out of the '80 acres' Camp. The mosquitoes were the worst he had ever experienced and he found it all but impossible to sleep. He determined to try to get back to the camp he had left at Mangan, but now he could not get permission. It was 'too dangerous', he was told. Too many Japanese soldiers about. He told the camp leaders that he found this hard to believe, but they were adamant. It was too dangerous.

At four-thirty the following morning, when they were woken with the news that a Japanese attack was anticipated on the '80 acres' camp, Arthur felt that perhaps the leaders had been right and that he had been hasty in not believing them. Most of the group were to head towards another camp in the Tunkutiga area, while he and a few others that they called 'special' troops would go to 21 Camp at Serakek, the camp where Doug had gone to fix a Vickers machine-gun.

It took them almost four days to get there, mainly because they were held up by numerous Japanese troop movements in the district. At Durian Chin Chin, where they decided to spend the first night, they had word from friendly Malays in the kampong that eighty Japanese had arrived at 10 pm and had pitched camp less than a mile from where they were. As there was almost a full moon and they feared the possibility of a night attack, they were on alert for most of the night. They had planned to move on during the day, but it was thought to be safer to stay where they were, waiting to see what the Japanese would do. They were prepared in the event of an attack and could easily escape into the jungle. Most of the day was spent in catching up on sleep lost during the night and, by the afternoon, when it started to rain heavily, they learnt that the Japanese soldiers had gone.

As the rain continued and most of the day's light had gone, they decided to stay another night. Again they had no sleep, this time because of the hordes of mosquitoes. They lit smoke fires to try to drive them away, but to no avail.

When they arrived at the Serakek camp the next morning, Arthur once again met up with Doug and Maurice. Maurice had been moved back to the Number 5 Company group which had since moved to Serakek, while Roy had stayed at the Q Camp.

Arthur found he was impressed with the camp. It was under the command of Lee See, the man from Headquarters who had been in charge of guarding the concert tours. From the way the other guerillas addressed Lee See and the fact that, when speaking to Arthur, Doug and Maurice, they referred to him as 'Number 1', it seemed to Arthur that Lee See had been doing some ladder-climbing in the guerilla hierarchy. He was taller than most of his companions, about thirty years old, with close-cropped hair. He was quiet and friendly towards Arthur and his companions, but, Arthur thought, totally without humour.

The camp seemed to have plenty of food, almost too much in fact. There were good supplies of fruit all around them and on his first day in the camp, a guard shot a pig and later in the afternoon someone else shot a large monkey, so it was pig and monkey for dinner that night, and pig and monkey for breakfast. They expected the same for dinner that night but in mid- afternoon one of the men shot a fifteen hundred pound seladang. Unfortunately, it was a good two hours away from the camp. Carrying-parties were sent out and the first loads began arriving in the camp at around 9 pm. Some of the meat was cut up and cooked immediately, for a late supper, while huge amounts of meat kept coming in. Much of it was sent off to other camps, but even so, for several days they had nothing but meat for nearly every meal. Arthur was surprised to find that, although he always enjoyed eating meat--most of the time in the jungle he was, of necessity, vegetarian--he found so much meat hard to take. His gums began to get sore and he felt bloated with wind.

By the time the camp had finished eating the seladang, Arthur, Doug and Maurice, as well as six others, were moved off to another camp only an hour's trek away. A very profitable little cottage industry had been established there, grating coconuts for oil. Hundreds of coconuts were being brought in to the place continuously. Arthur and the new arrivals were quickly conscripted into the labour force. They would all take turns in doing different jobs in the process, which involved grating the white coconut meat, washing it, squeezing large amounts of it in cloth to get the milk and then boiling that down until it turned to oil. It took about ten or eleven coconuts to produce one bottle of oil, which could be sold for eight dollars, and they could easily produce around ten bottles a day.

At this camp they seemed to eat endless amounts of fruit- - bananas, papaya, pineapples and, of course, coconuts--as well as the occasional monkey. Arthur had been eating well for so long now, he had put on considerable weight, almost regaining the weight he had lost in the earlier part of the year. But, unfortunately, being well-fed and looking healthy seemed to provide no guarantee against illness and, within little more than a week of their arrival in the new camp, Arthur began to feel the first twinges of what he knew would be another bout of malaria. He dreaded it. Day by day it got worse. On the first day he felt slightly off-colour, the next, desperately tired. Then his legs became shaky and he was confined to bed for several days. Although he was not delirious, he was alternately drenched in perspiration as his fever raged, or wrapped in blankets shivering uncontrollably. He found he could not face any food, or hold it down if he tried to eat any, so he began to lose weight again.

For the next six weeks he suffered recurrent bouts of fever which ranged in severity from being bedridden and unable to move, to days at a time when he could function quite normally with only a vague feeling of being slightly tired or off-colour. And then, suddenly, he would be laid low again, with violent vomiting and diarrhoea. He felt that it was probably a lot more than just malaria that he was suffering from, but no-one could tell if there really was something else, nor did they have any effective medication. One 'treatment' he received was from a Chinese herbalist who was in the camp one day, passing through to somewhere else. He maintained that the only thing to be done for Arthur's illness was for his sinews to be pulled. So he set to work pulling on all of the sinews in Arthur's body that he could lay his hands on, pinching the skin quite painfully all over. A week later, another Chinese doctor came through the camp and prescribed a special herb for Arthur to drink. He also assured him that, unless his sinews had been pulled, he would not have survived.

"How long would I have lasted?" Arthur asked him.

"Four or five days," the doctor said, "not more."

Arthur nodded gravely, not really convinced. Although he had no doubts that the illness from which he and several others in this and nearby camps had been suffering was serious--one of the soldiers at 'Hill Camp', not far from them, had died a few days earlier from what seemed to be the same condition-- somehow he still couldn't bring himself to believe that pinching and pulling sinews had saved him.

He felt fortunate, however, that during these long periods of illness, there had been no need for urgent activity, such as escaping from Japanese attacks. There was little or no Japanese activity in the area for many weeks. During this time the other members of the camp were involved in a process of consolidation--hut-building, food-planting and gathering, and coconut oil production, all of which kept them constantly busy.

Early in September 1944, Roy arrived to join the camp. His group had split up, with members being sent off in different directions. Roy's arrival meant that, for the first time in many months, there were now four Europeans in the one camp, and the possibility of a fifth. They received a letter from Bennett, who said that he was now well and was still hoping to join them. There had also been a letter, during the worst days of Arthur's illness, from Les, Mac, Bluey and Gaje who were also well and working in a big clearing down near Muar, planting and growing vegetables, with Mac working as assistant cook. It had been so long since Arthur had heard from any of them that he often wondered if they were still alive. He had written a couple of letters which never reached them, but now that there was definite news that they were all right, he felt they could probably keep in touch more regularly.

The camp continued to prosper and grow, numbering almost ninety during September and October and, although they heard reports of up to a thousand Japanese troops arriving in Segamat, with smaller contingents at Buloh Payu, Buloh Kasap and Selumpoh in preparation for a new campaign against the guerillas, for some reason it never eventuated. Nevertheless, their presence in so many centres nearby had the camps on tenterhooks for long periods, ready to fight or run.

That the Japanese did not mount any major offensives was fortuitous, because, almost as soon as Arthur began to get over his illness, Doug and Roy became sick. They were sent 'up the hill' to a separate part of the camp which, although it was only about eighty feet higher than the main camp, took half an hour to reach. It was regarded as a much safer spot for any of those who were sick or injured, as it would allow considerable extra time for escape if any attack was launched against the main camp.

Roy's illness was like Arthur's, a fever, almost certainly malaria, while Doug had a badly infected and swollen ankle which made it almost impossible for him to walk. For a few days Roy seemed all right, but then he took a turn for the worse, becoming slightly demented in the process. He would wander around with a vacant look on his face, talking absolute rubbish. Then he would develop, as Arthur had, a burning temperature, but surprisingly, no perspiration. When this happened, Arthur and others would bathe him to try to bring his temperature down and then put him to bed. This went on for several days before they could get a word of sense from him and then he slowly began to show signs of recovery.

Arthur was glad of Roy's recovery for more reasons than one. During the last week of October, the concert tours started again and Doug Stewart and Arthur were asked to join the touring group. Maurice was also approached again and this time, after having heard all of Arthur and Doug's stories of the previous concerts and realising that he had missed out on quite a lot by not going with them, he agreed to join the new tour.

The new group performed one concert in their own camp, to an enthusiastic reception. Maurice, who seemed to have quite readily overcome his initial reluctance or shyness, stood on

*15. Lord Louis Mountbatten, Supreme Allied Commander
of South East Asia Command, accepts the Japanese surrender,
Singap[ore, 12 September 1945. General Itagaki signs the
documents. (Australian War Memorial negative no. 116237*

386

CHAPTER TWENTY-FIVE

*16. Arthur Shephard in British Army uniform.
Photograph taken in Segamat, shortly after leaving
the jungle in September 1945.*

stage and told a couple of stories and several jokes in fluent Malay, much to the delight of the audience, which laughed uproariously. This seemed to give him confidence and he was full of enthusiasm for the tour when they took off, early in the morning of the following day. They headed back towards the areas in which they had previously performed and Arthur soon recognised tracks they had been on during the first tour and a rubber plantation, now deserted, where they had once given a concert. At about four in the afternoon they reached a large coffee plantation and stopped at a house occupied by a friendly Chinese man. After resting a while, they moved on a short distance to another plantation where the concert was to be held and where they had an excellent dinner of dry rice with plenty of chicken, fish and vegetables. The first concert was a success. A crowd of more than a hundred people turned up and when, towards the end of the night, donations were asked for, the money poured in with many in the audience giving as much as one hundred Malay dollars.

For the next few weeks, life in the camp remained fairly stable. Arthur, who was free of any bouts of malaria at this stage, found the food-gathering excursions very enjoyable. Walking in the open, through rubber plantations and clearings in the early morning, with the mist just lifting and the sun coming over the hills and trees, was always beautiful. The only sour note, during one of these early morning excursions, was when they came to a village which had been burnt to the ground. The beheaded skulls of at least forty people were left lying around--as a gruesome warning from the Japanese.

Apart from this, though, there were no upsets except for a couple of small moves they made to new, safer locations further into the jungle. The first was to a place called Sin Lee Swan Camp. Maurice had his fortieth birthday on the day of the move. They had planned to celebrate with a chicken and some sugar, which had been promised them by Lee See. Although the sugar-cane had been 'lost' in the process of moving camp, they were perfectly happy with just the chicken.

The second move, a week later, was only a quarter of a mile further along the nearby stream to a place which was not quite so muddy. It was there, on the first afternoon of their arrival, that a major confrontation erupted between the Europeans and the Chinese.

The new site had previously been occupied as a camp and had been vacated only a month previously. Why it had been left, Arthur couldn't establish. It seemed to him to be a very pleasant spot on the banks of a fair-sized stream, quite high from recent rains. The soil was sandy, instead of the mud-bowls they'd been used to in the previous two camps, and it was relatively free of mosquitoes. The buildings, however, were in a poor state and they had to set to immediately to fix enough huts to sleep in. The hut allocated to the three Europeans had fallen down. Doug and Arthur managed to re-erect part of it with a strong, forked tree branch, while other supports and ties were placed under and around it. When these were in place, Doug asked one of the camp leaders, standing nearby supervising some of the other repair operations, if he should remove the forked branch.

"Yes," he said in Malay, "go ahead."

But as Doug shifted the fork out of the way, the whole roof slipped and tilted badly.

"Sarquar!" the man shouted at Doug in Chinese, "you stupid idiot."

Doug's face flushed and he grabbed a bayonet which he had been using to cut vines.

"Don't call me names, you little bastard," he shouted, raising the bayonet threateningly.

The officer's eyes blazed with suddenly increased anger at the sight of Doug menacing him. Lee See, who saw the fracas developing, came running, pistol in hand and accompanied by two riflemen, to stop the argument. The three guerillas simply aimed their weapons at Doug and told him to drop the bayonet. There was nothing he could do.

Then, Arthur, Roy and Maurice could only stand by helplessly as Doug was tied with his back to a tree. He would be fed and given water, Lee See said, but no cigarettes.

Arthur then entered into a heated argument with Lee See about the unfairness of the situation. He explained that the guerilla officer had abused and ridiculed Doug and that it had been a flair-up of tempers on both sides. Arthur also tried to stress that it was a relatively unimportant issue and unfair to punish Doug for it.

But his efforts were to no avail. Doug was kept tied to the tree for more than a week, despite continued entreaties from Arthur, Maurice and Roy. He was allowed to be untied to go to the latrine and for a supervised wash once a day, but the rest of the time he was tied firmly to the tree, sometimes so firmly that the circulation in his hands was affected.

The incident soured relations between the Europeans and the Chinese badly, with the situation deteriorating rapidly. The Chinese began to pick on Arthur and the others for the smallest things. On 1 December, eight days after Doug had been tied up, Wong Tek Liong, Tek Chiong's older brother, who had been sending books to Arthur during the past year, turned up in the camp. He immediately acted as a mediator in the affair. Although Arthur had corresponded with him by mail, and Tek Liong had sent several books to him, they had never met until now. Nor did Arthur understand exactly what Tek Liong's relationship was with the guerillas. Technically he was not one of them, because he still lived in Segamat, but he obviously had considerable authority and was probably a member of the Party. In any event, Doug was released shortly after his arrival. Tek Liong also apologised, as much as he could without undermining his comrades' authority, for Doug having been tied up for so long. "It was all a mistake," he said.

"Difficult for them to go much further than that," Maurice said as the four Europeans sat together in their hut, shortly after Doug's release, discussing the sudden change in attitude. "It's important for them to keep some 'face'."

The four men didn't press the subject any further or look for redress. They just asked if they could move to another camp. Arthur felt it was unfortunate that relations had deteriorated so badly that they wanted to go, because the camp itself was in such a good position. Under the circumstances, though, they felt there was really no alternative. In all of the many months they had been in the jungle, they had got on extremely well with the Chinese and although they knew of clashes with other Europeans, this had been the first time it had affected them.

It was agreed that they could go to a camp called Foo Ee Kong, where they would be provided with food until their garden, which they were expected to plant, started producing. It seemed to Arthur to be a fair enough arrangement, enabling them to live separately from this particular group. But it wasn't to be so simple. On 6 December, the day after Arthur's twenty-seventh birthday, they were told they could leave on the following day but a warning of Japanese troop movements in the area delayed their departure. On several of the days following Doug's release, Arthur had felt ill and weak and now, as they waited to leave for the new camp, things got worse. He became very tired and could not eat any food for two days.

On the morning of 9 December, it was decided that Doug and Roy would go to the new site, while Arthur and Maurice would remain until Arthur's condition picked up a little. In the middle of the same afternoon, everything went suddenly blank for Arthur. For four days he knew nothing and only afterwards, from what he was told by Maurice, did he discover he had hovered near the brink of death for those days as a terrible bout of fever had struck him down.

Maurice had gone out with a food-gathering party that morning and had returned in the afternoon to find Arthur lying on the ground near their shelter, unconscious. No-one knew how long he had been there.

"For the next few days you were absolutely delirious," he told Arthur later. "You had raging temperatures and shocking attacks of shivering. You were in a coma. We were all convinced you were dying."

Four days later, Arthur had started to come around and to regain some consciousness. Everything seemed strange and unreal to him, unearthly, as though he was watching it all in a cinema. He felt completely detached. He was given rice to eat and he managed to eat a little and to hold it down. The following day, he had some sweet potato and said he liked the taste. As each day passed he showed gradual improvement, but he was still desperately weak and could not move from his bed.

Then, as if to set the seal on the fact that they would not be leaving this camp for some time, the rains came. After a period of what had only been sporadic rain, the monsoon began to set in. The rain fell in torrents, all day and all night for days. Not only Arthur, but everyone else in the camp was confined to their shelters unless it was absolutely necessary to leave. It was a bad time for Arthur. The grey monotonous rain made the days dark and depressing and he felt weak and useless.

Two days before Christmas, two weeks after he had fallen ill, he managed to get up for the first time and to hobble around slightly, with the aid of a stick, in the shelter he shared with Maurice. He felt ninety-seven instead of just twenty-seven. After a meal of potatoes, panjan and katchan (long beans), he spent the next day vomiting it all up again. His stomach couldn't handle it.

On Christmas Day 1944, he was allowed to eat a few strips of pastry boiled in water, and some unsweetened tea. Christmas dinner! In the evening he was given some coffee with sugar in it.

The next week, the last of Arthur's third year in the jungle, passed in an equally uninspiring fashion with unending rain beating down until he thought he would go mad. But, despite the conditions, he felt his strength gradually returning and he tried to convince himself, although he found it hard to do, that the rain would eventually stop that he would be able to leave with Maurice to join Roy and Doug and to start the new year on a brighter note. He also wanted very badly for this to be his last Christmas and New Year in the jungle.

26

DURING THE FIRST WEEK of 1945, Arthur took things very easily around the camp, but, after the unpleasantness of the period preceding his illness, both he and Maurice wanted to move to the Foo Ee Kong campsite where Doug and Roy had gone, or to the small clearing not far away where less than a dozen or so others were camped and running quite a productive vegetable garden. The camp commandant, Lee See, had been sent away on an extended assignment, so they raised the subject of moving with the new camp leader, a stocky man in his early forties called Lee Cheng Foo. He said he thought Arthur was still too weak to go. For some reason, Cheng Foo treated both him and Maurice with a degree of suspicion. Arthur and Maurice could only guess that it was because he had not had much contact with Europeans before. In any event, they never really got to know Cheng Foo well, but under steady pressure from the two men, he eventually agreed in principle for the move to take place and, within a few days, they were given a 'chit' confirming that permission had been granted. '

"Bureaucracy rearing its ugly head," Arthur commented as they said goodbye to the camp. "Good riddance."

As they approached the new campsite at 'the clearing', after a trek of about an hour, they hoped their experiences there would be better than the last. And from the very beginning, their hopes were fulfilled. Firstly, they were given a hut of their own. Normally one of the other men slept in the hut but he was off on a mission somewhere and no-one seemed to know when he would be returning, so they had the hut to themselves.

It was a very simple set-up. There were only six Chinese in the clearing, all of whom addressed each other with the simple

'Ah' in front of their names: Ah Chee, Ah Kow, Ah Leong, and so on. Their main task was to grow vegetables, so there was already established an efficient routine of either hoeing, sowing, weeding, cropping or picking. It was a routine into which Arthur and Maurice were launched almost immediately. It was extremely difficult for Arthur at the beginning, as he was still very weak and was plagued by diarrhoea. In addition, because they were in a clearing and not protected by the canopy of jungle trees, the temperature was considerably higher than in previous camps and this tended to make the work in the fields more arduous than normal, particularly for Arthur, in his weakened state. But, apart from a few days on which he was forced to rest, he made gradual progress, over the following weeks, back to normal health.

During this period they were told that a family of eleven would be moving in to another small clearing about a hundred yards from their own. Arthur was initially a little upset when Ah Leong and some of the others from his small camp were pulled away from planting to help build a simple house for the family, due to arrive any moment, but his attitude changed a few days later when the family moved in and he met one of the sons, seventeen-year-old, Teo Ten Chew.

As he spoke quite reasonable English, Ten Chew dropped into the clearing camp on the morning of their arrival to chat with Arthur and Maurice. It seemed that his father, Teo Ee Lim, had been working in Segamat as the chief detective in the police force there, but all the time secretly acting as an agent for the Communist guerillas. He had been given away by a captured guerilla who had been subjected to Japanese torture, but had been prudent enough to foresee the possibility of exposure and managed to send his family into the jungle for protection and to escape himself. He was presently at 23 Camp, a site not far from '80 acres', where he was working amongst people from nearby kampongs, as well as Segamat, collecting money for the guerilla cause. It would be some time before Arthur and Maurice would meet Teo Ee Lim, but in the meantime, Ten Chew and the rest of Ee Lim's family, which included his parents, a brother and his wife and their two children, settled down to life in the jungle and to the planting routine that Arthur and Maurice had established at the clearing.

Another regular diversion for Arthur and Maurice, duly noted in Arthur's diary, was spotting Allied planes flying over. This occurred with increasing frequency as the weeks passed by and whenever they saw the big American B-29 bombers going over in groups of forty, fifty or sixty at a time, heading for raids on Singapore, Ipoh, Penang and other centres, they would cheer and wave to wish them luck.

More important to Arthur than the B-29s were the changes in the air: changes in attitude of both the Japanese in Malaya and the civilian population outside, particularly the Malays. It was as if everyone now sensed the inevitability of an eventual Japanese defeat. The war between the Japanese and the guerilla forces in the jungle still continued, but there was no longer grim determination on the part of the Japanese to exterminate the guerillas. They seemed resigned to the fact that the guerilla forces were there to stay and that all they could hope to do was contain them.

On the civilian side, there had been a remarkable turnaround in attitudes. The Malays, who for the past three years would have nothing to do with the largely Chinese guerilla forces and may have actively worked against them, now began showering food, cigarettes and money on the guerilla camps. Discreetly, of course, because it was still an extremely dangerous practice to be friendly to the guerillas. All over the country, people who had been convinced otherwise during the early part of the war now began to see the writing on the wall and wanted to hedge their bets.

"Bloody cynical bastards," Arthur once said to Maurice when they were discussing the apparent turnaround in opinions and attitudes. "Six months ago half of them would have turned us in without batting an eyelid."

Maurice nodded. "Yes, but I don't see that they've had much choice, really. It's pretty much an exercise in self-preservation on their part. They've got to back the winning side, whichever it is."

While Arthur could understand this sort of reaction on the part of the civilian population who were now switching their allegiances, he couldn't really like them for it, having been on the receiving end for so long.

After one of the big B-29 raids on Singapore in mid-February, they had word that one of the aircraft had been hit and brought down in Negri Sembilan State near Malacca. Three of the crew were reported killed, four were captured alive while another four had escaped into the jungle. The Japanese were offering rewards of a thousand dollars for any information, or ten thousand dollars per head for the capture of an actual airman.

They heard no more of the incident until the last few days of February when a report came in that the four escaped men, one of whom was badly burnt, had been brought safely to a camp near Palong, a long way from where the plane was supposed to have been shot down. Arthur and Maurice tried to obtain what information they could on the fliers from other surrounding camps, but several weeks passed before they heard any more of them.

At this time, in the early days of March, heavy rain fell virtually every day. There would be some sunshine during the mornings, then gradually the huge thunderhead clouds would build up until they could no longer hold their enormous load of water. Torrential downpours would fall all afternoon, every afternoon, until four or five o'clock. Then the rain began to extend into the night, and then through the night and into the following morning, when it always seemed to become even heavier.

Their main worry was the potatoes, many of which were going rotten. They had to pick as many as they could, even though they weren't fully matured, in order to save them.

They also had to go out to other areas, near Buloh Payu, Selumpoh and Por Twee to get other foodstuffs as the rain had wreaked havoc with their normal system and they were now experiencing a real lack in supplies.

On 31 March, during one of these food-collecting sorties to Por Twee, Arthur was stopped by a guerilla guard at a crossing point by a stream on the approach to the Por Twee kampong. He stood for a few seconds in surprise before speaking. There was no need for the man to bar his way. Arthur knew him and he recognised Arthur. He had been along the same path only the previous day.

"I want to go to Por Twee," Arthur said. "Let me pass."

"I am sorry," the man replied, holding his rifle across his chest, "no-one can go through."

"Why not?" Arthur asked angrily. The man simply shook his head.

Arthur beckoned to another man he recognised, asking the same question.

The man hesitated a moment and then said, "No-one is allowed there. There is an important meeting."

"What sort of meeting? Who is there?"

"I think there are Americans there, fliers, from a plane."

"The B-29?" Arthur felt a sudden wave of excitement. "The men who crashed in the B-29, the bomber in Malacca, two months ago?"

"I do not know," the man said. "I know only that they were from a plane."

"But I must see them." Arthur said. "They are friends, Allies. It is important for me to meet them." He turned to the original guard and spoke in Chinese, "Don't you see? They are friends. I must go to meet them."

He felt a tremendous urge to make contact with people who spoke his own language, understood his culture and had been in the outside world as recently as only six or seven weeks ago. But the guard shook his head and adopted an even more determined stance. The other man also shook his head.

"It is no use," he said. "We must obey our orders."

Arthur returned to camp, frustrated and angry, to tell Maurice what had happened. He asked others in the camp if they knew what was happening at Por Twee, but they were genuinely ignorant of the whole story.

Life continued as usual for a few days, the breaks in the rain allowing them to do some salvage work on the garden. On 4 April Arthur went again to Por Twee. This time he was not stopped when he entered the kampong compound and he learnt, after a few questions, that three American pilots had in fact been there on the day he was not permitted entry.

"But why couldn't I come in to see them?" he asked.

Several excuses, such as 'security reasons', were offered, none of which he found satisfactory.

"Where have they gone now?" he asked.

No-one seemed to know--or if they did, they weren't prepared to say. However, Tek Chiong, who had been in to Por Twee at the time they were there, was able to give Arthur some details of the men and their condition. One of the four survivors had died of burns at Palong, but the three others, although they had suffered a few minor wounds, were now in reasonable health. Arthur learnt that their names were William Duffy from Chicago, Donald Humphrey, of Pottsville, Iowa, and Clifford Saltzman of Washington DC.

The guerilla leaders weren't about to tell him, but Arthur felt sure that somehow the men were going to be evacuated from Malaya, either by air or boat, because when he enquired whether they would be going to a camp, the answer he received was a definite 'no'. Arthur felt certain that was the main reason they had been kept out of contact with him or any other Europeans in the jungle. The guerillas were probably concerned that if they were seen to be setting up elaborate escape mechanisms for three American pilots, there would be pressure from the remaining Europeans to have the same treatment, and then resentment on their part when they were told it could not be done.

Whatever the reasons, Arthur and the others were upset about the whole incident but there was little they could do. Within a couple of days, Arthur was diverted by a letter from Chew Ee Poo, one of the other camp leaders, saying that he had heard that Roy had died, three days earlier, on 6 April. He had no other information, but said in the letter that he would try to find out more.

Several days later, two letters came from Doug, who had been with Roy when he died. One letter told how Roy had suffered from fever for most of March and then seemed to go crazy. He started mixing tobacco into his rice, to verbally abuse people in the camp and to prowl around at night, sometimes with a bayonet in his hand. Everyone in the camp became frightened that he might do something dire, either to them or to himself, so efforts were made to hide the bayonet and any other weapons from him. There was also discussion about the possible need to tie him up. But on the night of 5 April, he fell into a deep coma and died at six the next morning.

According to a Chinese doctor, Doug's letter continued, Roy's spleen had burst, but whether this was true or not, Doug did not know as Roy was buried on the same day. Arthur wrote to Doug asking him to keep Roy's personal effects until they next met. He said he would try to return them to Roy's family at the end of the war.

After he had written the letter to Doug, Arthur sat quietly under a tree, holding it in his hands and thinking about Roy and some of the things they had been through together. He had been just nineteen years old when they left Australia and he had died two weeks short of his twenty-third birthday. Arthur remembered how he used to reminisce about the corner shop in Springvale, where he went to meet his mates. He remembered, too, how difficult Roy could be at times--the time he had refused to get out of bed in one of the guerilla camps. Everyone was supposed to 'stand to' at 4 am, some six hours before breakfast. Roy thought it was a stupid exercise, so lay in bed. As punishment, his rifle was taken from him for a period of time. He was a headstrong bugger, Arthur smiled sadly to himself, and now he's gone. The three years he's survived in the jungle and all he's been through, will mean nothing to those who've been waiting for him and hoping he's alive. All they'll know is that he died in the jungle. Arthur wondered, for the ten-thousandth time, how much longer the war would last. He wondered how much longer Roy would have had to hang on, to have survived. He wondered that for himself and the others, too.

There was now a definite feeling that the end was much closer. There was the feeling of 'don't mess it up now, don't make a mistake, don't get sick and die when it's all nearly over'. And, as every day went by, there seemed to be more and more news to confirm their hopes. By the end of April, they had news from several sources, including a Japanese paper, that Berlin was surrounded and could not hold out much longer.

But this good news was accompanied by a sudden spurt of Japanese activity against the guerileas, following an audacious guerilla attack on the military establishment in Segamat. A small party consisting of Teo Ee Lim, the former secret agent in Segamat, Lim Tek Sing and Kok Ching went into Segamat and, in a well-planned and executed raid, killed the chief police officer there, a Japanese. He had been a military officer, but since he had taken over the police role, not long before, he had employed various forms of torture on many of the prisoners held in Segamat.

His death immediately sparked increased anti-guerilla activity. The Japanese had come to accept the fact that the guerillas might assassinate some of those Malays or Chinese that co-operated with them. But a Japanese officer, that was quite different. About four hundred Japanese soldiers now poured into the area around '80 acres' and began arresting people indiscriminately. They questioned people and tortured some, fortunately without serious harm to any of them, but were unable to find out anything about the raid and the assassination. They did not remain in the area long, nor did they try to penetrate the jungle around '80 acres'. Within a couple of days they had withdrawn to Segamat once more.

During this time Doug arrived from the Foo Ee Kong camp to join Arthur and Maurice, bringing with him Roy's small parcel of belongings, including his pay book, some other papers, reading material and a string of rosary beads. He also brought the news of the end of the war in Europe. A local newspaper, printed in Malay by the Japanese, told of Hitler's death, the fall of Berlin and the German surrender.

Although they were all used to taking rumours with a grain of salt, the fact that this report was in an officially sanctioned, Japanese-controlled newspaper gave it credence and it was taken by all those in the camp as fact. It was the cause for general celebration, for everyone knew that, with the war in Europe over, the full weight of the Allied strength could now be swung into defeating the Japanese. The newspaper, however, dismissed the German collapse and surrender as being of no importance to the Japanese. They would fight on in every theatre of the war, the report said.

And fight on they would have to. On Sunday, 13 May, in an extraordinary series of coordinated attacks on cities and towns all over Malaya, the Chinese guerillas turned the tables on the Japanese, at least temporarily, giving them quite a shock. It was a clear demonstration of the guerillas' ability to strike hard, almost wherever they pleased.

For several days Arthur, Maurice and Doug had sensed that something was in the air in their own area. Dozens of riflemen were passing through the camp on their way to 23 Camp. Amongst them, Arthur saw Sou Young and the three who had carried out the successful assassination of the Segamat police chief, Kok Ching, Tek Sing and Teo Ee Lim, whom Arthur met briefly for the first time. Although he had a seventeen-year-old son, Ee Lim seemed very young himself. Arthur calculated that he must have been at least thirty-eight or forty years old, yet he looked no more than thirty. He spoke excellent English and was extremely personable and friendly to Arthur and Maurice during their short meeting. Some two hundred and fifty guerillas had gathered in the '80 acres' area that day, moving off in trucks (in itself an illustration of how quickly events were changing) towards Segamat, Buloh Kasap and Batu Anam.

In the Segamat raid, the guerillas entered the town from different directions, carrying their Tommy guns and other weapons in bags and other disguised coverings as they mingled with market crowds and made their way towards various specified objectives. Then, at the sound of a prearranged burst of submachine-gun fire from the centre of Segamat, the guerillas opened up on Japanese soldiers and threw grenades at the police headquarters. The Japanese provost marshal (the chief of the military police) in the town was caught in his car during the fracas and shot, at point-blank range, through the window, by Kok Ching.

The Japanese forces retired to an area around their headquarters, near a large water tower on a hill near the centre of town. From there they exchanged fire with the guerilla forces, but the guerillas were able to dominate the town for the night, roaming freely to collect large quantities of arms and ammunition and then returning by truck in the early morning to '80 acres'. Only two of the Segamat raiders had been wounded: Tek Sing had received a body wound (no-one knew exactly where, except that it could be serious) while another guerilla had been shot in the shoulder.

The success of the whole mission was largely due to Teo Ee Lim, whose knowledge of Japanese operations, their timetables and patterns of work, was invaluable. Prior to the Japanese occupation he had worked as a customs officer in Malaya under

British rule, and when the Japanese took over, he rose to the position of chief detective in the police force. In this post he had lived a daring double life, sending foodstuffs and information to the guerillas, including the radio Arthur's group had received back in September 1943. He used to secretly notify the guerillas about people who were collaborators and traitors to the guerilla cause. He carried on his work undetected until he was given away.

After his escape, the Japanese set huge rewards on Teo Ee Lim's head--half a million dollars--yet, during the raid on Segamat, he was able to move into the town with the guerillas, and to mingle with police and detectives whom he knew, without them giving him away.

The attack on Segamat was regarded as highly successful, but it was only one of many. Virtually every fair-sized town in Malaya was attacked at the same time. The widespread success of the raids was a major shock for the Japanese occupation forces, as well as a tremendous boost to the morale of the guerillas. However, in addition to being shocked, the Japanese were also enraged. They sent immediate reinforcements to many towns, including Segamat, and began making preparations for counterattacks.

In the meantime, Kok Ching and Tek Chiong came to the clearing to see Arthur and his friends. Kok Ching was wearing the murdered provost marshal's britches and puttees, while Tek Chiong had on his shirt and sword, a large, double-handed samurai sword of the kind usually reserved for officers of high rank. They were full of excitement about the success of the mission and spoke as if it was only the forerunner of many more similar attacks on Japanese establishments.

The following day there was considerable movement between the various guerilla camps in the region, mainly to transfer the sick and wounded, as well as women and children, to safer areas. Arthur was in Por Twee when Tek Sing, who had been injured in the Segamat attack, was brought in from another camp on a stretcher. He was fully conscious, talking a little, although with some effort, but he was spitting blood. Arthur did not see his wound, but he assumed it was in his stomach. He was taken from Por Twee a short distance into the jungle to a reasonably secure camp where he could be treated. Most of the guerillas from 23 Camp also arrived in the Por Twee area during the same day to be dispersed to other surrounding camps in the jungle.

Reports now began to come in from all around them of Japanese troops arriving in the vicinity. A guerilla patrol met a large party of Japanese soldiers in the '80 acres' area and exchanged fire with them for some time before escaping into the jungle. The following day another patrol operating between Por Twee and '80 acres' reported that the Japanese had found the track which led to the clearing camp where Arthur, Doug and Maurice were based. They had followed it a short distance and then returned to '80 acres' during the afternoon. This was taken as a strong indication that they would return in the morning. With the little encampment right in their path, Arthur felt sure they would be in for trouble.

There was no way that they could carry everything with them, so, determined not to leave anything for the Japanese, a number of carriers were enlisted from other camps to help move out as much of the vegetables they could crop and carry. The rest they put into bags and hid in the jungle around the clearing. By mid-afternoon they were ready to run at a moment's notice, even though there had been no indication yet that the Japanese were coming.

At dusk, a runner came with some news. At two in the afternoon, some of the people carrying vegetables had been moving down a track when they heard noises in the jungle not far from Arthur's camp. They stopped, listened and then carefully found a position from which they could see what was happening. A force of Japanese soldiers was busy cutting its own track through the jungle. The carriers were not seen by the Japanese so they hurried on to report the situation. It was clear to Arthur, Doug and Maurice that the Japanese could very easily strike at their camp without even passing through any of the intermediate camps like the one at Por Twee. But for some unknown reason, the Japanese did not continue cutting through the jungle to reach their trail and campsite.

That night the three Europeans went to Por Twee seeking extra arms and ammunition and while there they learnt a little of what had been happening outside. Segamat had evidently been closed off completely. A public meeting had been called at which the Japanese Commander in Segamat had harangued the local populace, saying that, as only Japanese were killed during the raid, then the townspeople must be working with the guerillas. They then began arresting people. The guerilla informant who witnessed the meeting remained at the scene only until it became unsafe for him to stay longer. By the time he left, however, at least half of the people at the meeting had been arrested.

Another incident concerned a guerilla they knew well from previous camps, called Lim Yong. He was stopped for questioning by two Japanese who had come to '80 acres' with a large party of soldiers a couple of days after the attack on Segamat. He was found to be carrying between six and seven hundred dollars on him, far more than a civilian would reasonably have. One of the Japanese grabbed Lim Yong by the left wrist to hold him. Lim Yong then threw the money into the air and, as the second soldier tried to catch and collect it, Lim Yong drew a knife and stabbed the first soldier in the arm, causing him to let go and giving Lim Yong a chance to dive into the bush and escape.

They also heard the story of a group of eight Malay police who returned to their kampong near Batu Anam on the night of 14 May, after the Segamat attack, taking their weapons with them. When a group of guerillas turned up at the kampong in the morning, the Malay police willingly brought out their weapons and handed them over to the guerillas--six shotguns and a .303 rifle. Arthur and his companions heard this with amazement and took it as yet another indication of the rapidly changing attitudes in Malaya.

Even better news came the following day: the Japanese had withdrawn from the '80 acres' area with no major success in their efforts to exact some retribution for the Segamat attack. All at Arthur's camp were able to relax a little once again. They celebrated in the morning by starting back to work on the potato beds in the clearing. But by midday the temperature had risen well over 100°F and with the high humidity that accompanied it, they were totally immobilised. It was one of the hottest days Arthur could remember. In the evening, however, there was some compensation in a spectacular thunder and lightning storm. It was like a fireworks show that lit up the whole sky. It was some

404

distance away from their position and so they experienced only a little rainfall, but the thunder was loud and continuous and the forked lightning kept the sky alight for more than two hours. None of them, including the Chinese guerillas who had spent their whole lives in Malaya, had seen anything quite like it before. Arthur noticed that some of them, although they tried to hide it, were a little frightened by the event. It was something he found surprising, considering some of the terrifying situations they had lived through during the past three years.

They now settled into a period of relative stability, working in their garden, planting, weeding and cropping, and sawing wood for fires. Within a short time, Doug and Arthur had planted over a thousand new potato plants. "Not bad for a couple of bloody amateurs," Doug laughed as they finished a row and hit the thousand mark. "Plays havoc with your back, though."

Without interruption from the Japanese, the set-up at the clearing was, in Arthur's opinion, the best they'd ever had in the jungle. When the weather was good their vegetables grew at an amazing rate, so that although their main task was to supply other camps around them with food, they always had enough left over for themselves and for a little bartering outside for other kinds of food and supplies when they needed them. For example, their excess in potatoes, sweet potatoes, kankong, long beans and several other vegetables was readily exchanged for such things as oil, fish, chillies, sugar, tapioca flour, coffee and rice and even chicken or pig.

One item on a menu, though, Arthur could not stomach. One day Ah Leong and Ah Chee cut down a large hollow tree for firewood. It turned out to be a home for a colony of bats. They managed to catch a couple of hundred and for the evening meal they cooked some up and ate them. Doug and Maurice, and this time Arthur, all said 'no thank you' to Ah Kow's offer.

"Come on, Arthur," Doug laughed, teasing, "I thought you could eat anything."

"No bloody fear. Rats and snakes are one thing," Arthur said, "but this is the bitter end." The sight and smell of the bats being cooked turned his stomach and he had difficulty in preventing himself from vomiting.

They sat and ate their vegetables, while several, but not all, of their Chinese companions ate bats. They quite expected those who ate them to come down with some dire illness, or at least an upset stomach or diarrhoea, but they suffered no ill-effects at all. There were, of course, plenty of bats for future meals, but nothing would persuade Arthur to change his mind. "I'd rather eat tapioca for a month than one meal of those bloody bats."

In the early part of June, Doug suddenly became seriously ill with what seemed to be some kind of dysentery. It began with him feeling sick in the stomach and not being able to eat. A day later his condition worsened, with very bad diarrhoea, at one stage taking him to the latrine twelve times in less than an hour, accompanied by bouts of vomiting. He vomited until he had nothing left to bring up except bile. This situation continued, to a lesser degree for four days. There was little anyone could do for him. They tried to get him to drink as much water as possible because, losing fluids so rapidly as he was, they all knew he might easily die of dehydration. But on most occasions when they tried to get him to drink, he was unable to hold even water down.

Arthur had gone, on the first day, to Por Twee seeking medicine, but they had been unable to supply anything. They felt totally helpless as they watched Doug lose weight dramatically, and gradually become weaker and weaker. They were anxious for him to be able to eat at least a little rice or, they felt, he would be unable to pick up again. But Doug just continued to throw up virtually anything that passed his lips.

On the sixth day, however, he showed a slight improvement and in the evening he managed to take a little rice and a couple of spoonfuls of mashed vegetables. A further day passed where he showed no change, but managed to eat a little again in the evening. Then, on the eighth day, he was down again, suffering from diarrhoea and vomiting. His condition calmed slightly during the night and then one more day went by where he lay as if in a coma, deathly pale and gaunt through losing so much weight.

And then it passed. On the tenth day he suddenly began to pick up. Some colour returned to his cheeks and he could talk to his friends. He was still terribly weak as a result of the ordeal, but the most important thing was that he could now eat and drink without immediately throwing it all back up.

There was very little respite as, within a week, as Doug slowly recovered, Maurice began to fall ill with what they suspected was jaundice, or hepatitis. He felt desperately tired after only the slightest effort or movement and his face and body began to turn quite yellow. He found, though, that, after a short while, he could live with the condition without too many problems, as long as he wasn't required to do any major work. He just had to take things fairly easy.

One day towards the end of June, they were awakened at about one in the morning by two planes flying very low overhead. "They're not Japanese," Doug said, as he sat up to listen. "They're ours."

For a while the planes seemed to be circling the area, flying low. Then, after ten minutes or so, they flew off.

"Well, what do you make of that?" Arthur said to Maurice, who was also sitting up on his mat, wide awake.

"Maybe it was only one of ours being chased by Jap one," Maurice said.

"But what would they be doing here at night?" Arthur asked. "We've never heard planes at night before. They must be on a raid."

"Maybe one of ours was hit and was hedgehopping, trying to get away from a Jap plane," Maurice insisted.

But they were just guessing and they knew it. Nevertheless, the mystery of the two planes had them intrigued. The Chinese in their camp were also at a loss to explain it. The planes had, of course, been heard at Por Twee and other places, but when Arthur enquired over the next few days, no-one in the surrounding camps seemed to know any more than he and his companions did.

Although there were no more night flights, the general level of air activity seemed to be picking up during the first weeks of July and on several occasions they saw Allied planes at quite close quarters. One afternoon a B-24 flew over very low, heading to the east. It was followed by several fighters flying protective cover at a higher altitude. A little later, two B-24s came over from the north-east, flying so low that the markings on the side of the planes were easily visible to Arthur and the others in the camp. Again they could only guess at the aircrafts' mission, but they had great hopes that something important was happening.

A few days later, when Arthur, Ah Chee and two others from Sin Kok Swan camp were called to Por Twee to help build a store hut, they were shown pamphlets that had been dropped over several towns in the area by the B-24s they had seen. There were two different types: one written in English on one side and Chinese on the other, the second in Malay on one side and Hindi on the reverse. The pamphlets carried the message that the war was nearly over. The Philippines and many of the islands in the South-West Pacific had been retaken by the Allies. Okinawa had been taken, after an American invasion and a bitter four-month campaign, in June, the pamphlet said, and Japan would soon be invaded, as would Singapore, Malaya and the other occupied countries in the region. It called on the local people to cooperate with the Allied soldiers when they landed and to help them in every way against the Japanese.

The pamphlets sent a wave of excitement through Arthur, Doug and Maurice, and it now became difficult for them to concentrate on their work in the clearing, knowing that wonderful developments were going on all around them in the outside world. And yet they knew there was nothing they could do, until there was a landing and Allied forces were actually in Malaya. So, after a few days of relative unrest and discontent, they pressed on with their planting regimen and general daily routine. Except for Maurice's jaundice, which prevented him from doing anything energetic, they were all now in reasonably good health and, most of the time, in very good spirits. They looked forward now to the weeks and months ahead, which they all saw as being the final phase of the war with Japan.

Arthur celebrated the new mood by shaving his beard off and once again having his hair cut so short that he was almost bald. He had to wear a hat continually for some time to avoid getting sunstroke.

Around this time, while Arthur was in Por Twee collecting salt he met Tek Sing. Arthur's last sight of Tek Sing had been a few days after the May raid on Segamat, when the young Chinese guerilla had been carried in on a stretcher, spitting blood.

Tek Sing showed Arthur the healed scar from his wound--a big one in his stomach. But what Arthur found more interesting about Tek Sing's condition was that he was outfitted in entirely new gear and equipment. His khaki pants, shirt, webbing and boots were all brand-new. It was the first new uniform he had seen in the jungle in three years. Looking around he now noticed that several of the other guerilla leaders in the Por Twee camp were also fitted out in new uniforms.

"Where did you get the clothes?" Arthur asked him. "They have been dropped in by plane. Many supplies are coming now. There are British commandos who have also been parachuted in-"

"What?!" Arthur interrupted, incredulous. "British commandos? Where?"

"They are in a secret position in the jungle. They will help organise the invasion."

"But when? And how many of them are there?"

"Forty." '

"And when did they come?"

"Earlier this month."

"Can I, can we--that is, Maurice, Doug and I--see them? We must meet them."

"I do not know," Tek Sing said, looking around the camp. "I do not think it will be possible. There are very few among us who know exactly where they are. I do not know myself, but perhaps I will be sent there."

"When?"

"I do not know"

"If you go, you must take a letter for me," Arthur said, sitting down immediately to write a note to the commanding officer of the group, whom Tek Sing informed him was a captain. Arthur wrote of their situation and of their desire to meet up with the commando group.

"Give this to the captain," he said, handing the note to Tek Sing.

"But I do not know when I will go," Tek Sing protested, "or if I will go at all."

"Then give it to someone you trust who is going to see them."

A few days later, 29 July, which Arthur noted as being the fourth anniversary of his departure from Australia with the 2/29th Battalion, Tek Sing came out to visit him and Doug and Maurice at the clearing. He brought some parachute material, which he said could be used to make and repair clothes. He told them, too, that he was leaving soon for the place where the British commandos, which he said were called Force 136, were living in the jungle. He said he still had Arthur's letter and promised to deliver it to them.

"How far is it?" Arthur asked.

"I am not sure, but it is at least three or four days. I do not know exactly where it is. I am going with others who know the way."

They said goodbye and wished Tek Sing luck, hoping to soon hear the results of his meeting with the commandos.

For a few days in early August, life went on as usual. Doug and Arthur continued to tend the vegetables in the clearing, going out to Por Twee every couple of days for additional supples like rice, coffee and sugar, and occasionally as far as Sin Kok Swan camp for tapioca, which they ground into flour to make cakes. They often saw Teo Ee Lim and his family who now lived in one of the houses at Por Twee. He always gave Arthur and his companions a particularly warm welcome and laid on cakes and samsoo wine whenever they called on him. Arthur found him pleasant company and the fact that Ee Lim enjoyed a good chat in English made their visits there something to look forward to.

A few times during the first week of August they met two more guerillas who were wearing new clothes. Both of them, Sung Poo and Lou Kwan, Arthur had known from previous camps. The three Europeans eyed their new equipment, including the shiny new pistols protruding from holsters on their belts, with envy. Some quantity of this gear was apparently now being parachuted in.

"If you need any new equipment, or clothes," Sung Poo told them, "you must ask Ho San."

"Ho San? Who is Ho San?" Arthur asked. "And where is he?"

"He is the new commander of Number 5 Company. He will supply you with some new clothes."

Back at their camp that evening, the three men made a modest list of clothing requirements, which they planned to send out to Number 5 Company at the first opportunity. To Arthur, the prospect of new clothes seemed too good to be true and he didn't really expect any results, but felt it was at least worth a try. The fact that others were now wearing good new clothes could have been just 'the luck of the draw' with the first ones on the scene having the opportunity to pick from a pile of new equipment until it was all gone. After all, he told himself, that was how things had been in matters of clothing and equipment during the whole of his stay in the jungle. It was hard to believe that it was all suddenly changing now.

Several rainy days followed, during which there was very little activity at the clearing. B-24s were flying over with increasing frequency and, even if they couldn't see them, they could now tell the difference between their distinctive engine sound and that of the Japanese planes.

When the rain seemed to ease towards the middle of August, they began to resume their visits to Por Twee, always stopping to visit Ee Lim for a cup of coffee and a chat. There seemed to be less work to be done at the clearing and for some reason nothing seemed to matter quite so much any more. The Japanese were extremely quiet. It was as if they were all waiting for something to happen.

Then, on 14 August, while Arthur was in Por Twee early in the morning to collect some coffee and cooking oil, Ee Lim rushed out of his house, waving a piece of paper and yelling hysterically in Chinese and then, when he saw Arthur, in English.

"The Japanese have surrendered! They have surrendered! The Japanese have surrendered!

There was a moment of amazed silence and immobility. Everyone looked at him as if he had gone mad. Then they looked around at each other and suddenly started shouting and laughing and cheering and rushing about, jumping in the air and repeating the news to everyone they saw.

Arthur and others crowded around Ee Lim to find out more. A runner had just brought him a letter from Chew Ee Poo, the guerilla leader who had sent them the news of Roy's death. He read it to them. "It says that the Japanese High Command in Tokyo has surrendered, unconditionally, on 15 August. Russia has also entered the war and has already advanced two hundred miles into Manchuria."

"Has Japan been invaded?" Arthur asked, incredulous. "Why have they surrendered when they still occupy so much of Asia?"

"I don't know," Ee Lim said. "It just says I must report to 23 Camp in one hour."

Arthur rushed back to the clearing to tell Doug and Maurice, and, although both men normally never took any news as being true unless there was something really solid and believable to back it up, there seemed to be something different about this. They took the rest of the day off and, to celebrate, made up ten cakes each for the night.

The following day there was an air of exhilaration in the camp but it was tinged with caution. The thing that worried them most was the question of what the Japanese Army in Malaya might do. After all, it was only the politicians in Japan who had decided to surrender. It might still need an invasion here to end the war.

Several people were called from their camp to go to Por Twee and Segamat. How they could go to Segamat, quite openly while hundreds of armed Japanese were still in the town, Arthur and the others didn't know. Perhaps it was safe, and perhaps it wasn't. They would soon know. He and Doug and Maurice waited in frustrated anticipation. On 16 August, a runner came back with news for their camp and the others in the area that it was now official. The Japanese headquarters in Singapore had hoisted the white flag of surrender for the whole of Malaya. The war was over.

27

ON THE MORNING OF FRIDAY, 17 August, three Japanese trucks rumbled down the road between Buloh Kasap and Batu Anam. The trucks contained forty bags of rice and eighty bags of sugar. In the back of each truck there were also six armed soldiers. As they turned a bend in the road, which was lined on both sides with rubber plantations, a group of guerillas from '80 acres' stood blocking their path. Two trees had been felled across part of the road making it almost impossible to pass.

As the trucks braked and came to a halt, the guerillas crouched behind the fallen trees, in the ditches at the edge of the road and behind the cover of shrubs and rubber trees on the embankment, their rifles and automatic weapons all aimed at the Japanese trucks. The slightest sign of aggression on the part of the Japanese would have triggered a fusillade of fire from the guerillas. It was the first time that an attempt to intercept a Japanese convoy had been made in this area without blowing up the lead truck, then shooting first and asking questions later. There were many among the guerillas who felt that that was the only way to deal with the Japanese, but now that Japan had surrendered and there was a ceasefire, things should be different. But how many of the Japanese knew about it? And, more importantly, how many would accept it? Nevertheless, the leader of the guerilla patrol had insisted that no shots be fired at the trucks unless the Japanese fired first.

The Japanese offered no resistance. They sat in the trucks and waited. There was a sort of hiatus as the guerillas shouted questions at them from behind their cover. "How many men are in the trucks? What sort of goods are you carrying?"

The driver of the first truck replied in broken Malay, explaining that there was rice and sugar in the trucks, as well as eighteen soldiers. Then he added, "If you wish to kill us, then go ahead. Or if you wish to tie us up, we will not resist."

A few moments passed as looks of amazement were exchanged amongst the guerillas and then their leader ordered all of the Japanese to alight slowly, without their arms, from the trucks. He also ordered the Japanese to transfer the supplies from one of the trucks to the other two. Then the Japanese soldiers were tied up, placed in the empty truck and driven back to '80 acres'. There they were taken from the trucks and tied up again, either to be released later, or to be used as hostages if necessary.

In the days that followed, other trucks were stopped and confiscated in a similar way. Any food they were carrying was invariably distributed to nearby kampongs. If the cargo was benzine, petrol or other non-edible supplies, the guerillas took it to Durian Chin Chin where they were beginning to form a central supply depot.

Although most Japanese soldiers surrendered without resistance, caution was still necessary as not all accepted the ceasefire so readily. For many Japanese soldiers, steeped in the traditional warrior code of Japan, surrender to an enemy involved such a loss of 'face' and dignity that it was not acceptable. Four armed Japanese soldiers, who obviously felt this way, made their way to Simpang township where they entered a coffee shop. They told the proprietor that they wanted to fight the Chinese guerillas, to die honourably. The shop-owner sent word to Tek Liong and others who were staying in a house nearby and then discreetly made himself scarce.

Within minutes, the street outside the coffee shop became, almost magically, deserted and, shortly afterwards, in a scene not unlike a western movie, Tek Liong and Ho San, the commander of Number 5 Company, accompanied by several other guerillas, all of whom were armed with Tommy guns, began to make their way quickly along the colonnaded sidewalks towards the coffee shop. The Japanese, who began shooting the moment they saw the guerillas, clearly wanted to die for they took no cover and were soon shot down in a hail of guerilla bullets. Tek Liong and his men suffered no casualties.

Later in the day, four truckloads of Japanese soldiers arrived, collected the bodies of their dead comrades, then proceeded to ransack several shops and to drive off with the trucks filled with food supplies which they took to their headquarters in Segamat. There, a large group of about one hundred Japanese and some thirty Malays, having laid in a substantial store of provisions, intended to hold out until some sort of security system was worked out for them. There was no doubt it was now dangerous for them to walk about in the township where they could be confronted and killed in direct shoot-outs with guerillas, or picked off, one or two at a time, by snipers.

The group on the water tower hill had several artillery pieces which could be aimed at various parts of the town, so the situation showed all the signs of developing into a siege. The Japanese move to retire to the hill had followed a meeting in the Simpang area between the guerillas on the one side and, on the other, the chief police officer of Segamat, a Chinese man called Kai Wong, and the Japanese officer in command of Segamat. The Japanese officer did not turn up, sending his second in command in his place. The meeting, as reported to Arthur by EC Lim, who was there, confirmed that the Japanese High Commands in Tokyo and Singapore had surrendered. The guerillas therefore called on the Japanese party to arrange for all Japanese soldiers in Segamat and the surrounding areas to lay down their arms and to turn them over to the Communist Party. The Japanese objected strongly to this, as it would leave them no guarantee of their personal safety. It was pointed out to them that the prisoners they had taken at the beginning of the war had no guarantee of their personal safety either. The Japanese response was to return to Segamat to barricade themselves into their makeshift fortress around the water tower.

In the meantime, Arthur, Doug and Maurice had been keen to get out of the jungle, to find out what was happening and to meet up with some of their own people, the British commandos they had heard about, but they were prevented by the erratic and often dangerous situation outside. Guerilla headquarters sent word to them asking that they stay in the jungle until they could be escorted out to their own headquarters. The three men reluctantly agreed, hoping that they would not have to wait too long.

Unfortunately, although the war was technically over, there were still people fighting and dying. On 22 August they heard a considerable amount of artillery-fire from the direction of Segamat during the night. The following morning there was more, this time coming from the direction of Gemas. Later in the day they learnt that the action in Segamat had been around the Japanese water tower which, the previous afternoon, Sou Young had ordered the 3rd Independent Guerilla Company to surround. The Japanese had opened fire with their artillery and a battle of sorts had continued into the night. In the morning the guerillas found the water tower hill deserted and no-one knew where the Japanese had gone, or how they had slipped through the cordon around the hill. It was thought that they may have headed for Gemas to link up with other Japanese forces there. This was confirmed by the sound of artillery fire that they had heard coming from the direction of Gemas that day.

In the last week of August, there was continued activity in the camps around them, with people coming and going, many of them in new uniforms, carrying new weapons and equipment. There was a real air of excitement and purpose which only tended to increase the sense of frustration Arthur and his companions experienced at having to stay put in their camp. It was as if everything had been finished and wrapped up outside while they were left, forgotten, in the jungle.

They went out each day to Por Twee to visit Ee Lim or his wife and people sometimes came through to the clearing to visit them. Ah Leong and Ah Kow brought a young rooster and a bottle of samsoo wine one afternoon. They cooked the bird with vegetables and ate it, then sat around the campfire talking late into the night over cakes, coffee and the wine. After Ah Kow, Ah Leong and Maurice had gone to sleep, Arthur and Doug continued drinking the samsoo until they had finished the bottle, getting exceedingly drunk, for the first time in years. After so long without any alcohol, they found it extremely powerful.

They awoke next morning with equally powerful hangovers which did nothing to improve their general feelings about being stuck in the jungle. Although life was relatively comfortable and safe now, they were becoming so desperate for news that Arthur decided to do something about it. On the morning of 1 September he left for '80 acres', heading first to Por Twee where a pile of cast-off clothes from the Japanese had arrived. He collected some trousers and three heavy Australian army-issue singlets and then mentioned his intention of going to '80 acres'.

Suddenly everyone, including Ee Lim, became rather agitated, telling Arthur he should not leave without permission. He would be in danger and big trouble with the guerilla authorities. They said he should first write to Wong Tek Liong before he took things into his own hands. Arthur returned to the clearing where he wrote a strong note to Tek Liong requesting news from outside and an explanation of why they could not leave.

The following day, Teo Kong Am, Ee Lim's brother, arrived to tell them that the letter had been received and would be considered promptly. But two more days passed with no reply. Thick thunderclouds now filled the sky and although they brought no rain, they made the days dark and gloomy and tended to aggravate their feelings of isolation and depression.

In Por Twee, during the afternoon of the second day, they came across an old man, sitting alone under a tree, burning joss sticks and chanting softly to himself. He was bemoaning the fact that two of his sons had died, but thanked Buddha for bringing him and the rest of his family through the war. A set of Chinese throwing sticks lay on the ground beside him and when there was a pause in his lament, Arthur asked him to work on the sticks to see if he could predict when they would leave the jungle. The old man looked at Arthur for a few moments without saying anything. Then a small smile came to his face. He held the sticks in his hand a short while, mumbling over them in Chinese before dropping them on the ground. After examining the positions in which they had fallen, he confidently informed Arthur, Doug and Maurice it would be at least half a month before they could leave. The three men were crestfallen.

The next day Arthur went again to Por Twee, telling Ee Lim of his plans to go out to Sin Kok Swan to see Chew Ee Poo about getting an answer to their requests. Although Arthur had not had a great deal to do with Chew Ee Poo, he thought he had more authority than Ee Lim, Lee See, or perhaps even Sou Young. Again, Ee Lim and others there said 'No', putting even greater pressure than before on him not to go.

"If you go against the Party's wishes now," one of them said, "you will end up with a knife in your back, or a rope around your neck."

Deciding that discretion was the better part of valour, Arthur returned once again to the clearing, fuming with anger, partly because he could not go out, but also because he felt so impotent.

The following morning, a written message came through saying that they would soon be able to leave the jungle. It was in Malay and used the words 'sediki thari' to describe the length of time they might have to wait. Sediki thari meant literally 'small days'.

"It generally means 'in a few days time'," Doug said, "but I'll believe it when I see it. It could also mean a week or more. They'll bloody well keep us here for ever."

Later in the morning, Tek Liong arrived in camp with a long face and some disturbing news which leant weight to the advice that it was too dangerous for them to go out right now.

"There are many massacres happening," he told them in almost shocked tones. "When the British and Australian troops landed in Singapore, they freed prisoners from Changi Prison and there has been some killing of Japanese since then. Also the Ghurkhas have been killing the Sikhs and the Chinese have been killing Malays. Here in Malaya, at Chaah and at Muar, Malays have been killing Chinese and now Er Sin has gone to Chaah with one thousand guerillas to take revenge on the Malays. It is very bad, a big mess." '

They talked about the chaos that was raging outside and came to the conclusion that, if only half of it was true, then headquarters was probably right in making them stay inside. It would be far safer in the jungle than out there.

For a while their frustration and impatience subsided as they resigned themselves to waiting for the time when Allied troops reached Segamat, whenever that might be. They decided, nevertheless, that they would move to Por Twee to live. It was cooler and brighter than the clearing and there were fewer mosquitoes. They also felt they would be in a much better position to keep in touch with what was happening outside.

The next day, 7th September, while they were still at the clearing, a letter arrived from Ee Lim, saying that he had interviewed Soo Sin, the guerilla commander in Segamat, on their behalf. Soo Sin had indicated that it was all right with him for the three Europeans to come to Segamat, but they should first wait for the approval of Lee See, the overall Area Commander.

"Two steps forward, one step back," Maurice said wearily as the letter was read.

The next morning, Arthur decided, on the spur of the moment and without telling anyone, to walk along the track leading to '80 acres'. He had covered about four miles through several of the old Camps which the Japanese had raided during the previous year and had just arrived at the deserted site of one more camp, when he met Ah Kow, Ah Leong and Ah Wee Coming along the track in the opposite direction. They were as surprised to see Arthur as he was to see them, but they were also pleased, immediately telling him that they were carrying a letter for the three Europeans saying that they could at last come out of the jungle.

Arthur could hardly believe it. Even though they had been waiting and wanting the word to come through every day, the reality came as a surprise. Now that it had come, he wasn't quite sure what to do.

"Shall I go on from here?" Arthur asked, "or what?"

He realised, as he asked the question, that there was really no need for him to return to Por Twee at all. He was wearing a clean set of khaki clothes and, as he was carrying the only possession of any importance--his diaries--there was nothing else he needed to collect.

"I think it might be dangerous if you continued alone," Tek Liong said. "You should wait here until we return with your two friends."

Arthur reluctantly accepted their suggestion and sat with Ah Kow in the shade of a large tree in the deserted campsite, awaiting the return of Ah Leong and Ah Wee with Doug and Maurice, both of whom were in a state of high spirits and excitement when they arrived.

*17. The Melbourne Sun's front page story, on 13
September 1945 of Arthur's survival.*

CHAPTER TWENTY-SEVEN

4   THE STAR, Friday, June 3, 1977

Former soldier tells of three years in jungle

A MAN who survived for more than three years in the jungle when the Japanese occupied Malaya during World War II, is back to visit old friends.

He is Arthur F. Shephard, formerly a sergeant with the Australian Military Forces. He is now 59.

In January 1942, he and 11 other soldiers including eight British, were

PENANG, Thurs.

with a force of 250 at a small town near Muar in Johore when a 20,000-strong Japanese force attacked.

"I was left behind in a swamp when the Allied Forces evacuated to Singapore after being beaten soundly by the Japanese," said Mr. Shephard.

He was wounded in the neck during the battle.

Mr. Shephard together with the 11 soldiers then escaped into the jungles near Segamat before the Japanese could reach them.

They joined up with a local guerilla force called the Anti-Japanese Imperial Army, and formed camps in the jungles in Chaah, Labis, and Segamat.

"I used to train the Chinese guerillas in jungle warfare to fight the Japanese," Mr. Shephard said.

As time went on, the others with him died leaving him with two other Australians.

Mr. Shephard who spent exactly three years and 10 months in the jungle, said they had very

little communication with the outside world and his family presumed he was dead.

He lived by eating cats, dogs, rats, snakes, elephants and wild pigs.

He also helped the

FORMER Sergeant in the Australian Army, Mr. Arthur Shephard and his wife, Nancy, in Penang yesterday

guerillas who in 1945 formed a headquarters for two British forces preparing to invade Malaya from India.

"I nearly died of malaria three times during my stay in the jungles but a Chinese sinseh gave me medicine and made me well again," he said.

"About three years after I entered the jungle, a price was put on my head.

"First the Japanese offered a bag of rice which was equivalent to $15 Japanese dollars and later it went up to $250,000."

Mr. Shephard said besides training the guerillas, he was also responsible for helping in printing jungle money and leaflets, growing vegetables and rice, drawing maps and

did patrol duties with them.

"I think some of the guerillas I knew are still in the jungle today and a number have died," he added.

He and the guerillas were always on the move in the jungle from the north of Pahang till Johore in the South.

ATTACKED

They were attacked by the Japanese a couple of times.

Mr. Shephard came out of the jungle with two other Australians on Sept. 13, 1945, to see if the war was over.

"We went to Segamat town and found out that

the war was indeed over," said the former Sergeant who was later flown home to his family in Victoria.

Today, Mr. Shephard is an engineer. He married and lives in Adelaide with his wife, Nancy.

He has a number of diaries, papers and Japanese notes as well as letters which he wrote while in the jungle.

Mr. Shephard, who arrived in Singapore on May 14, has visited Segamat to look up a few friends.

He is now in Penang for a four-day visit.

He hopes to give away his collections of diaries and notes to a museum and also hopes to have a book written about his days in the jungle.

18. the Penang Star's report of Arthur and Nancy Shephard's 1977 visit to Malaysia.

After a brief rest, they set off together shortly after one in the afternoon, arriving in Simpang, around 4.30 pm. They walked out of the jungle onto the main Segamat-Simpang road a short distance from the town and then followed the road into the town itself.

As they approached, walking confidently and directly down the centre of the road, people stopped in their tracks and stared open-mouthed. Adults as well as children, pointed and gabbled excitedly to each other. "You are the first European people they have seen for over three years," Tek Liong explained.

It was the first time that Arthur, Doug or Maurice had been into a town for three and a half years and, although Simpang was very small, as far as Malayan towns were concerned, it seemed an extremely busy centre to them.

Although their clothes were reasonably clean, they were nonetheless rather tattered. They were all unshaven, with varying lengths of hair. Arthur carried a pistol on each hip as well as a bayonet hanging from his belt. Doug was wearing a pistol on his side, but also carried a .303 rifle. Maurice carried only a rifle.

From the first contact, on the outskirts of the town, they waved and smiled at the stunned locals who reciprocated immediately, laughing and calling out 'hello, Joe' or 'hello, John', then fell in behind the men as they walked down the narrow main street lined with wooden verandahed buildings and Chinese shops. They were determined to see where the three Europeans were going and what they planned to do.

And they weren't disappointed. Arthur and his companions proved a great source of amusement for the crowd by going directly to the nearest barber-shop and having a shave and a haircut. Although, under normal circumstances, such an event would not be exceptionally funny, the group blocking the pavement outside the shop to watch the proceedings enjoyed themselves immensely. They joked and laughed, and Arthur, Doug and Maurice, infected with the sense of merriment, laughed back at them.

When they had all been shorn, Tek Liong and his companions led them to a house in the town where Ee Lim was also staying. They were welcomed there and told they could stay until they knew where they should go next. They bathed, revelling in what was their first hot shower in years, and were then issued with some new clothes.

"Are there any Japs still here?" Arthur asked as they set out in the fading afternoon light for a brief look around the town.

"Oh yes, about thirty of them," Tek Liong replied. "They are staying in the public school until transport arrangements are worked out for them."

"Transport to where?"

"To Japan I suppose."

"But that might be a long time."

"Yes, perhaps."

"Are they armed?"

"Yes, they are armed in their compound, to defend themselves. But, if they come out into the town, they must be unarmed and wear a white armband."

"Do they come out at all?"

"Yes. They come out to get their own supplies and so far there have been no problems. The local people have been ordered by the Party to leave them alone. If there are any Japanese wanted for crimes, they will be sought out and dealt with by the Party. But in the meantime they must be treated properly."

Arthur was surprised to hear that the Party and the local populace were behaving in such a civilised manner, considering the terrible acts that had been perpetrated against them by the Japanese occupation forces over the past few years. They heard later, however, of several violent acts of retribution and revenge. On their short stroll through the town that evening, they met three Japanese soldiers returning to the schoolyard from the main street. As Ah Leong had said, they were not carrying arms and were all wearing white armbands signifying their surrender. When they saw Arthur, Doug and Maurice, the effect was quite startling. They stopped immediately in their tracks, came to attention and all simultaneously executed a deep bow from the waist, keeping their heads down, looking at the ground until the three Europeans had passed them. Arthur found it a strangely gratifying experience. Neither he nor the others stopped to talk to them or to ask them anything, nor did they say anything between themselves until they had passed. It could have been a moment of levity, an opportunity to gloat or put them down, but somehow they found it a sober and significant moment that contained, at the same time, a sense of immense satisfaction combined with relief and gratitude at having come through the war alive.

After an excellent meal and a good night's sleep in a comfortable bed, they arose to face their first day out of the jungle. It was Sunday, 9 September. After they had breakfasted with Ee Lim, he left them for a few moments to go to another room. When he returned he handed them each a bundle of banknotes.

"What's this?" Arthur said in amazement.

"It is for you," he smiled. "You can spend it now, for enjoying yourself."

They all looked down at the pile of notes sitting in their laps and began counting. It was one thousand dollars in Japanese currency. More money than any of them had had for themselves during the entire war.

"But. . .so much?" Arthur queried. "It is a lot of money."

"Yes, well, never mind," Maurice moved the subject quickly on, trying to shut Arthur up. "Thank you very much, Ee Lim. This will come in very handy. We will need to buy several things in the town."

Ee Lim smiled. "It is not as much as it might seem. Prices have gone crazy--inflation--and, of course, who knows what Japanese money will be worth when the British return."

They soon discovered the truth of Ee Lim's words when they went into the Segamat town marketplace. One pound of salt cost thirty dollars and a hen was one hundred and seventy. Nevertheless, they still had plenty left over after buying some additional pieces of clothing and a few beers in a local cafe.

They were told, later in the day, that two Australian war correspondents had arrived in Segamat and wanted to see them. The two journalists, Noel Monks from the Melbourne Sun and Allan Dawes from the Sydney Sun, finally met up with Arthur, Doug and Maurice in the evening as they were being entertained to a sumptuous Chinese meal by the manager of a local Chinese bank. There was considerable excitement on both sides at the meeting. The two correspondents were fascinated and stunned to find people who had survived in the jungle for so long, on the run from the Japanese. Arthur and his companions were elated, on the other hand, at meeting the first people from the outside world in three and a half years--free people who had lived through the war at home in Australia, or with the Australian troops in different theatres of the war.

What a different war we've had, Arthur thought as they spoke. The questions flew thick and fast: "Where did you live? Did the Japanese try to hunt you down? What sort of food did you have? Was there any illness? How did you meet with the Communist guerillas? How did they treat you?"

Arthur felt a great chasm of understanding, or the lack of it, yawn between them. He and Doug and Maurice answered the questions as best they could, but Arthur felt the enormous difficulty of getting across to these two young men what they had been through in the jungle. It was like trying to explain the complexities of human relations to a four-year-old child. Not that the correspondents were ignorant or uninformed of the military situation that had existed, but to impart anything other than the most basic aspects of their three-and-a-half-year ordeal was all but impossible.

They sat and spoke with the journalists for almost an hour before the two men said they had to leave. They had borrowed a car and driven it from Singapore. Arthur found it difficult to believe that such a thing was possible. That you could just get in a car and drive so far from Singapore. But they had made the trip with only minor interruptions and now had to head back to send their stories to Australia. They planned to radio them back, which meant that by the following day, the newspapers would be carrying the news that they were alive. Arthur hoped that his mother or some relative would see it or hear about it, or that at least someone would tell them about it.

The fact that the two correspondents had left Singapore and returned so easily convinced Arthur, Doug and Maurice that they could do the same, very soon. It was strange saying goodbye to the two men after such a brief meeting. They had arrived suddenly out of nowhere, and then disappeared, leaving Arthur and his companions living, not quite as they had been in the jungle, but in a sort of limbo world.

28

THEIR INVOLVEMENT WITH THE CHINESE was now gradually lessening. It was as if an umbilical cord, through which they had been nourished and protected over the years, was gradually withering, or being cut. The guerillas were still acting as their protectors, but only until Allied troops arrived to disarm the Japanese, whom they now saw quite regularly in the town, usually in the evenings. There was some concern, though, that unless Allied forces came soon, trouble would erupt in several areas.

Kluang was one potential trouble spot. Apparently there were about three thousand armed Japanese confined there, without proper sleeping quarters or adequate food supplies. But, as they heard, it was not only the Japanese who were a possible danger. A small group of radical Malays, determined to prevent the return of the British colonial government to Malaya, was reported to have come from Batu Pahat to Segamat with the intention of stirring up trouble and even 'eliminating' any whites in the area, which included Arthur, Doug and Maurice. This information came from Ee Lim, who suggested they be armed at all times and careful whenever they were in the town.

On 11 September, the same day that they received this warning, they had the exciting news that several British commandos had arrived in Segamat to take over and that they should report to them as soon as possible.

The commandos were members of Force 136, the group which had been parachuted in some weeks earlier. They were taking over a house close to the centre of Segamat, with a Colonel Miles of the British Army in charge. He greeted the three men with great enthusiasm and warmth.

"Wonderful to see you," he smiled, shaking their hands. "We've heard so much about you over the past few weeks, but somehow we couldn't get anywhere near your camp. The Chinese kept insisting that it was too difficult."

"Yes," Doug raised his eyebrows. "We're not surprised. We've had quite a bit of that from them over the past few years. But never mind, better late than never."

"Cup of tea?" the colonel said. "Sorry there's nothing stronger at the moment, but we'll organise that before long."

There were seven commandos altogether, including one Australian officer, a Lieutenant Geoffrey Frank, whom they met only briefly before he left to drive down to Kluang to see what could be done to sort out the problems faced by the large Japanese force there. He went alone, with one Chinese driver, and, as they learnt the following day, had an extraordinary experience on the way.

His car had a blow-out and overturned in a ditch. Fortunately, neither man was hurt. The driver went off along the road to try to get some help, leaving Lieutenant Frank by the car. After spending a tedious half-hour waiting for the driver to return, the young lieutenant heard the sound of trucks coming towards him from the direction of Kluang. Two Japanese army trucks rounded a bend in the road. They slackened pace at the sight of the Australian officer standing beside his upturned car and, when Frank ran into the centre of the road, waving at them, they pulled in beside him.

About a dozen armed Japanese soldiers stepped down from the trucks. Lieutenant Frank hesitated a moment and then, having no alternative, spoke in English to one of the men who was clearly an officer, a captain.

"My car has overturned," he waved at the car. "Tell your men to pull it out of the ditch."

Neither the Japanese officer nor any of his men could speak any English, but they understood what Frank was saying and, after a curt direction from the officer, set to work to extract the vehicle from its upturned position in the ditch and to set it on its wheels on the road. The operation required some ropes and about ten minutes work, but it was completed without any fuss.

After checking the car and finding no major damage apart from large dents in the bodywork and a door that wouldn't close properly, Frank pointed to the blown tyre and indicated he would like some help in changing it. The spare wheel was quickly fitted by two Japanese soldiers and, when it was complete, the Japanese officer saluted Frank and bowed. Frank thanked the officer and let him continue on his way.

Fifteen minutes later, Frank's driver returned with another truck to find the young officer sitting in the car on the road, waiting for him. He was incredulous. The truck was sent back to Segamat and the two men continued on their way to Kluang.

Not long after Arthur's first meeting with Colonel Miles, there was an emotional reunion with young Peter Koran, the boy Arthur had known when his unit had been camped in Segamat prior to the Japanese invasion. He rushed into the British commandos' temporary headquarters calling, "Mr Shep, Mr Shep--I knew you were alive."

Arthur was taken completely by surprise and, in fact, hardly recognised Peter, who was now fifteen years old and almost a foot taller than when Arthur had last seen him.

Arthur laughed and embraced the young man, and they both began to talk at once.

"We knew there were Australian soldiers alive in the jungle," Peter said, "but I did not know for sure if you were one of them. But I knew you were alive."

Arthur introduced Peter to Doug and Maurice and to Colonel Miles, who was interested in Peter's advice on dealing with the local populace. He sat Peter down and began asking him many questions about life in Segamat under the Japanese.

During the following two days there was much excitement generated in Segamat by several airdrops of supplies parachuted onto the local school playing fields: supplies of clothing, equipment and food, the likes of which Arthur and his two comrades and young Peter Koran had not seen since before the war.

Peter insisted that Arthur come to his house and meet his parents. Arthur was given a great welcome by Peter's mother and father and his brothers and sisters and asked to stay to dinner. He did so with pleasure as it was a meal of curried chicken and vegetables that again surpassed anything he had eaten for the duration of the war. During the dinner, Peter produced a glass jar in which he had hidden the two pieces of brass insignia Arthur had given him in late 1941.

"I buried them in the garden," he told Arthur, "in case the Japanese found them. I knew you would come back and I could return them to you."

"No," Arthur smiled, "they are yours. I don't need them now. You keep them."

The next afternoon, 15 September, an Australian soldier, a sergeant, suddenly turned up in Segamat driving a Japanese staff car. He was a tall man, about six feet two inches, in his middle to late forties. He introduced himself simply as 'Lofty'.

When he presented himself at Colonel Miles's office, Arthur, Doug and Maurice and a couple of commandos were sitting around, sorting out some of the supplies from the latest airdrop. He looked gaunt and sunburnt, leading Arthur to believe, at first, that he had also just come from the jungle.

"Nope, spent the bloody war in Changi," he replied airily to a similar query from Colonel Miles.

"And, er, is that where you've come from now?" the Colonel asked, a little nonplussed by the Australian's manner, "Singapore?"

"Too right! As soon as they let us out, I stopped the first bloody Jap car I saw and took off, heading for Gemas."

"For Gemas?" Miles said incredulous. "You mean you drove all the way from Singapore, alone? How did you get permission?"

Lofty laughed aloud. "Permission? I didn't need any permission, sir. They're processing everybody down in Singapore, getting ready to send us all home. There's a few days to spare before our boat leaves, so I just grabbed a car and came up."

"And the car? Who provided the car?"

Lofty smiled. "Heh, heh. Nips of course. Just chucked the little bastard out and took it. Got some petrol along the road the same way. Nobody stopped me anywhere. Couldn't waste any time, got something important to do."

By this time, Colonel Miles's mouth had fallen open in amazement. "You just commandeer a vehicle in Singapore, drive a hundred and forty miles up here, without anyone knowing, or even anyone stopping you on the way?" It was too much for him. He leant back in his chair and burst out laughing. "Would you like a cup of tea--or perhaps a beer?"

"A beer would do fine thank you, sir. I haven't seen too many of them in the past three and a half years."

A sergeant who had been standing to one side, listening to Lofty's story, stepped into the next room and brought back a bottle of Tiger Beer from the icebox there.

"Now then," said Colonel Miles, "what's so important for you up here?"

Lofty said nothing for a moment or two and, for the first time since his arrival, an air of seriousness came over his face. He lifted his eyebrows and sipped from his glass. "Well, it's like this. When the Japs came down through here, back in January '42, I was with the 2/30th Battalion at Gemas."

"Galleghan's mob?" Arthur said. "We were just behind you at Buloh Kasap--2/29th."

"That's right," Lofty nodded, sipping again at his beer. "Well, I...my son was also in the 2/30th."

"Your son? Surely that's not usual," Colonel Miles said. "They don't normally allow a father and son to serve in the same unit."

"No. It's very rare, but we managed to arrange it. Anyway, we were very close. Good mates. He was just twenty years old when we set up the ambush at Gemas--and, as you probably know, it was a bloody big success. We stopped the Nips in their tracks. They didn't know what struck them."

As Lofty spoke, his voice became lower and lower. The half- dozen or so people in the small room listened intently.

"Well, Bill and I were in the same company, but different platoons. We'd see quite a bit of each other under normal circumstances, but when you get into situations like that ambush and what happened after it, well...it becomes pretty difficult. You see the Japs had so many troops coming up behind them, reinforcements, that we were soon so badly outnumbered, there was no way we could hold them for more than a couple of days. They started swinging around through the jungle and the rubber on all sides of us and in no time they were hitting us so hard, we had to back off." Lofty took a long breath and then sighed deeply. "It was during our withdrawal from the area just beyond Gemas that it happened. Bill was hit."

Nobody said anything. Lofty paused, his voice very low. "I was with my platoon. We were told to move back to the rear from our positions, while Bill's platoon which was closer to the front if you could call it a front--they were coming from all around us--was to cover our retreat. Well, my platoon eventually got back to a small ridge where there was some temporary cover and we could look back to where Bill's platoon was, but all we could see were Japanese troops running and taking up positions in the same area. I saw two Aussie soldiers shot down. I'm pretty sure neither of them was Bill, but of the rest of them-- we couldn't see a thing."

Lofty's voice faltered. He pursed his lips and looked at the ceiling and for a moment Arthur thought he might not be able to go on. His eyes were moist.

"We couldn't go back. We couldn't go back, you see. The bastards had already overrun the place. It would have been suicide. I wanted to go back for Bill. But I couldn't." His head dropped. He swallowed hard a couple of times and he wiped his eyes. "I couldn't."

He straightened himself up and took another deep breath. "I kept thinking all the way down to Singapore, while we were retreating over the next month, maybe he got out of that place, maybe he got into the jungle and will meet up with us. That happened with a lot of the troops, you know, they met up with us further down. But no. And then, after the Allied surrender, in Changi, I used to keep hoping, as they brought in late prisoners, stragglers who'd come in from the jungle, that maybe he'd be among them. But he never was and slowly, as the months went by, I knew that he had died there at that spot."

He looked up at the circle of men sitting around him, listening. "And that's why I've come back here. I've got to go back to that place, to say goodbye."

Nobody said a word, nor moved for several moments. Lofty looked out of the window.

The colonel stood up from his chair. But will you be able to find the place?" he said. "Do you remember..?"

"It's bloody well burnt in there," Lofty interrupted, tapping his head and recovering some of his former manner. "It's burnt into my memory. I'll never forget it."

It was late afternoon and, with dusk approaching, too late for Lofty to drive on to Gemas. The colonel suggested he stay the night with his group and go on to Gemas, with a couple of them accompanying him, in the morning. Lofty agreed and that evening, after dinner, they all sat around drinking beer and talking about their various, very different experiences of the war.

All of the men found it an interesting night. The circumstances were sufficiently out of the ordinary that the regular protocol that dictates relations between 'officers' and 'men', at least in the British Army, were set aside. They were all just 'men' together, talking, getting slightly drunk and contemplating a suddenly different world and an entirely different future. It was 2 am before they finally called it a day and went to bed.

In the morning, Lofty was up early and wanting to be on his way to Gemas. The colonel directed Arthur and Doug to go with him and shortly after breakfast they left on the twenty-mile drive with Lofty at the wheel of his commandeered Japanese staff car. Arriving in Gemas, they drove straight through the town and out along the road on the far side leading west and on to Tampin. For a short while they travelled through rubber estates with trees closely lining the road on both sides. Then the country opened up slightly and Lofty began scanning the road on the left intently. He slowed as they passed patches of open ground, a railway cutting, some small areas of rainforest coming close to the road and then an area of open ground stretching back from the roadway for several hundred yards to a rising hill, sprinkled, on the lower part, with rubber trees. The open ground was covered with a thick growth of lalang grass, in some places almost shoulder high. Lofty brought the car to a stop beside the road.

"This is it," he said. "I'd know it anywhere. The grass is much higher, but I've seen it over and over in my sleep, in my dreams, for years. This is it."

Arthur and Doug said nothing as Lofty headed off immediately into the lalang grass with them following a little behind.

"What do you reckon he expects to find?" Doug said softly, as they trampled through the grass. "Surely he doesn't think. . ."

"I think it's just the principle of it," Arthur said. "The idea of coming back to where he last saw him. Laying the ghost."

Neither of them really expected Lofty to find anything after three and a half years, but they were wrong. He knew almost exactly where his son's position had been at the time of the action and he began scouring around in the long grass for anything, anything at all that could connect him in time and space to that moment. There were a surprising number of small articles that first Lofty, and then Arthur and Doug, turned up as they flattened and rummaged through the grass at ground level. Spent bullet shells, a rifle magazine, a rusted ammunition box, a broken bipod from a Bren Gun and then--a soft cry from Lofty. "Oh, Jesus!"

He was holding a steel helmet. Part of it was badly rusted and the webbing liner was tangled with grass and soil, but the helmet had belonged to Lofty's son.

"There's his name, you see. Can you see it?" he said urgently, showing Arthur and Doug the faded letters on part of the webbing liner. He looked at the helmet for a few moments then held it to his chest and closed his eyes. A minute or so passed without any movement or word from the other two and then Lofty turned to them. "Okay," he said, "that's it. That's all I needed. Let's go. I'm off now. I'm heading back to Singapore." He turned and led the way back to the car, tears streaming down his face.

When they returned to Segamat, Lofty dropped Arthur and Doug off, went in briefly to say goodbye to the colonel and the other commandos, and then drove off for Singapore, where he was due to leave on a boat within a few days time.

The following day, the British Army, or at least part of it, arrived in Segamat. A battalion of Seaforth Highlanders were deposited by a convoy of trucks, which also carried a large number of Indian soldiers. Arthur found it a strange experience to see such large numbers of European troops again, all in smart uniforms and moving about in an ordered and disciplined manner. Arthur, Doug and Maurice spoke to several of them as they were establishing themselves in a camp in the school grounds. They were amazed to find that the three men had spent the entire war in the jungle. They looked at them wide- eyed, as if they were some kind of freaks, but after a few minutes they were laughing and exchanging jokes and, later, when they had some free time, several of them joined Arthur, Doug and Maurice for some drinks in the town.

Talking to the Scottish soldiers, Arthur felt a yearning to be in the world outside again. He was becoming impatient and anxious to move on, to get on his way home. He and his companions spoke on several occasions during the next couple of days to Colonel Miles to check when they could leave. Although he was friendly and helpful, there was apparently nothing he could do.

"You see," he said, "I'm just waiting for word from Singapore for you to leave. They're very interested to see you down there, but evidently there's a couple of other Aussies who'll be going down with you, probably in a day or so."

"Other Aussies?" Arthur said. "Who are they? Where from?" He thought immediately of Mac, Bluey and Les, whom he hadn't seen for more than two and a half years. But Colonel Miles did not know.

Suddenly, on the afternoon of 20 September, Arthur and his companions were given half a minute's notice to pack whatever belongings they had and to board a truck heading for Muar, en route to Singapore and home. They dashed around excitedly collecting their few things together in packs. Arthur said a hurried goodbye to Peter, who was with the men when they received the news.

Peter was crying. "Will you come back, Mr Shep?"

"I will," Arthur said. "You keep those badges for me and I'll come back."

"I will keep them, " Peter said, "so you will come back to Segamat one day."

Arthur ruffled the boy's hair then turned and headed for the truck. He stopped in his tracks just before reaching it, realising that he must also say goodbye to his guerilla friends, Tek Liong, Tek Chiong, Kok Ching, Teo Ee Lim, Sou Young, some of whom were in the town.

He told the driver.

"No time for that, pal," the man said peremptorily, without a thought for what was involved for Arthur: three and half years of constant connection with a group of people, a tie that would suddenly now be broken. The bond had been partly broken when Arthur arrived in Segamat. He had spent all of his time with his companions, Colonel Miles and his crew, and had seen Ee Lim and Tek Liong occasionally in the town and Sou Young only once.

They were, however, still in contact. Now, it seemed desperately wrong to suddenly leave without any farewells and yet that was what was happening.

"Come on, Aussie," the driver yelled again. "We haven't got all day. D'yer want to go or not?"

Arthur hesitated a moment longer, then piled into the back of the truck with Doug and Maurice. Maurice wasn't sure which direction he should head, towards Singapore or to Kuala Lumpur. Although Kuala Lumpur was the capital of Malaya, Singapore seemed to be where most of the organisation for the repatriation of Allied troops was happening. But Maurice had been a civilian at the outbreak of war and wasn't sure which was the best place to go to start picking up the threads. As Arthur and Doug were heading for Singapore, he decided to stay with them.

In Muar they were met by a major of the Seaforth Highlanders who informed him that he would be leaving for Singapore the next day with two other Australians, the first of whom Arthur met a few minutes later. It was Mac...Lieutenant Bill McCure.

"G'day, Shep," he smiled. "Long time, no see. How're you going?"

"Bloody good, Mac...er, sir," Arthur laughed. "Bloody good. How about you?"

Mac looked well and fit to Arthur, although he knew that, like any of those who had spent years in the jungle, he certainly must have passed through periods of illness and malnourishment, when he would have been all but unrecognisable. Arthur introduced Doug and Maurice to Mac and then spoke animatedly with him for some time. They questioned each other about people, times and places, fitting some of the missing pieces into the jigsaw pattern of their lives over the past three years.

"Who else is coming with us to Singapore?" Arthur asked.

"I don't know. I think it might be Bluey. He's been over near Batu Pahat. I think they either want us to go over there, or for him to come here to meet up with us."

"And what about Les?" Arthur said. "And Gaje? Have you seen them?"

"No. I don't know anything about either of them. They've been out of touch for ages."

Muar was quite a sizeable town. Arthur knew nothing of it from his previous visit to the area in January 1942, as their convoy had stopped a mile or so past Bakri township and about nine miles east of Muar. The Muar River, which ran into the sea at this point, was about a quarter of a mile wide and flowing strongly. The town was on the southern side of the river, while the northern side was relatively empty, apart from the thick vegetation which lined its banks. The town itself consisted mainly of two-storey buildings which were either shops, offices or houses that sprawled parallel to the river towards the sea front. There had been considerable damage to some parts of the town by Allied bombing of Japanese installations, but the general feeling in Muar was one of good humour as the local populace went about the task of cleaning up the mess of a long and awful war. Arthur was aware of a few sour notes. The Communist Party guerillas had adopted a relatively uncooperative stance towards the Allied troops who were moving back into Muar.

"They're not telling us anything at all," the major said to Arthur and the others at one stage. "They take whatever supplies they can legitimately lay their hands on, but give us no help at all. They feel they've beaten the Japs and now they've got us to contend with. I think they're going to be a problem for us in the future."

"Yes," Arthur said quietly, "I think you're right." His thoughts flashed back over some of the Party's harangues against colonialism during those years in the jungle. "In the long run, you won't be able to stay here either."

Later the following afternoon, Arthur, Doug, Maurice and Mac_drove to Batu Pahat, intending to meet up with Bluey before leaving for Singapore the following morning. Bluey, who expected them earlier, had been on tenterhooks all day and was now excited and pleased to see Arthur and Mac again and to meet Doug and Maurice. They sat until late at night exchanging stories about their separate experiences in the jungle. Bluey had some discouraging news about Les.

"Les is still 'inside' somewhere," Bluey told them. "He was at a camp about ten or twelve miles from me and for a while we wrote to each other, but he got sick and when I tried to find out what happened to him, I got no response. Eventually I heard that he had been moved to another camp for the sick, further in. That was several weeks ago. I've tried since then to find out what's happened to him, but I can't get any news at all. I think he could have gone."

Arthur nodded. Les gone too. So many dead. So many who could have walked out like he had, if only...

29

IN THE MORNING, AS THEY prepared to leave, the five men saw hundreds of unarmed Japanese soldiers being marched past under the guard of a few British soldiers. There were, they were told, twenty-two thousand Japanese in this area alone. The British were now confronted with the huge problem of feeding and housing many troops all over Malaya, as well as keeping them under control until arrangements were made to ship them back to Japan.

Arthur felt glad that it was not his concern and at 10 am, as he boarded a truck leaving for Singapore, the problem disappeared from his mind. As they travelled inland from Batu Pahat towards Ayer Hitam, he felt as if the world had suddenly opened up. The road trailed behind them as the countryside whizzed by, the sky was clear, with a few fluffy white clouds on the horizon. It was hot, but they had plenty of breeze coming through the open front of the truck as they barrelled along the road. They shouted like children and waved at people they passed. They stopped for half an hour for lunch at Ayer Hitam, then continued on towards Singapore, crossing the causeway from Johore Bharu at about 2 pm and arriving in the centre of Singapore about half an hour later. As they disembarked, they saw a large number of Japanese officers being marched away to board a number of trucks.

Arthur was swept once more with strange emotions. Returning to Singapore after four years, he found it hardly recognis- able. There had been extensive bomb damage to much of the city and there was none of the colour and commercial bustle that had made Singapore so lively. There was, however, bustle of a different kind with teams of people at work everywhere, cleaning up rubble and beginning the process of starting over again.

The five men went first to an office of RAPW&I, the organisation for the Repatriation of Allied Prisoners of War and Internees, in central Singapore, where they gave their names and some basic details of their wartime experience. Arthur, Bluey and Mac were advised to present themselves at the Australian Army Headquarters office at Changi, while Doug was told to report to British Army Headquarters. Maurice, as a civilian was really free to do what he pleased, but, as a British citizen, he was also advised to report to British Army Headquarters.

Suddenly, they now found themselves at a parting of the ways. They made plans, if they were to stay in Singapore for some time, to meet up for a drink in town, but as no-one could guarantee what might happen to them, or if in fact they would see each other again, they said their goodbyes. Arthur found it unexpectedly difficult. His thoughts flashed back to the weeks before Christmas 1944 when Maurice had nursed him from near death back to some degree of health. He clasped Maurice's hand, then Doug's and turning, wiped a tear from his eye as he, Mac and Bluey headed one way and Doug and Maurice went the other.

It was late in the afternoon when the three Australians arrived at Changi. They were given quarters and told to report to a debriefing session in the morning. Mac was disgruntled at the idea. He wanted to look someone up in the town. He said he also had a plan for getting home more quickly than waiting for a troop ship to arrive, so the following morning, instead of going to the debriefing session, he went off on his own into town.

When Arthur and Bluey turned up for the debriefing procedure, after breakfast, they were directed to an officer, a young man with a blond moustache, who had a desk set up outside the building, under a coconut tree. The desk was covered with papers which he seemed to be rearranging randomly. When Arthur presented himself, it was clear the man knew nothing of Arthur's situation.

"Fill this in, please." He handed Arthur a piece of paper. It was a form for 'Prisoners of War' with headings like: 'Date and place of capture', 'Camps', 'Japanese atrocities witnessed' and so on.

Arthur handed it back to the officer. "Excuse me, sir. I wasn't a POW. I was never captured."

"What's that?" he said in surprise. "You say you haven't been a prisoner of the Japanese?"

"That's correct, sir."

"Then what...I mean how...well, where have you been?"

"In the jungle."

"The jungle?! For the whole time?"

"Yes, sir. Three years and eight months. We've been with the guerillas."

"Gorillas?!"

"The Chinese partisans, sir, guerillas."

"Oh, ah yes," he said, writing the information on a note-pad in front of him.

From Arthur's position, in front of the desk, he could read what the officer was writing: '...spent time with gorrillas in the jungle.'

Arthur leant across and pointed at the word. "Excuse me, sir, you've spelt guerillas wrongly."

"What? Oh yes, of course," the officer said. "There's only one 'r' isn't there?" He changed the spelling to 'gorillas'.

Arthur felt, for a moment, that he should correct the man's spelling again, but then decided to leave it. Give them something to think about, he thought.

"Now, these are communist gorillas, are they?"

"Yes, sir."

"Anti-British, aren't they?"

"No, sir, anti-Japanese. They weren't at all anti-British during the whole time I was with them. They were very Communist and pro-Russia and pro-Marx and all that sort of stuff, but not anti-British. Well, not to us anyway. They saw us as their allies. What they'll be like towards the British now that the war is over, I don't know, but they were definitely friendly to us, otherwise we couldn't have survived."

"No sign of any revolutionary plans against British interests for after the war?"

"Nothing definite, sir. There was a good deal of talk about wanting Malaya to be an independent country, but nothing I heard in the way of revolutionary plans."

They talked at some length, with the officer taking copious notes, often holding up his free hand, asking Arthur to pause so that he could catch up. But at the end he seemed no wiser about how to treat Arthur.

"I really don't know what to do about you," he said. "You're a bit of a mystery. You're not a POW, but you haven't been serving in the AIF, and yet, at the same time, you have technically been on active service. I suppose you could say you've been on secondment to these Chinese gorillas, just as if you'd been with the Yanks or the Brits. Something like that, eh?"

Arthur nodded.

The officer also nodded, as if reassuring himself. "Yes, that's it. Well, as far as I'm concerned, you're still on active service and you've had no leave for three and a half years. I think we'll get you home as soon as possible. From what you've told me, I think Military Intelligence will want to talk with you when you get back home. There's a plane leaving early tomorrow morning. I'll have a talk with your mate in a moment, but if his situation is the same as yours, I'll be putting you both on that plane. Report here at 1900 this evening for transport to the 'drome."

A wave of excitement swept through Arthur. It meant that, instead of waiting for a troop ship to arrive and then spending weeks on board, they would be home in a matter of days.

"You'll have to go to Q for an issue of some warm clothes. It gets pretty cold up there," he said, writing out a slip of paper and handing it to Arthur.

He waited on the steps of a nearby building while Bluey went through much the same sort of interview and then the two men went together for an issue of heavy drill uniforms and greatcoats. Back at their quarters, there was still no sign of Mac, who must still have been in town. By 1900, when they left to go to the aerodrome, he had not turned up.

Arthur left a note, explaining what had happened and that they were taking a plane which would be leaving in the morning for Australia.

"He's going to be mad as hell at missing out on this," Arthur said.

"Yeh," Bluey agreed. "But he's got no-one to blame but himself. He should have come with us."

At the aerodrome, when they arrived about 7.30 pm, they were directed to a Nissen hut where a group of very ill soldiers were being readied for a flight to Perth, via several other stops along the way. They were mainly men from Changi and the Burma railroad who had undergone terrible privations and had to be evacuated as soon as possible. Arthur and Bluey were allocated bunks for the night and told they would be leaving at 7 am on a Dakota aircraft. '

"You're lucky with the flight," the flight-sergeant who showed them their quarters said. "You're going with General Callahan."

"Callahan?" Arthur said, "You don't mean Galleghan?"

"No, that's Colonel Galleghan. This is General Callahan, the bloke who took over the 8th Divvy when Gordon Bennett shot through."

Major General C.A. Callahan was the most senior Australian offlcer imprisoned by the Japanese after the fall of Singapore. The controversial escape from Singapore and return to Australia by Lieutenant General Gordon Bennett had left Callahan in command of all Australian Imperial Forces in Malaya, including the 8th Division. In August of 1942, he and other senior officers had been taken by ship to Formosa and then, in 1943, to a remote prison at Lia Yuan Chow in northern Manchuria. Since his release in Manchuria at the end of the war, General Callahan had flown back to Singapore to help oversee the repatriation of Australian troops from Changi and the Burma railroad.

The night passed with interminable slowness. Arthur found he could not sleep at all, he was so excited and tense with anticipation. He spoke softly to Bluey a couple of times during the night, hoping he might be awake and that some conversation would help pass the time. But Bluey was sleeping soundly.

Eventually they were woken before dawn and there was plenty of activity to keep them busy until they took off at seven. It was the first time either Bluey or Arthur had flown, so they were both like a couple of children, anxious to be able to get some sort of view as they took off. But because it was a C-49 troop transport plane, there were no windows. They were seated with the other passengers, including General Callahan, a couple of other officers and several other former POWs from the Burma camps, on bench-type seats along the sides of the plane, facing each other. But for Arthur and Bluey, even that was exciting. And what made it especially satisfying was the fact that the plane was carrying them home.

Their first stop, after four and half hours, was Labuan, a tiny island off the north-west coast of North Borneo. The triangle-shaped island is only thirty-eight square miles in area: but it sits in a commanding position in the entrance to Brunei Bay and with its deep, well-sheltered harbour, good roads and large airfield, it had become an important base for the Japanese during the war. Originally, they were landing there only to refuel and check the aircraft, but once on the ground, the passengers were advised that it would be an overnight stop.

It was extremely hot when they landed, but they were greeted with enthusiasm by Australian airmen on the ground and taken to the sergeants' mess where, with some of the other passengers and the airforce ground staff, they ate an excellent lunch, washed down with their first Australian beer in over three and a half years.

The following morning, 25th September, they took off again, heading for Morotai, in the northern Moluccas. Morotai, although it was also an island, was quite different from Labuan, It was big (some seven hundred square miles), mountainous and heavily wooded with tropical rainforest. It had been developed into an important Japanese base for their naval and air operations in the islands and when the Allies captured it in 1944, the Americans developed it further as a strategic airbase for raids on Japanese forces throughout South-East Asia.

Morotai had become a staging point for large numbers of Allied prisoners of war coming from Borneo and the Philippines, as well as from Singapore, Thailand and Indo China. The military authorities were facing major logistical problems in caring for the men, Australian, British, Dutch and American servicemen, many of whom were seriously ill and in extremely bad condition. They were trying to get them home as soon as possible. Many were being flown out, while others, less ill, were waiting for ships. The army was also faced with the problem of how to deal with the estimated twenty-seven thousand Japanese soldiers spread throughout the Moluccan islands. Many of them had still not accepted the fact that Japan had surrendered and were attempting to continue fighting, although such incidents were becoming increasingly rare.

While there, General Callahan made immediate calls on the sick and wounded POWS in the field hospitals and, after spending a good part of the day with them, decided to fly to Manila to visit more POWs there. These men had been flown to the Philippines by American rehabilitation teams from prison camps in Formosa, Hainan, Manchuria and Japan. The general's decision to go to Manila meant a delay in their flight plans, which was a disappointment for Arthur and Bluey, but there was nothing they could do about it, and they could see that it was clearly the right thing for the general to do. They were to wait on Morotai for a couple of days for the plane to return.

There were a great many Americans on Morotai and Arthur and Bluey found it amazing to visit them. Their PX stores were crammed with luxuries that they had not seen for years, particularly sweets and chocolates, which they naturally sampled eagerly. The Americans had also set up an open-air cinema and playhouse which was showing two or three different movies a week, as well as staging regular concert performances.

After three days on Morotai, they were advised that their plane had returned from the Philippines and they would be flying out first thing in the morning.

When they reported to the aerodrome, they were surprised to see that their plane was no longer a Dakota transport aircraft, but a B-24 bomber. They were told that General Callahan was still in the Philippines and would not be flying to Australia with them. The B-24, although a reasonable bomber, was not really equipped to carry passengers. Arthur, Bluey and the others were squeezed into every available nook and cranny and Arthur found himself travelling in the nose of the aircraft with a spectacular view, through the plexiglass gun-turret there, of everything in front of them. Before landing at Darwin a few hours later, however, all of the passengers were told that, for reasons of weight distribution, they must crouch in the empty bomb racks in the middle of the plane.

When they came in to land at Darwin, none of them could see a thing, but as they touched down, all on board broke out into spontaneous applause and cheering.

As they taxied towards the hangar, they could immediately feel the heat. It seemed to be at least a hundred degrees Fahrenheit, and the plane began to warm up like an oven. In their thick, woollen uniforms, necessary for higher altitudes, they now began to sweat profusely. But it was not long before the plane came to a halt and they all clambered out onto the tarmac. Arthur felt tears and laughter coming together as he, Bluey and several others lay down to kiss the ground, much to the amusement of the RAAF ground crews.

"Have a good holiday?" one of them called with a smile.

"Yeah," Arthur said, "I can recommend it. Visit the fascinating Orient, relax in beautiful tropical surroundings, meet interesting people and soak up the ancient cultures of South-East Asia--just the trick." He laughed. "But I don't think I'll be doing it again for a while."

Once again they were taken to quarters in a large Nissen hut where they were told they would probably have to wait in Darwin for a couple of days before flying south. They were able to change what Malay and Singapore (Straits) money they had into Australian currency. Arthur had a total of £29.3s.4d ($58.34), which he felt was more than enough to last him until he started getting his pay again. Both he and Bluey had been told they would be getting all of their back pay for the time they had spent in the jungle and they were looking forward to it.

"Three-and-half-years pay in one hit will be quite a little nest egg to start off with," Bluey said.

In the meantime, there wasn't much for them to spend their money on. All of their food and accommodation was provided, they had been issued with one hundred cigarettes and were given one bottle of beer a day.

On Sunday, 29 September, the day after their arrival, they were both put through a thorough medical examination which fortunately showed them to be in reasonably good condition. They were then driven in to the centre of Darwin where the two men were interviewed by Intelligence officers. They were extremely interested in everything Arthur and Bluey had to say, al-

though, at the beginning of the interview, they could hardly believe what they were hearing.

"This is vital information you chaps have," one of the in-
terviewing officers kept saying. "We'll have to get you down to
Victoria Barracks in Melbourne, as soon as possible."

"That's fine by us, sir," Arthur said earnestly. "We're ready
to go, just as soon as you want us to."

"Good, good," the officer said. "Very important stuff."

Before his first interview in Singapore, Arthur had wondered, now that the war was over and the Japanese had surrendered, why all this was so important. But it had soon become
clear to him that the main reason Intelligence was so interested
in their activities in the jungle was that the British authorities returning to Malaya already feared that the Chinese guerillas, who
had been their allies during the long Japanese occupation of the
Malayan peninsula, would soon be their implacable enemies.
Many of the guerilla units had not come out of the jungle yet and
those that had still maintained their secret dumps of arms and
ammunition which they had no intention of surrendering. So it
seemed that Arthur and Bluey's knowledge, not only of locations,
but of the whole pattern of guerilla warfare, tactics, habits and
general procedures was now of crucial interest to Allied Intelligence.

Arthur was in two minds about the line of questioning. He
was naturally pleased to be amongst his own people, but found
that he could not make the mental leap of regarding the Communist guerillas as 'enemies', or even 'potential enemies'. The
Japanese had been the enemies, while the guerillas had been
their friends. He thought of Tek Liong, Tek Chiong, Sou Lim, Sou
Young, Teo Ee Lim. True, there had been difficulties, animosities,
arguments, even fights between him and some of the guerillas,
but he knew that without them he would have long since been
dead. He gave his questioners information, but nothing which he
felt would directly harm the guerillas. At the same time, his
comments contained considerable praise for the guerillas and
their efforts against the Japanese.

When their questioning session was over, Arthur and
Bluey went into the town and saw something of the mess that

CHAPTER TWENTY-NINE

Japanese bombers had made of Darwin. They had done quite a job on it.

The following day there was little for them to do but sit around and talk with some of the RAAF people on the base. They were issued with new, lighter-weight uniforms, smarter than their old ones. They were also shown a copy of the Melbourne Sun, a couple of weeks old, which had printed a picture of Arthur. It carried the story that had been written by one of the correspondents who had driven up to meet them in Segamat. Arthur found it quite amazing to see the story. He kept wondering what his family and Nancy would have thought when they saw it, because until that time, they almost certainly would have thought him to be dead.

That evening, they were told they would be leaving at six the next morning and that reveille would be at 3 am.

"Why three o'clock in the morning?" Bluey protested. "We don't need three bloody hours to get ready for the flight!"

"Doesn't worry me," Arthur said. "I'm so glad to be on our way again, I'd stay up all night if they wanted us to."

They took off on time, now flying in a 'Liberator' and, because they'd got rid of their heavier uniforms, as the plane gained altitude they became really cold. Arthur was able to find a warmer spot, where the sun shone on him, in the tail-gunner's turret at the rear end of the plane, and he huddled there for the whole flight to Alice Springs.

As the brown, arid land rolled by beneath him, with a blue haze above, his thoughts flew, free and clear, like a tune ringing in his brain. Home, he thought, I'm home, home, home!

When they landed at Alice Springs for a refuelling stop, they were surprised to find it cold and windy, but they were taken inside to the mess where they were given a good meal and some hot tea before taking off again on the last leg to Melbourne. Arthur returned to his place in the tail-gunner's glass bubble and, with the sun now high in the sky, found it warm and comfortable. He gazed back into the empty, cloudless sky and down at the sandy ridges of the Simpson Desert, then dozed into a dreamless sleep. Some time later, he woke and, glancing off to his left, saw what he thought must be the great dry lake, Lake Eyre, shimmering, mirage-like, in the distance. Then he fell back to sleep again, waking shortly before the plane touched down in Melbourne at 6 pm.

After a few brief preliminaries at the aerodrome, he and Bluey were taken by army car to Heidelberg Military Hospital, arriving there around 8 pm. Both Arthur and Bluey felt in top form and were surprised that they were being treated like hospital cases. They were given beds in Ward 8A and told that they would have to go through a series of tests during the next couple of days.

"Now listen," Arthur said to the sergeant who had shown them to the ward, "we haven't had a day's leave in three and a half years and here we are, in our own home-town, where everyone has thought us dead, and you're going to keep us in here?" Arthur slammed his fist down on a sideboard table. "Why can't we have a bit of leave first, to see our families?"

The man hesitated a moment, surprised at the vehemence of Arthur's reaction. "It's not up to me," he said. "I'll have to check with the major." He turned to leave, then pointed to a phone on a nearby desk. "You could make some phone calls in the meantime."

Arthur picked up the phone and dialled a number, a number he hadn't used, or even thought of, in four years, but one which was imprinted indelibly in his memory.

"Hello, Mum. It's me, Arthur."

A moment's silence and then---"ARTHUR!!" The scream down the line nearly deafened him. "Arthur!..Oh, Arthur, where are you?"

Arthur explained where he was and why he couldn't come home immediately. He stopped talking. There was sobbing on the other end of the phone. "It's all right, Mum," he said. "I'm okay. I'm home again."

"They told me you'd been killed," she whispered. "Only two months ago they sent a telegram saying you were dead in the jungle. And then we read in the newspaper that two correspondents had met you, so we knew you were alive. But we didn't know where you were or how long we would have to wait."

"What about Frank?" Arthur asked. "And Jack and Bobby and Lucy and Joan?" In all the time he had been away he'd had no idea what had happened to his brothers and sisters. He laughed, "And Laurel and Lucy and Myrtle?"

There was another silence at the end of the line. A brief one. "Frank's dead, Arthur. He was killed in action in Bougainville, during the landings there. It was last year. It took ages for us to learn about it."

"And Jack?"

"Jack's home," she said. "Safe and sound, thank God! He was in Balikpapan. Bobby's home here. He's a big boy now, six foot three. Lucy's married, and so is Joan. Lucy's got a baby."

"Married? A baby?" Arthur laughed in amazement. His little sisters both married. They talked animatedly for several more minutes before Arthur had to relinquish the phone to an impatient Bluey. Before hanging up he told his mother that they were trying to get permission to leave the hospital temporarily and as soon as he was able to, he would come straight home.

Shortly afterwards, the sergeant returned with word that they could take leave until midnight of the following day. So, without a moment's hesitation, Arthur and Bluey grabbed what belongings they had and raced from the hospital.

The two men were headed in different directions, Arthur to Coburg, only six or seven miles west of the Heidelberg Military Hospital, Bluey to the inner-city suburb of Collingwood. Within minutes of their leaving the hospital, Bluey was on one of the frequent trams which ran past the front entrance of the complex, heading into the city and waving goodbye to Arthur.

"I'll see you back here tomorrow," he cried.

"Okay," Arthur yelled back. "But don't hold your breath." He planned to do everything possible to stay out of the hospital.

He stood for a few minutes, debating with himself whether to wait for a tram that would get him to Coburg, or try to find a taxi, but before he had come to any decision, a tram arrived.

Arthur boarded and, although the night was quite cold, decided to sit on the hard, wooden seats in the open, middle section of the tram. The only other occupants of the vehicle, as it rumbled along Bell Street towards Coburg, were sitting in the closed sections at either end.

Arthur sat facing forward, the wind chilling his face as he gazed out into the night, watching the warm yellow windows of the houses glowing in the darkness as they flashed by. All those people inside, he thought, sitting eating supper, or around a nice cosy fire. Maybe they've had members of their families in the war also. Of course they have, he said, almost aloud, to himself. Everybody has. And some of them would have died.

He looked more closely at the houses, almost as if he was trying to guess at the stories behind each lighted window. In some there would be only sadness and sorrow. Others would be full of happiness. Some, like his own, would have both.

As the tram trundled on, he slipped down in his seat, stretching his legs out underneath the bench opposite, and leaned his head on the back of his seat, looking up and out into the clear night sky. He closed his eyes, and images flashed before him: images of Claude and Leo, buried by a lonely jungle swamp. Scottie and Pete, Jock Smylie Bomber and Roy, old Tom Percival--all gone. He saw himself, lying beside Bomber, cold and hard on his makeshift bed, with the rain pouring down in torrents around them. He felt a tear run down his cheek.

"You all right, mate?" The young tram conductor was leaning over him.

"Huh? Oh, yeah," Arthur said, looking away. "Yes, I'm okay."

"It's just that I thought you might be feeling sick," the conductor persisted. "Where are you heading?"

"I'm heading home," Arthur said, turning to face him. "Home."

POSTSCRIPT

During the period of Arthur Shephard's extraordinary sojourn in the jungles of Malaya, over twenty thousand Australian soldiers were held prisoner by the Japanese. Seven thousand, seven hundred and seventy-seven died in captivity, more than three times the number killed in battle in the 9th Australian Division during its four campaigns. Of the 13,872 who were recovered, only a handful, including Arthur Shephard, had never been captured.

Arthur Shephard was given a hero's welcome on his return home, with the Coburg municipal band leading a parade through the streets. Arthur was reluctantly swept into the festivities and, although at first he found the public attention flattering, it quickly became an embarrassment to him and he took whatever opportunity he could to avoid it.

For a long time he found it difficult to adjust to normal civilian life. He continued to carry his long-bladed commando knife for many months, much to his mother's concern, and for several years slept with a pistol beneath his pillow.

Not long after he was demobilised from the Army, he returned to school, the Melbourne Technical College where he gained his matriculation, going on then to take a degree in mechanical engineering.

He had also, during this time, renewed his relationship with his pre-war sweetheart, Nancy Muller, who had spent the war serving in the Australian Women's Army Service. Arthur and Nancy were married on 31 August, 1947.

Arthur joined the British Petroleum Company as an engineer, based in Melbourne, and worked, over a period of twelve years, on installations as far afield as Darwin. In 1958 the company transferred him to Adelaide. His family--which now included two daughters, Judith and Wendy--went with him.

After another eighteen months he left BP to join the American engineering firm Kelloggs, for which he worked a further two years before taking up a position with the earth-moving company Roach Brothers in Adelaide. The post was well-paid but it was hard work and involved a lot of travelling and a 6 am start every morning.

In the mid-sixties he changed jobs for the last time, accepting the offer of a job from the local Unley Council in offices which were just five minutes from his home.

He retired in 1976 and in June of the following year he and Nancy made a trip to Malaysia--his first since the end of the war, more than thirty years previously. In Segamat he met several of the people he had known during his time in Malaya, including his friend Peter Koran. Peter, by then forty-seven years old and head of the Segamat Water Works Department, was delighted to see Arthur again and introduced him and Nancy to his own wife and children.

In the years that followed, Arthur continued to play an active part in his community. He was a prominent member of the local Lions Club and for five years was President of the Unley RSL, the Returned Servicemen's League.

He died of heart disease, 8th November 1984, aged sixty-six.

Arthur Shephard's story is only one of the many thousands of tales of heroism, courage and endurance that could be told of the dark and brutal days that unfolded during the Japanese occupation of South-East Asia. Unfortunately, the vast majority off them remain untold.

Perhaps the most encouraging message from Arthur's experience during three and a half years in the jungle is the fact that, despite all of the violence, death and destruction he was exposed to, despite deprivation, starvation and all kinds of sickness and injuries, despite the emotional anguish of witnessing and participating in executions and the bizarre rituals of eating human organs, he survived and went on to live as what most people would consider a normal member of society.

What went on in Arthur's mind to enable him to make the adjustments, after all he had been through, we can only guess. My interviews with him gave no hint of any emotional trauma and his wife Nancy talks of Arthur as an exceptionally stable and basically calm man.

I like to think of Arthur's survival, not only in the grim days of the war, but in the years that followed, as a triumph of the human spirit.

BIBLIOGRAPHY

Arneil, Stan, *One Man's War*, Alternative Publishing Cooperative, 1980

Barber, Noel, *Sinister Twilight*, Collins, 1969

Bateson, Charles, *The War With Japan,* Ure Smith, 1968

Bennett, Gordon, Lt Gen. H., *Why Singapore Fell*, Angus and Robertson, 1944

Blair, Joan and Clay, *Return From the River Kwai*, Macdonald & Janes, 1979

Chapman, F. Spencer, *The Jungle is Neutral*, Chatto & Windus, 1949

Dilley, Roy, *Japanese Army Uniforms and Equipment 1939-1945*, Almark Publishing,

Pacific War Research Society, *Japan's Longest Day*, Souvenir Press, 1968

Trotsky, Leon, *Terrorism and Communism*, University of Michigan Press, 1961

Tsuji, Matsanobu, *Singapore: The Japanese Version*, Ure Smith, 1960

Tweedie, M.W.F., *Mammals of Malaysia*, Longman Malaysia, 1978

Wigmore, Lionel, *The Japanese Thrust*, Australian War Memorial, 1957

Zich, Arthur and editors, *The Rising Sun*, Time Life Books, 1977

A History of the 2/29 Battalion-8th Australian Division AIF, 2/29 Battalion AIF Association, 1983

Ofiicial War Records, 2/29 Battalion, Australian War Memorial

Some of the Malay and Chinese words used in the text:

Attap	A type of long leaf used in roof-making
Barang	Baggage
Berak	Dysentery
Blachan	Shrimp or fish paste
Brinjel	Egg-plant
Bubor	Rice porridge
Chunkel	A shovel or hoe
Claddy	A type of potato
Gantung	About a gallon
Gulemelaca	A sugary sweet
Ikan bilis	Small, dried fish
Kacan	A long bean
Kangkong	A type of spinach leaf
Kattie	1.25 pounds (weight)
Kelame	Vegetable
Kepala / Kapela	Village headman
Ketchang	A medium-sized deer
Labis	A tortoise (also place name)
Lalang	Tall grass (about 6 feet)
Mee Foong	Cakes
Musang	A civit eat
Nasi goring	Fried rice
Nebong	Cabbage palm
Nehoong	A meal of ubi, flour and rice
Padang	A playing field
Panjan	Chinese cabbage
Parang	A large bush knife
Pelandok	A mouse deer

GLOSSARY (Contd)

Pikul	l = 100 katties (125 pounds)
Rotan	Thin, bamboo—like cane
Rusah	A large deer
Reubon	Bamboo shoots (for eating)
Sakai	Small nomadic jungle natives
Sam soo	A Chinese wine
Selatlang	A buffalo
Tahil	About 1 ounce (weight)
Tikka	Sleeping mat
Towkay	A rich or influential man
Ubi	A type of potato

Read about other titles by
Iain Finlay:
The Azanian Assignment
A Hitch In Time

By Iain Finlay and Trish Clark:
*Africa Overland
*South America Overland
*Across the South Pacific
Good Morning Hanoi
The Silk Train

Titles marked with an asterisk were originally
published under Trish's previous name,
Trish Sheppard.

For more details and video coverage
visit
\<highadventureproductions.com\>

457

THE AZANIAN ASSIGNMENT
Iain Finlay

Banned in South Africa on its first release in 1978, this fast-paced, fictional drama stands the test of time as an en- grossing thriller set against real-life situations in eastern and southern Africa at the time. Set in Apartheid-era South Africa, in what was then a few years in the future (1981), this is a political intrigue adventure novel, which predicts the downfall of the apartheid system, albeit more than a decade earlier than when it actually occurred and more violently than the real event.

The mysterious hi-jacking in Johannesburg of a plane reportedly carrying a secret gold shipment to Europe, sees Tony Bartlett, the East African correspondent for a London newspaper, flying south to a small town in Tanzania where the hijacked plane is reported to have landed. Escaping a murder attempt on the TanZam Railway, and directed by his editor to continue following up the story in South Africa, Tony finds himself simultaneously swept into the opposing worlds of the country's right-wing extremists and the underground revolutionary movement of the Azanian People's Army.

Nelson Mandela is still in prison on Robben Island, but elaborate plans are underway to release him and other leaders of the African National Congress (ANC). The apartheid regime faces military and diplomatic pressure from all sides, both within the country, from neighbouring African states, and the major powers.

Meeting and moving among real politicians and diplomats of the time. as well as running afoul of BOSS, the dreaded Bureau Of State Security, Tony becomes intimately involved with Ingrid, a beautiful, but dangerous Afrikaaner political extremist. The connection leads him to uncover a vast conspiracy that will drastically affect the country's future, whichever side wins the looming battle.

(Available 2015)

A HITCH IN TIME
Iain Finlay

In a journalistic career spanning almost sixty years, the author has lived, worked and traveled in over a hundred countries on every continent. As a Foreign Correspondent , documentary producer, photo-journalist and Radio and TV reporter, he has covered the Viet Nam and Indo-Pakistan wars and co-founded the internationally successful and long-running TV science program Beyond 2000. Now aged 80 he looks back on his first great adventure in Africa while still in his teens.

This is the true story of a young man's passage to adulthood in the most extraordinary circumstances. In 1954, not quite nineteen years old, the author left his home in Melbourne, to travel by ship to Italy and to hitch-hike, with two young friends, through Europe.

But within a year, he finds himself flat broke in the North African city of Casablanca, at the beginning of what are to be two incredible overland journeys through Africa. These amazing treks...covering some 30,000 kilometres... and viewed now in the light of over fifty years of historical change in continent... have become, in effect, journeys in time.

Hitch-hiking across the top of North Africa, from Casablanca to Cairo, then from Egypt south into East and Central Africa, he and his young Australian friend, Noel White, see an Africa that has long since disappeared ... an Africa in which every country, from West to East and North to South is under some form of colonial rule or European influence.

Robbed in Casablanca, chased by lions in Kenya, sleeping in grass huts in Tanganyika and working on the copper mines of Rhodesia, they dream of somehow making it back to Melbourne for the 1956 Olympic Games, where Iain hopes to find work as a journalist. He heads for South Africa to work as a professional lifeguard on the beach in Durban, before turning north again, to hitch the length of Africa once more... this time with a South African friend, Shorty Bronkhorst and over a different route, north, through the Belgian Congo and down the Nile River by barge.

Back in Europe, he finds a job on a ship to Perth in Western Astralia, from where he hitches across the continent to Adelaide and Melbourne, arriving little more than a month before the Olympic Games are due to start. With boundless optimism he sets out to try to land his first job as a journalist and in the process, perhaps see the Games at the same time.   (Available 2015)

TRAVELING WITH CHILDREN:
THREE INCREDIBLE ADVENTURES
By

IAIN FINLAY & TRISH CLARK

Africa Overland
South America Overland
Across the South Pacific

You'd love to travel to remote and exotic places but...you have kids. So? Why let that stop you? You're worried about their education...think you should wait. Don't!

Iain and Trish didn't. They made three big journeys through some of the toughest territories in Africa, North and South America and the South Pacific with their two young children. Using public transport; buses, trains, trucks, trading vessels, sometimes hitching, each of them shouldering their own backpack, they spent months at a time on the road.

Spread over a period of just on four years, during the 1970's, their travels took them first from Capetown to Cairo. Eighteen months later they journeyed overland from Canada to Tierra del Fuego, at the bottom tip of South America and within another year and a half, they island hopped across the South Pacific from Chile to Australia.

Not only did they survive to write the books, which also look at the history, politics and way of life of the countries through which they traveled, but, with the passing of the years they have come to realise how much their travel adventures truly sealed an on-going adult friendship with their children.

Africa Overland is the first in the series. The following hard copy illustrated titles will be available during 2014/2015. Digital eBook versions available shortly after.)

AFRICA OVERLAND
Iain Finlay & Trish Clark

Capetown to Cairo! A magical phrase...the journey of a life-time.Around 12,000 kilometers, nine countries, four months on the road with nothing booked or arranged in advance. With their two children; a son aged eight and daughter nine, carrying their own back-packs and often sleeping in rough circumstances (like in the back of a truck laden with copper ingots), Iain, Trish and the kids get to see: Kruger National Park, Victoria Falls and travel on the TanZam railway. They experience the vast herds of game in Serengetti, Lake Manyara,Ngorongoro Crater and Am-boseli, go to the source of the Blue Nile in Ethiopia, travel on 'Kitchener's Railway' across the Nubian Desert from Khartoum to Wadi Halfa, Aswan and the great temples of the Nile Valley... all the way down to Cairo and the Pyramids.

(Available late 2014)

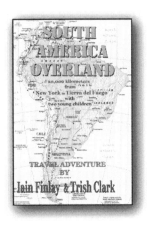

SOUTH AMERICA OVERLAND
Iain Finlay & Trish Clark

This amazing journey includes much more than just South America. It starts in Canada as Iain, Trish, their ten-year-old son and daughter, aged eleven, set out in a blizzard that covers most of the US, to deliver a car cross-country to San Diego. Then they travel by train and bus through Mexico, Belize, Guatamala, El Salvador, Honduras, Nicaragua and Costa Rica to Panama. Along the way they visit the great Aztec and Mayan temples of Tenochtitlan, Palenque, Tikal and many others.

Then on to Ecuador and Peru, where they puzzle over the mysterious lines in the Nazca Desert and visit the fabled Lost City of the Incas at Machu Picchu. Across the Andes, on the Amazon headwaters, at Pucallpa and down-river, they find barges, ferryboats and a trading boat for a 3,000-kilometer, month-long journey down the Amazon to Iquitos and Manaus.

On through the Matto Grosso to Bazilia, Rio and Sao Paulo, Iguasu Falls, Montevideo and Buenos Aires, before hitching for much of the way south through Patagonia to the amazing glaciers of southern Argentina, the Magellan Straits and Tierra del Fuego. Here they reach the southernmost city in the world, Ushuaia, Six months, 17 countries, 23,000 kilometers:

(Available late 2014, early 2015)

ACROSS THE SOUTH PACIFIC
Iain Finlay & Trish Clark

Leaving Santiago, Chile after a frightening night of earth tremors, Iain, Trish and their two children, now 12 and 13 years old, fly to Easter Island, where, using their own tents, they camp out in remote corners of the island as they explore the huge, enigmatic stone monoliths. From there, its Tahiti and the stunning beauty of Bora Bora, Morea and the unbelievable Tuamotu atolls. In the Cook Islands they board a copra trading vessel for a journey through the island chain; Aitutaki, Rakahanga and Manihiki. When it breaks down, mid-ocean, they go overboard with the crew to swim in water 3,000 metres deep. American and Western Samoa are next, in the midst of a typhoon. Then the pleasures and beauty of Tonga, the Fiji Islands, Vanuatu and New Caledonia, before finally returning to their home in Australia. The message about travelling with your kids is: do it before their teens. By then its too late. Iain & Trish only just made it.

(Available late 2014, early 2015)

463

GOOD MORNING HANOI
Iain Finlay & Trish Clark

When Iain Finlay and Trish Clark arrive in Hanoi on an 18-month work assignment for the English language service of the communist government-run radio network, they can hardly foresee the intense and exceptional experiences that await them. Coming to Vietnam for an Australian aid agency, their intended role is to coach and instruct, or at least to share their knowledge, with a small group of young reporters. But they find that they learn more than they teach.

As friendships with their colleagues grow, Iain and Trish are involved in developing and presenting a daily radio program - the first run by Westerners on a regular basis - and they become immersed in the stimulating life of one of Asia's most enchanting cities. In the process, they gain fascinating insights into Vietnamese society and culture, as well as a greater understanding and respect for the new Vietnam.

Good Morning Hanoi also illuminates the lives of a group of people dwelling in crowded conditions around a small courtyard in central Hanoi where Iain and Trish find a house to rent, and who become like an extended family living in the heart of the city.

In Good Morning Hanoi, Iain and Trish, two of the founders and producers of the international television program Beyond 2000, return to a country from which they had reported during the Vietnam War. They find an extraordinarily friendly people whose resilience and irrepressible good nature enable them to put the past behind them and move into the future with confidence.

(Illustrated hard copy version available now from
<www.amazon.com> Kindle eBook version in 2015)

464

THE SILK TRAIN
Iain Finlay & Trish Clark

The Silk Train is travel adventure with a geo-political backbone. Veteran journalists Iain Finlay and Trish Clark set out to travel 21,000 kilometres from Singapore to Venice, by hopping on and off trains up through South East Asia, across China, Central Asia, the Caucasus, Turkey and the Balkans. Much of their route covers territory along which the ancient Silk Road trails wound their way over the past two thousand years. They planned to use rail lines that form part of an embryonic, UN-backed Trans-Asian Railway network, that will eventually create unbroken freight and passenger corridors all the way from China's far-eastern seaboard, to Europe.

While visiting some of the great historic sites of China and Central Asia, among them: Xi'an, Dunhaung, Samarkand and Bukhara, they also become aware of the changing dynamics of Big-Power politics across the vast Central Asian steppes, once the stamping grounds of Genghis Khan and Tamerlane, which now include the newly independent countries of Kazakhstan, Kyrgyzstan and Uzbekistan. They very quickly realise that, by far the most important items of trade along the modern equivalents of the Silk Road, are now oil and natural gas. Oil is the new silk. It is the new trans-national currency of the Silk Road, with China and its voracious, seemingly insatiable appetite for energy, emerging as the most significant factor in the political and economic arena of Central and South East Asia.

Further west, Russia's increased pressure on the Caucasus, particularly Georgia, is just another indication of how vital the world's dwindling energy resources are and will remain for most of the twenty-first century. By journey's end, in Venice, they realise they have travelled a very different Silk Road than that of Marco Polo.

(Illustrated hard copy version available now from:<<www.amazon.com>> Kindle eBook version in 2015)

Iain Finlay

Iain Finlay has been a journalist for over fifty years, including six years covering Asia, including the Viet Nam and Indo-Pakistan Wars, as a foreign correspondent. He served more than five years in Australia's Citizen Military Forces during which time he was commissioned as an officer in 30 Battalion, the NSW Scottish Regiment.

He has travelled and worked on every continent and was co-founder and presenter of the acclaimed science and technology series *Beyond 2000*. He has written a novel, *The Azanian Assignment* and co-authored five non-fiction books.

HIGHADVENTUREPUBLISHING.com
AND
HIGHADVENTUREPRODUCTIONS.com
ARE PART OF
High Adventure Productions
PO Box 111
Tumbulgum, NSW 2490
EMAIL: IAINTRISH@MAC.COM
AUSTRALIA

23176514R00288

Printed in Great Britain
by Amazon